"This is a monumental piece that provides an entry point for learners—and their mentors, too—to explore key dimensions of global mental health research and practice. It is grounded, wise, and practical. An inclusive approach is critical, and here the many diverse authors show us a path forward."

Dr. Elizabeth H. Bradley, *President of Vassar College, and Founder of Yale Global Health Leadership Institute*

"Global mental health can often be seen as something that academics write about—and discuss with—other academics in scientific conferences. The book by Acharya and Becker clearly and conclusively demonstrates that key lessons of global mental health can be learned and practiced much more widely and can change the way mental health is conceptualized and delivered. A must read for all teachers, students, and practitioners of mental health everywhere!"

Dr. Shekhar Saxena, *Professor of the Practice of Global Mental Health, Harvard T.H. Chan School of Public Health; Former Director, Mental Health, World Health Organization*

"This Introductory Framework relies on the distillation of decades of work in global mental health to offer learners and their mentors an outstanding balanced grounding in this increasingly fundamental approach to overcoming the worldwide impact of racism, colonialism, and economic exploitation. Its chapters cover conceptual foundations, history, overall practical guidance, specific applications, case examples, research agendas, and current critiques. It's a terrific one-volume introduction to everything one needs to know in global mental health."

Dr. Roberto Lewis-Fernández, *Professor of Clinical Psychiatry, Columbia University; Director, Center of Excellence for Cultural Competence and Research Area Leader, Anxiety, Mood, Eating and Related Disorders, New York State Psychiatric Institute*

"The Global Mental Health field has matured. It's the urgently needed "next system" to deliver on the increasingly acknowledged priority of safeguarding mental health across all levels of governance. It brings an overdue makeover to long dominant Global North over-medicalized traditions, and rigor and space to a more Global South epistemology that converges holistic, social, and empowering ground rules. A harvest of wisdom on how to grow and teach that is wonderfully brought together in this important and timely volume."

Dr. Gary Belkin, *Director, Billion Minds Project, Columbia University Mailman School of Public Health, and Chair, COP²*

Global Mental Health Training and Practice

The enormous health and social burdens associated with mental disorders have global reach and persist in the setting of unmet needs. To address these, the pipeline of global mental health trainees must be expanded and nurtured as the next generation of practitioners, investigators, and educators advance innovation in mental health prevention, promotion, and health delivery. This book offers a much-needed introduction to the rapidly evolving field of global mental health. The editors bring their extensive expertise and experience in global mental health research, practice, and training, which includes working in academic and non-profit settings, building collaborations, and teaching hundreds of students and trainees. The volume's 12 chapters—authored by over 60 contributors from multiple disciplines—offer a breadth of content that comprises an introductory framework.

This volume is an essential read for learners and educators who seek to explore or deepen their interest in the field of global mental health. Its orientation to fundamentals of practice and training and contextualization with social science perspectives will also be invaluable to health professionals, social scientists, policymakers, and other professionals who are invested in training the next generation of global mental health practitioners.

Bibhav Acharya, MD, is an associate professor of psychiatry at UCSF, where he sees patients, conducts research, and directs a fellowship in global mental health. He is the co-founder of Possible, a non-profit that has administered over $35 million in healthcare innovation in rural Nepal.

Anne E. Becker, MD, PhD, is the Maude and Lillian Presley Professor of Global Health and Social Medicine, Professor of Psychiatry, and Dean for Clinical and Academic Affairs at Harvard Medical School.

Global Mental Health Training and Practice

An Introductory Framework

Edited by Bibhav Acharya and Anne E. Becker

Routledge
Taylor & Francis Group

NEW YORK AND LONDON

Cover Image © Getty Image

First published 2024
by Routledge
605 Third Avenue, New York, NY 10158

and by Routledge
4 Park Square, Milton Park, Abingdon, Oxon, OX14 4RN

Routledge is an imprint of the Taylor & Francis Group, an informa business

© 2024 Taylor & Francis

Library of Congress Cataloging-in-Publication Data
Names: Acharya, Bibhav, editor. | Becker, Anne E., editor.
Title: Global mental health training and practice: an introductory
framework/edited by Bibhav Acharya and Anne E Becker.
Description: New York, NY: Routledge 2023. | Includes bibliographical
references and index.
Identifiers: LCCN 2023000956 (print) | LCCN 2023000957 (ebook) |
ISBN 9781138064126 (hardback) | ISBN 9781138064133 (paperback) |
ISBN 9781315160597 (ebook)
Subjects: MESH: Mental Disorders | Mental Health Services | Global
Health—education | Mentoring | Teaching
Classification: LCC RA790.8 (print) | LCC RA790.8 (ebook) |
NLM WM 18 | DDC 362.2071—dc23/eng/20230515
LC record available at https://lccn.loc.gov/2023000956
LC ebook record available at https://lccn.loc.gov/2023000957

ISBN: 978-1-138-06412-6 (hbk)
ISBN: 978-1-138-06413-3 (pbk)
ISBN: 978-1-315-16059-7 (ebk)

DOI: 10.4324/9781315160597

Typeset in Galliard
by Deanta Global Publishing Services, Chennai, India

This book is dedicated to the memory of Paul Farmer—with gratitude for his vision and capacious aspirations for global health that have lighted a path for learners, educators, and practitioners toward realizing a future with health, well-being, and mental health equity—and to students, mentors, advocates, communities, caregivers, and persons living with mental health conditions who continue to inspire, fortify, and advance this commitment and work.

Disclaimer

The content of this book is provided for educational purposes only. The information should not be used for clinical decision-making for any particular patient or population or as a substitute for medical advice or clinical judgment from a doctor or other qualified clinician overseeing patient care or clinical operations.

The content of this book is drawn from the contributors' expertise and experience as well as their synthesis of relevant medical and other research and scientific literature; however, no representation can be made regarding the content's ongoing accuracy or comprehensiveness, since scientific knowledge evolves quickly. Its application to clinical practice and global mental health educational, research, service delivery, and other kinds of collaborative engagements is anticipated to change over time and vary across settings.

Contents

Acknowledgments

There is a long list of individuals to whom we owe gratitude for their part in supporting the intellectual architecture and completion of this book. Among them are colleagues, mentors, students, other learners, and collaborators, as well as individuals living with mental health conditions and caregivers who have courageously shared insights about their lived experiences, needs, and priorities. We also thank communities, clinical sites, schools, academic centers in various parts of the world, non-profit organizations, and other community-based services who have been generous teachers and collaborators for their contributions to advancing the quality of prevention and care for mental health and to the learning and understanding—including our own—that have shaped many ideas and successes in the field. We are also grateful to funders, program officers, and other supporters of our research, teaching, and other scholarly work that provided, in many ways, the scaffolding and impetus for this book.

We must also thank our family members who have always been in the background, offering edits, encouragement, and very helpful critiques. For BA: my sons, Nirav and Aneesh, and my wife Elen provided a balance of encouragement and trepidation with the question universally dreaded by writers and editors: "Is the book done?" I thank all three for always energizing me, regardless of how tough my day has been. For AEB: my two daughters, Isabel and Juliet, who in a burst of generosity with their excellent editing skills and a bit of down time during their respective COVID gap years, provided not just invaluable copy-editing assistance but also a candid and discerning perspective as learners on one end of the range of readership. I also thank my husband Eric and our son Henry, who have been a reservoir of encouragement and backup with every kind of pragmatic support.

We thank many, many students and other learners. For BA: this includes students at Haverford College who took a not-for-credit course that I co-taught when I was beginning my career as a global health scholar, forcing me to articulate and sharpen my views, which had been shaped by a very diverse set of experiences: as a recipient of global programs while living in Nepal, and as an implementer of such projects while traveling as a global health practitioner to low-resource settings. I thank all the fellows I have worked with in the University of California, San Francisco (UCSF) Psychiatry HEAL Fellowship in Global Mental Health: your critiques, idealism, and energy will never let me stagnate. I thank numerous brilliant mentees I have had from the non-profit Possible, UCSF, and elsewhere. You continue to approach the field of global mental health with novel perspectives and you make me optimistic about the direction of our discipline. For AEB: I am especially grateful to the students who have taken various iterations of SW25 and Gen Ed 1093 (most recently, *Who Lives, Who Dies, Who Cares? Reimagining Global Health*) at Harvard over the past nearly decade and a half, who have been a constant and generative source of creativity, incisive critique, and aspirational thinking. Students: every year the course grows wiser and better not just because of your feedback to the faculty and teaching fellows, but also because of the questions and critiques you raise. I hope you know that your questions, engagement, and commitment continue to inspire us and hope you will recognize that inspiration in the pages of this book. Also among the students whose examples and commitments have inspired this book are Harvard Social Sciences MD-PhD students, MMSc in GHD students at Harvard Medical School, doctoral students in the Harvard Department of Anthropology, and each of the extraordinary teaching fellows who has found new ways to engage learners in the intellectual excitement and moral imperatives that animate the field of global mental health. I am especially indebted to—and proud of—the former students, with whom I have been fortunate to work, who agreed to collaborate with their peers to write so eloquently and generously in sharing their experience and perspective with educators and other learners.

There are countless others whose contributions to our intellectual growth and its continued revitalization have been both foundational and immeasurable and to whom we are grateful for their support. First and foremost, for BA: my parents, Meena and Bishnu Acharya, instilled in me the importance of pursuing educational opportunities, not just as a conduit to economic security for myself but as a pathway to serve the broader society. My mentors at Haverford College, Leslie Dwyer and Kaye Edwards, introduced me to medical anthropology and public health, and encouraged me to pursue global health practice that is never free of self-reflection, critical examination of the inadvertent harm one may be causing, and the constant need to course-correct in the pursuit of equity. Bruce Agins, then at the New York AIDS Institute and now at UCSF, not only hired me despite his peers worrying about my immigration status, but also taught me to think in systems and modeled for me that mentorship can be intellectually demanding yet interpersonally warm. My mentors and role models at Yale, Robert Ostroff and Robert Rohrbaugh, showed me that psychiatry, a discipline that is often stigmatized and marginalized, including by my own younger self, can be rewarding and fun. At UCSF, my mentor and colleague Maria Ekstrand helped me sharpen my research skills when I was a new investigator, and is now a collaborator as we carry out National Institutes of Mental Health (NIMH)-funded global mental health research studies. Thank you for showing me that a researcher can build a successful career while directly mentoring learners from low-resource settings and expanding access to crucial health services in marginalized communities. I thank Craig Van Dyke and Barbara Kamholz, the co-Directors of the UCSF Global Mental Health Fellowship, for their generosity, time, and zeal while we train some of the most inspiring young leaders in the discipline.

Everyone associated with the non-profit Possible deserves my deepest gratitude. My fellow co-founders—my brother Bijay Acharya and my colleagues Jason Andrews, Sanjay Basu, and Duncan Maru—for joining forces in starting Possible, even when we had hardly any resources other than a deep-seated and shared desire to address health inequity in rural Nepal. The numerous donors, whether they invested $2 or $5 million, who were compelled by our vision to build a healthcare system in Achham, Nepal, where previously, there had not been a single physician. I am thankful to the late Paul Farmer for providing the Possible team his mentorship and support and for personally supporting my career. I am grateful to all the patients who entrust us with their health, and the families who invite me into their homes in rural Nepal and teach me about not only the senselessness of suffering but also teach generosity and optimism. Possible's staff and leadership, including Sabitri Sapkota, Sikhar Swar, Madhur Basnet, Pragya Rimal, Rekha Khatri, Kripa Sigdel, Kim Lipman-White, Duncan Maru, and Srijana Shrestha, have become my family and provide an environment where unremitting values are turned into positive impact on health equity.

Various leaders and colleagues have helped to build unique settings that have helped me grow. Yale was unusually flexible and supportive of us going off to rural Nepal to build a hospital and hire doctors and nurses, while attending medical school. I am grateful that my medical training included guest lectures from several people living with mental illness, who came to our lecture halls not as helpless victims, but as authority figures who shared their expertise and inspired me to become a psychiatrist. For the last decade, the UCSF Department of Psychiatry and Behavioral Sciences has been my academic home. I thank the Department Chair, Matthew State, for sharing the vision of investment in global mental health, and including research and training focused on equity as essential aspects of the Department's mission. I thank an anonymous donor who has quietly supported my work, allowing me to listen to people who are the most vulnerable and design interventions to address their worries, even when conventional funding sources may not see such issues as a high priority.

I thank various people that I have never met but whose generosity has helped me immensely. Many people donated to the scholarship funds that made it possible for me to attend Haverford College and Yale School of Medicine. Anonymous reviewers supported my immigration petition—allowing me to build a career in the United States focused on global health—and grant applications that help me build a viable career in global mental health.

For AEB: I thank my colleagues in the Harvard Medical School Department of Global Health and Social Medicine: Arthur Kleinman, who has been a mentor and role model for so many of us, and also for me since I was an aspiring student of anthropology and medicine; Byron Good and Mary-Jo DelVecchio Good: also long-time mentors and then colleagues whose indefatigable efforts to integrate anthropology with cultural psychiatry and, later, with global mental health, mobilized a new generation of learners. Salmaan Keshavjee, as well as many other colleagues who have graced the course we have taught with Arthur Kleinman and the late Paul Farmer for so many years with their brilliant lectures and by sharing case studies: Marty Zeve, Jason Silverstein, Gene Richardson, Joia Mukherjee, Joe Rhatigan, David Jones, and Jeremy Greene, to name just a few. I also thank many others I have had the good fortune to teach with and learn from, including Vikram Patel, Mary Kay Smith Fawzi, and Giuseppe Raviola; close colleagues whose work in adjacent areas of global health has elevated the aspirations for global mental health, Megan Murray, Mercedes Becerra, Carole Mitnick; and, indeed, the exceptional academic community that comprises the Department of Global Health and Social Medicine at Harvard Medical School. A little beyond my academic home, I thank many, many others whose impactful and abiding commitment to the mental health and well-being in their communities has been generative, inspiring, and foundational not just to our own work but also to the global mental health field. Among these are Pere Eddy Eustache and the Zanmi Lasante-based Ekip Wozo—especially Reginald Fils-Aimé, Tatiana Therosme, Emmeline Affricot, Ermaze Pierre, Yoldie Alcindor, Jennifer Severe, and Alexis Erick—as well as Dr. Fadi Maalouf, Rima Afifi, Leyla Akoury Dirani, Rima Nakkash, Lilian Ghandour, and others on Dr. Maalouf's team at the American University of Beirut. I am grateful to the late Tui Sigatoka, Joana Rokomatu, her wonderful extended family, and community as well as collaborators, Asenaca Bainivualiku, Nisha Khan, and the late Kesaia Navara who brought great wisdom and warmth to our work within the *iTaukei* community.

Next, there are numerous colleagues who have made my work on this book possible through their leadership in creating an academic milieu where scholarly work, dialog, and ideas can flourish. Among these, I thank the leadership of Harvard Medical School, especially Dean George Q. Daley, and leadership of the Department of Global Health and Social Medicine, Allan Brandt, interim chair and also a long-time mentor, as well as the late Paul Farmer who has been a mentor and inspiration not just to me, but to the next generation as well. I also thank the leadership of the Massachusetts General Hospital Department of Psychiatry, including Maurizio Fava, and former residency training directors, John Herman and Gene Beresin, who, along with many others, have built a strong learning environment where careers in global mental health can flourish. Many others have also made the work possible through their practical support and accompaniment, and especially among them at Harvard Medical School are Jen Puccetti, Katie Kralievits, and Sara Nolasco.

We want to make special mention and give special thanks to several extraordinary research assistants who have lent their considerable editing and organizational talent to the book: Louisa Fresquez Hudson and Pragya Rimal, and, most recently, Anne Lheem, whose exceptional dedication to the project in the last sprint to finish it has been our good fortune. We thank them all for their support and stand in admiration of their energetic commitment to global mental health equity: another source of our optimism for how the next generation of learners, educators, and practitioners will advance global mental health and global health equity.

And finally, we owe immense thanks to the unparalleled cohort of contributors, whose aggregate expertise and experience comprises the intellectual centerpiece of this book, and whose work places them in the very vanguard of innovation in global mental health. To the extraordinary authors and co-authors who have been generous with their time and ideas through their contributions to this volume: Authors, we thank you not just for your collaboration on this book as contributors, but also for your work that has undergirded the aspirations and steady progress in the field of global mental health. We are also grateful for your abiding commitment to teach and empower the next generation of global mental health learners, educators, and practitioners.

Editors

Bibhav Acharya, MD, is the Founding Director of the University of California, San Francisco (UCSF) Psychiatry HEAL Fellowship in Global Mental Health. Dr. Acharya grew up in Nepal. Prior to leaving his home to attend Haverford College and Yale School of Medicine on full scholarships in the United States, he bore witness to the inadequacies in the quality of mental health care. Unfortunately, he would soon learn of deficiencies of mental healthcare delivery in the United States as well. As a psychiatrist, he has consistently worked in Nepal since 2007 as a co-founder and mental health advisor for the non-profit Possible, designing and improving mental healthcare delivery systems, testing National Institutes of Health (NIH)-funded innovative behavioral interventions to address domestic violence and chronic diseases, developing and disseminating culturally adapted self-help materials, and training primary care providers and counselors to deliver high-quality mental health to the rural poor in Nepal. As the Director of the UCSF Psychiatry HEAL Fellowship in Global Mental Health, he mentors and supervises both US-trained psychiatrists in their work in rural Nepal, Mexico, and Navajo Nation, and mental health professionals from Nepal, Mexico, and Navajo Nation in their local work. He is associate professor at UCSF, providing direct clinical care, conducting research, and overseeing educational programs in global mental health. During training and practice in San Francisco, he has provided care for and learned from disenfranchised communities in the region. These experiences have laid bare the reality that a high-income country (HIC) designation fails to guarantee equitable and effective access to mental services, whether observed through the mental health disparities characterizing Indigenous communities in the United States, people living without housing next to some of the most profitable corporations in the world, or persons for whom a mental illness diagnosis can mean shame, stigma, and suffering. Dr. Acharya is a co-author of Chapter 4, "Developing a Global Mental Health Training Curriculum," and is co-editor of this book.

Anne E. Becker, MD, PhD, SM, is Dean for Clinical and Academic Affairs, Professor of Psychiatry, and Presley Professor of Global Health and Social Medicine at Harvard Medical School (HMS) in Boston, Massachusetts (USA). A medical anthropologist and psychiatrist, Dr. Becker's areas of research focus include the social and cultural mediation of presentation and risk for eating disorders, social barriers to care for mental disorders, and school-based mental health promotion. She has led investigations on the impact of rapid social transition on eating pathology in the indigenous *iTaukei* population of Fiji and has served as co-principal investigator on school-based mental health interventions in Haiti and Lebanon. Dr. Becker is founding and past Director of the Eating Disorders Clinical and Research Program at Massachusetts General Hospital (MGH), former vice chair of the HMS Department of Global

Health and Social Medicine, and past president of the Academy for Eating Disorders. She has also previously served as a member of the American Psychiatry Association's (APA) DSM-5 Eating Disorders Work Group and DSM-5-TR Cross-Cutting Culture Review Group and as vice chairperson of the APA's Council on International Psychiatry; she is former associate editor for global initiatives of the *International Journal of Eating Disorders* and past co-editor-in-chief of *Culture, Medicine and Psychiatry* as well. She also served as a commissioner on *The Lancet* NCDI Poverty Commission, Reframing Noncommunicable Diseases and Injuries for the Poorest Billion. Dr. Becker has served as faculty co-director—alongside her colleagues, Drs. Arthur Kleinman, Salmaan Keshavjee, and the late Paul Farmer—of a large undergraduate course on global health at Harvard College, where they have taught over 1500 students over the past 12 years. She has been the recipient of a Mentorship Award in recognition of "Exceptional Mentorship of Women Faculty" in the MGH Department of Psychiatry and an Outstanding MD-PhD Advisor Award at HMS. She was the 2013 recipient of the Price Family Award for Research Excellence from the National Eating Disorders Association and the 2018 Leadership Award in Research from the Academy for Eating Disorders. Dr. Becker is co-author of Chapter 2, "Resocializing Global Mental Health: What Anthropological Perspectives Offer to Learners, Educators, and Practitioners," and is co-editor of this book.

Contributors

Sherein Abdeen, MA, is a clinical instructor in psychiatry at the George Washington University School of Medicine and Health Sciences in Washington, DC (USA), and a teacher, psychotherapist, and educational leader in West Bank Palestine, where she has developed school-wide programming that builds resilience broadly among Palestinian youth vulnerable for mental health problems and identifies individual students whose behavioral or learning problems merit specific professional treatment. Ms. Abdeen has provided training for the full faculties of school principals and teachers at numerous public and private schools in Jerusalem and West Bank Palestine. Ms. Abdeen is a co-author of Chapter 3, "Promoting Global Mental Health Equity in Training Programs: Establishing Ethical and Reciprocal Partnerships."

Nilanga Abeysinghe, PhD, is a Senior Lecturer at the School of Psychology, Faculty of Humanities and Sciences, at Sri Lanka Institute of Information Technology in Malabe, Sri Lanka. Dr. Abeysinghe started working in global mental health as a counselor in 2005 and continues to work as a private practitioner. He was also part of a mental health project that aimed to promote rights-based mental health services in Sri Lanka and contributed to establishing and capacitating mental health service user groups. Since 2010, Dr. Abeysinghe has been working as a psychology lecturer and a counseling trainer at university and community-level training programs. Dr. Abeysinghe was part of the team that translated and introduced Psychological First Aid (PFA) to Sri Lanka and continues to work as a trainer. At present, his research focuses on the role of common factors in counseling in Sri Lanka to enhance the quality of counselor training programs, clinical supervision, and assessment. Dr. Abeysinghe is a co-author of Chapter 5, "Mentorship in Global Mental Health."

Matthew Basilico, MD, PhD, is a Resident Physician in Psychiatry at Yale University in New Haven, Connecticut (USA), and a member of the faculty at the Department of Economics and the Department of Global Health and Social Medicine at Harvard in Cambridge and Boston, Massachusetts, where he teaches "The Economics of Development and Global Health." He is an Adjunct Assistant Professor at the University of Global Health Equity in Kigali, Rwanda, where he teaches in the first-year core medical school curriculum. He worked for several years with Partners In Health, including in Malawi, Haiti, and Rwanda, and has worked with Boston Healthcare for the Homeless and on advocacy projects for permanent supportive housing. As a physician-economist whose work focuses on the behavioral economics of health, economic development, and well-being, Dr. Basilico's research and teaching in economics has examined relationships between social environment, behavioral health, and economic decision-making. He has served as a Consultant to the President of the World Bank under Jim Yong Kim and is a co-editor of the textbook *Reimagining Global Health* with

Paul Farmer, Jim Yong Kim, and Arthur Kleinman. Dr. Basilico is a co-author of Chapter 9, "Student Engagement in Global Mental Health: Perspectives on Curricular, Extracurricular, and Advocacy Opportunities."

Madhur Basnet, MBBS, MD, is an Associate Professor in the Department of Psychiatry at B.P. Koirala Institute of Health Sciences in Dharan, Nepal, and a Mental Health Consultant for Nyaya Health Nepal, one of the training sites for Global Mental Health Fellows from the University of California, San Francisco (UCSF). During his psychiatry residency training, Dr. Basnet came across the reality of the vast gap between the need for mental health services across the globe and the available resources, as well as the evidence of immense impact with early and community-based interventions. Since then, he has developed keen interests in community psychiatry and global mental health. He significantly contributed to the front lines for mental health and psychosocial support during the Mega Earthquake in Nepal in 2015, an experience that further reinforced his interests in the subject. Dr. Basnet also contributed as a reviewer for the Mental Health Gap Action Programme Intervention Guide (mhGAP-IG) version 2.0 and worked as the coordinator in the implementation of the District Mental Health pilot project supported by the World Health Organization (WHO) country office in Nepal. Currently he is working as a mental health officer for the WHO's Special Initiative for Mental Health in Nepal. Dr. Basnet is a co-author of Chapter 4, "Developing a Global Mental Health Training Curriculum."

Concilia Tarisai Bere, MSc, is a clinical psychologist and global mental health researcher based in Harare, Zimbabwe. She holds an MSc degree in Global Mental Health (GMH) from King's College London and London School of Hygiene and Tropical Medicine, completed in 2017. She has played a pivotal role in training community lay health workers and implementing the Friendship Bench Project, Zimbabwe. Ms. Bere is currently the senior psychologist for a clinical trial sponsored by the National Institutes of Health, testing the effectiveness of a cognitive behavioral therapy (CBT)-based intervention to treat depression and non-adherence to antiretroviral therapy in people living with HIV. She was instrumental in the cultural adaptation of the intervention for this trial called NziraItsva (New Direction), which was published in the *Journal of Health Psychology*. Additionally, she is co-principal investigator in the International, Maternal, Pediatric Adolescents AIDS Clinical Trials (IMPAACT) 2016 study, a randomized clinical trial testing effectiveness of a trauma-focused group CBT intervention for treatment of trauma in adolescents living with HIV. Alongside these studies, Ms. Bere is the lead investigator for the Mindful Arts Hub program. The Mindful Arts Hub is a program seeking to improve mental health, viral load outcomes, and quality of life among adolescents living with HIV, using creative arts and CBT-based interventions for depression. She is also a PhD candidate and lecturer in behavioral science at the Faculty of Medicine and Health Sciences at the University of Zimbabwe. Ms. Bere is a co-author of Chapter 9, "Student Engagement in Global Mental Health: Perspectives on Curricular, Extracurricular, and Advocacy Opportunities."

Aaron L. Berkowitz, MD, PhD, is a Professor of Neurology at the University of California, San Francisco in San Francisco, California (USA), where he practices and teaches at the San Francisco VA Medical Center and San Francisco General Hospital. He also serves as Health and Policy Advisor in Neurology to Partners In Health and Senior Specialist Consultant to Médecins Sans Frontières. He previously served as an associate professor of neurology at Harvard Medical School and director of the global neurology program at Brigham and Women's Hospital. He collaborated with Partners In Health and its Haitian sister organization Zamni Lasante to develop the first neurology residency program in Haiti and a community-based epilepsy program in rural Haiti. He has written extensively on the practice of neurology in resource-limited settings including the chapter on this topic for the *Oxford Handbook of Humanitarian Medicine* and the book *One by One by One* (HarperOne) about the complexities of caring for patients with brain tumors in rural Haiti. He is also the author of the neurology textbook *Clinical Neurology and Neuroanatomy: A Localization-Based Approach* (McGraw-Hill). His work in global neurology has been recognized by the Kenneth Viste Patient Advocate of the Year Award from the American Academy of Neurology and the Mridha Spirit of Neurology Humanitarian Award from the American Brain Foundation. Dr. Berkowitz is co-author of Chapter 11, "Neurology in Global Mental Health Delivery and Training."

Arvin Bhana, PhD, is an Honorary Chief Specialist Scientist in the Health Systems Research Unit at the South African Medical Research Council and an Honorary Associate Professor at the Centre for Rural Health in the College of Health Sciences, University of KwaZulu-Natal. He has a PhD in Clinical and Community Psychology from the University of Illinois, Urbana-Champaign, and is a registered clinical psychologist in South Africa. His early research focused on developing behavioral interventions for adolescent well-being, including for adolescent HIV and mental health. Subsequently, a focus on health systems and global mental health followed as a function of work on multi-country collaborative grants to strengthen mental health systems in low- and middle-income countries through implementation research. His publications can be found at https://orcid.org/0000-0003-4235-0108. Dr. Bhana is a co-author of Chapter 6, "Implementation of Integrated Care Models: Lessons for Training and Practice in Low-Resource Settings."

Colin Buzza, MD, MPH, MSc, is an Assistant Professor of Psychiatry at the University of California, San Francisco (UCSF) in San Francisco, California (USA). His background incorporates training in the fields of medical anthropology, public health, and public psychiatry. Over the course of his training, he has cultivated interests in service innovation and medical education in low-resource settings. Dr. Buzza has enjoyed helping to develop curricula related to global mental health, mental health policy, advocacy, and structural competency. Most recently, he worked with Alameda County Health Care for the Homeless, helping develop a mobile buprenorphine program serving homeless encampments in Oakland, California. He currently teaches and practices at San Francisco General Hospital, where he serves on the Inpatient Psychiatry Asian Focus Team. Dr. Buzza is a co-author of Chapter 4, "Developing a Global Mental Health Training Curriculum."

Lydia Chwastiak, MD, MPH, is a Professor of Psychiatry and Behavioral Sciences and Adjunct Professor of Global Health at the University of Washington in Seattle, Washington (USA). She is the Principal Investigator of the Northwest Mental Health Technology Transfer Center, which supports the implementation of evidence-based practices for patients with serious mental illness across the Pacific Northwest region of the United States. She is a psychiatrist and internal medicine physician and over the past 18 years, her research has focused on improving the medical care and medical outcomes among individuals with serious mental illnesses. She has been the Principal Investigator on numerous research projects to develop and implement innovative integrated care interventions for complex patients in low-resource settings. A focus on global health research developed from opportunities to adapt, implement, and evaluate integrated care models for clinical settings in India and Nepal. Her published works can be found at https://www.ncbi.nlm.nih.gov/myncbi/1RgT10xNrJe54/bibliography/public/. Dr. Chwastiak is a co-author of Chapter 6, "Implementation of Integrated Care Models: Lessons for Training and Practice in Low-Resource Settings."

David Citrin, PhD, MPH, is an Affiliate Assistant Professor in the Departments of Global Health and Anthropology at the University of Washington in Seattle, Washington (USA), and an Adjunct Clinical Assistant Professor for the Arnhold Institute for Global Health at the Icahn School of Medicine at Mount Sinai in New York City, New York. Dr. Citrin also serves as a Senior Research Collaborator with Medic and an Implementation Research Advisor for Possible. Over the past 15+ years, his work has focused on the ethics of global health and global health partnerships; designing digital tools and health information systems for care coordination and M&E (monitoring and evaluation); and mixed-methods implementation research to strengthen public-sector healthcare systems. Dr. Citrin's work in global mental health began in 2015 when Possible adapted the collaborative care model to integrate mental health services into their primary care settings in rural Nepal. Dr. Citrin has taught a range of classes at the University of Washington, including *Labor, Identity, and Knowledge in Healthcare; Health and Development in the Himalaya; Comparative Systems of Healing;* and *Multidisciplinary Perspectives in Global Health*. He also served as the founding co-Director of the South Asia Center's Nepal Studies Initiative in the Henry M. Jackson School of International Studies. Dr. Citrin's work has been published in various journals such as *Global Health Action, Medicine Anthropology Theory*, and *Healthcare: The Journal of Delivery Science and Innovation*. Dr. Citrin is a co-author of Chapter 5, "Mentorship in Global Mental Health."

Hilary S. Connery, MD, PhD, is an Assistant Professor in the Department of Psychiatry at Harvard Medical School (HMS) in Boston, Massachusetts (USA) and serves as the Clinical Director for McLean Hospital's Division of Alcohol, Drugs, and Addiction. Dr. Connery's expertise includes treatment of opioid use disorders and integrated treatments for co occurring mental illness and substance use disorders (SUDs). She is a Distinguished Fellow of the American Psychiatric Association (APA) and has served within the American Academy of Addiction Psychiatry (AAAP) as New England area director and co-chair of the policy committee and as a national mentor within the national mentoring program through the Providers Clinical Support System (PCSS). Through these roles, she has been actively advocating for more effective responses to the drug overdose and suicide epidemics, as well as mentoring clinicians nationally in evidence-based treatment of SUDs. Her current research efforts are directed toward public health prevention strategies for addressing self-injury mortality, and patient-focused investigation regarding suicidal motivations contributing to drug overdose. Dr. Connery is a co-author of Chapter 12, "Substance Use Disorders in Global Mental Health Delivery and Training."

Joop T.V.M. de Jong, MD, PhD, is Emeritus Professor of Cultural Psychiatry and Global Mental Health at University Medical Center (UMC) Amsterdam, the Netherlands, Emeritus Professor of Psychiatry at Boston University School of Medicine, and Emeritus Visiting Professor of Psychology at Rhodes University in Grahamstown, South Africa. Dr. de Jong is an expert in public mental health, cultural psychiatry, and global mental health. He has published on cultural psychiatry, global mental health, public mental health, epidemiology, medical anthropology, and on the mental health of populations in humanitarian emergencies with a special focus on refugees. He is advisor to the World Health Organization (WHO) and other United Nations (UN) agencies, member of several boards of trustees, and member and advisor of various professional organizations. He received the ISTSS Lifetime Award in 2017. After obtaining his medical degree, Joop de Jong was trained in international and public health. He provided medical support in (post-)conflict situations in Senegal, Guinea-Bissau, and Angola. He returned to the Netherlands where he trained in psychiatry and various schools of psychotherapy. He returned to Guinea-Bissau to help establish a model for the country's mental health program. Upon his return from Africa, he completed his PhD combining an anthropologic and epidemiologic perspective. He has since established TPO (Transcultural Psychosocial Organization), an NGO specialized in mental health and psychosocial care, with a staff of approximately 1000 collaborators in over 20 countries. TPO focuses on traumatized, (post-)conflict and post-disaster populations, covering hundreds of thousands of beneficiaries worldwide. From 2011 to 2019, he joined the Amsterdam Institute of Social Science Research (AISSR) of the University of Amsterdam. Dr. de Jong has worked part-time with immigrants and refugees and has provided forensic psychiatric expertise. He supervised 24 PhD students, was involved in documentary films, has worked in four continents and over 35 countries, and speaks seven languages. Dr. de Jong is a co-author of Chapter 5, "Mentorship in Global Mental Health."

Brendan Eappen, AB, is currently studying medicine at Harvard Medical School (HMS) in Boston, Massachusetts (USA). Mr. Eappen graduated from Harvard College in 2016, where he studied Psychology and Global Health and Health Policy, completing a thesis on suicide contagion and stigma in the media under the supervision of Professor Matthew Nock and Dr. Evan Kleiman. After graduating, he received the Alexander G. Booth fellowship to support the mental health team at Socios En Salud, Partners In Health's sister organization in Peru, during the 2016–2017 academic year. In 2017, Mr. Eappen co-founded a non-profit nutrition startup, Fortify Health, which has received eight years of funding support through GiveWell Incubation Grants to scale up wheat flour fortification in India. He hopes to return his focus to global mental health as he continues his training, incorporating caregiving, advocacy, teaching, research, and scalable implementation into a career dedicated to serving people who are left vulnerable, impoverished, or otherwise marginalized by current systems. Mr. Eappen is a co-author of Chapter 9, "Student Engagement in Global Mental Health: Perspectives on Curricular, Extracurricular, and Advocacy Opportunities."

Rabih El Chammay, MD, is a psychiatrist and member of the faculty of medicine at Saint Joseph University in Beirut, Lebanon. Dr. El Chammay also serves as head of the National Mental Health Programme at the Ministry of Public Health in Lebanon. After founding the program, he led the development and implementation of the first National Mental Health and Substance Use Strategy 2015–2020, which has been renewed to 2030. The strategy aims to reform the mental health system in Lebanon toward community-based mental health services in line with human rights and the latest evidence that is currently under implementation. He has been working in public mental health, refugee mental health, and health system strengthening for more than 15 years. He has been working on these topics in the Middle East and North Africa (MENA) region as well as on the international level with various agencies such as the World Health Organization (WHO), United Nations Refugee Agency (UNHCR), United Nations Children's Fund (UNICEF), International Medical Corps (IMC), and many other NGOs. He was selected to serve on the newly established Strategic and Technical Advisory Group on Mental Health and Substance Use (STAG-MSD) by the World Health Organization. The STAG-MSD will advise the WHO Director-General on matters relating to mental health, neurological disorders, substance use, and addictive behaviors. Dr. El Chammay is the co-author of Chapter 10, "Training for Humanitarian Crisis Response and Mental Health System Reform."

Abdelrhman Elnasseh, BA, is a medical student at George Washington School of Medicine and Health Science (GWSMHS) and a research assistant at the Global Mental Health (GMH) Equity Lab at George Washington University in Washington, DC (USA). Mr. Elnasseh was drawn to global health after working with and eventually serving as the president of

United2Heal, a non-profit that collects and ships surplus medical supplies around the world. Later during medical school, he spent time in Mukono, Uganda, working with village health teams on multiple medical education projects through OmniMed. After finding a passion for psychiatry during medical school, Mr. Elnasseh became involved in global mental health research, where he primarily worked on WHO's Ensuring Quality in Psychological Support (EQUIP) project. Mr. Elnasseh is interested in providing sustainable solutions through medical education to strengthen mental health systems globally. Currently, he is finishing his last year in medical school at GWSMHS and will go on to pursue a career in psychiatry. Mr. Elnasseh is a co-author of Chapter 5, "Mentorship in Global Mental Health."

J. Reginald Fils-Aimé, MD, MMSc-GHD, is a PhD candidate at the global health program of the School of Public Health of Montreal University in Montreal, Canada, and is working with Zanmi Lasante (ZL) in Haiti, in the division of government accompaniment. Dr. Fils-Aimé is also a Haitian generalist physician who grew up in the Haitian rural area. He graduated from the State Medical School of Haiti and has a master's degree of medical sciences in global health delivery (MMSc-GHD) from Harvard Medical School. He has worked for 14 years with Zanmi Lasante in the Haitian rural area, successively serving patients in several clinical services such as emergency, HIV, multi-drug resistant tuberculosis, and mental health and psychosocial support. He took part in leading the design and implementation of the ZL mental health program for the last decade and led the Partners In Health–Liberia's mental health program from 2020 to 2022. Dr. Fils-Aimé co-published peer-reviewed articles on integrated mental health care, task-sharing in global mental health, school mental health, and transcultural psychiatry. His master's thesis research, conducted in 2015, explored the lived experience of recovery from psychosis and the care-seeking journey of people with psychosis and their caregivers enrolled in the ZL system. Dr. Fils-Aimé is co-author of Chapter 11, "Neurology in Global Mental Health Delivery and Training."

Bikash Gauchan, MD, is a family physician, working as the Executive Director at the Infectious & Communicable Disease Hospital in Gandaki Province of Nepal. He has been overseeing the hospital, which provides comprehensive primary health care, including treatment and control of infectious diseases and mental health care. Dr. Gauchan began directly working to provide mental health services, which were previously non-existent in rural Nepal. As a primary care doctor, he has treated many people suffering from mental illnesses and developed a passion for global mental health upon encountering the huge burden of mental illness in the community where he works. Currently, he works with government officers, public health professionals, mid-level providers, nurses, medical officers, female community health volunteers, community health nurses, and other family physicians to continuously improve primary and mental health services in resource-limited settings. He is also involved in ongoing continuing medical education sessions to improve mental health care in the community. Dr. Gauchan is a co-author of Chapter 5, "Mentorship in Global Mental Health."

Eshetu Girma, MPH, PhD, is an Associate Professor of Public Health at the Department of Preventive Medicine in the School of Public Health at Addis Ababa University in Ethiopia. Dr. Girma is the founder and current president of the Ethiopian Health Education and Promotion Professionals Association (EHEPA). He is involved in teaching health promotion and social and behavior change communication courses for undergraduate and postgraduate students. He is also involved in global mental health, specifically on issues regarding stigma and discrimination against people with mental health issues. Dr. Girma's interest in mental health stigma started while he was conducting a collaborative research project with a psychiatrist regarding the pathways and delay in health-seeking behavior for mental health service use. This study was intended to produce local teaching material specifically on health-seeking behaviors and explanatory models of disease for a medical anthropology course, which Dr. Girma was delivering for undergraduate students. In that study, he identified that there was a long delay in seeking mental health treatment and a complicated pathway to access services and stigma were identified as the main factors contributing to the delay. It was based on this finding that he became interested in understanding stigma and discrimination in the field of mental health. Dr. Girma's career in this area started while he was doing his PhD work in international health. All of his scientific publications and projects focus on global mental health. Dr. Girma also coaches postgraduate students in their research. Currently, he is running projects to understand and reduce both stigma and discrimination against people with mental illness and their family members in Ethiopia. Dr. Girma is a co-author of Chapter 5, "Mentorship in Global Mental Health."

Lidia Goveia, MD, MSc, PhD, is an Adjunct Professor of Psychiatry at the Universidade Eduardo Mondlane (UEM), current Mental Health Advisor to the Minister of Health, and the former Director of Mental Health for Mozambique Ministry of Health (MISAU). As the Director, she oversaw all neuropsychiatric programs in the 11 provinces of Mozambique and led the mental health policies in Mozambique for 13 years, developing the action plans that have led to sustainable task-shifting activities that provide care for those with neuropsychiatric disorders despite few resources. She is a mental health leader of Mozambique and has devoted her research activities to bridge the gap between research and practice to inform policy in Mozambique. She is a mentor in the Fogarty/NIMH-funded US/Brazil/Mozambique collaboration research training program in Mozambique and has joined the US/Brazil research team to design the Implementation Global Mental Health Research and Capacity Building Hub in Sub-Saharan Africa. Dr. Goveia is a co-author of Chapter 8, "Mobilizing a Range of Resources to Advance Research and Service in Global Mental Health Training."

Jeremy A. Greene, MD, PhD, is William H. Welch Professor of Medicine and the History of Medicine and Director of the Department of the History of Medicine and the Center for Medical Humanities and Social Medicine at the Johns Hopkins School of Medicine in Baltimore, Maryland (USA). His research focuses on the interaction between medical technologies, medical knowledge, and the practices of medicine and public health. His most recent book, *The Doctor Who Wasn't There: Technology, History, and the Limits of Telehealth*, was published by the University of Chicago Press in 2022, and his earlier book, *Generic: The Unbranding of Modern Medicines*, was published by Johns Hopkins University Press in 2016. Greene's first book, *Prescribing by Numbers: Drugs and the Definition of Disease*, was awarded the Rachel Carson Prize by the Society for the Social Studies of Science and the Edward Kremers Award by the American Institute of the History of Pharmacy. Besides publishing broadly about the history of disease in scholarly journals, Dr. Greene writes regularly for clinical and public health journals including *JAMA*, the *New England Journal of Medicine*, the *Lancet*, the *American Journal of Public Health*, and *Health Affairs*, and for popular audiences in the *Washington Post*, *Slate*, *Forbes*, *The Atlantic*, *AEON*, and *The Boston Review*, in addition to his broader public engagement via interviews on NPR, television news, and documentaries. Dr. Greene received an MD and a PhD in the History of Science from Harvard University in 2005, finished a residency in Internal Medicine at the Brigham and Women's Hospital in 2008, is board certified in Internal Medicine and a fellow of the American College of Physicians, and continues to practice primary care medicine in a community health center in East Baltimore. Greene's work has been supported by grants from the National Library of Medicine, the National Science Foundation, the Greenwall Foundation, and the Mellon Foundation, and he is currently working on a book on how medical technologies become medical waste. Dr. Greene is co-author of Chapter 1, "The Colonial and Postcolonial Roots of Global Mental Health Efforts."

Shelly F. Greenfield, MD, MPH, is a Professor of Psychiatry at Harvard Medical School (HMS) in Boston, Massachusetts (USA), and the Kristine M. Trustey Endowed Chair of Psychiatry at McLean Hospital, where she is also Chief Academic Officer, Chief of the Division of Women's Mental Health, and Director of Clinical and Health Services Research and Education in the Alcohol, Drug and Addiction Treatment Program. Dr. Greenfield received her BA from Brown University, her MD from Harvard Medical School (HMS), and her MPH in epidemiology from the University of North Carolina (UNC) at Chapel Hill. She is an addiction psychiatrist, clinician, and researcher. Dr. Greenfield completed psychiatry residency at McLean Hospital and a Robert Wood Johnson Clinical Scholars Fellowship at UNC. She has served as Principal and Co-Investigator on federally funded research regarding treatment, gender differences, and health services for substance use disorders (SUDs). She received a National Institute on Drug Abuse (NIDA) award in SUD patient-oriented research (2005–2016). With grants from NIH/NIDA, she developed a new evidence-based group therapy for women with SUDs, the Women's Recovery Group (WRG), and published the dissemination manual, *Treating Women with Substance Use Disorders: The Women's Recovery Group Manual*, in 2016. Dr. Greenfield led the alcohol implementation team for the National Institute on Alcohol Abuse (NIAAA)-funded IMPACT trial implementing alcohol and tuberculosis treatment in Tomsk, Russia. She is Past President of the American Academy of Addiction Psychiatry, current member and past chair of the American Psychiatric Association's Council on Addiction Psychiatry, and past Editor-in-Chief of the *Harvard Review of Psychiatry* (2002–2018). She is a member of the NIH/NIDA National Advisory Committee on Drug Abuse (2021–2023) and past member of the Advisory Committee on Services for Women for the US Substance Abuse and Mental Health Services Administration (2011–2017). She has been elected to the American College of Psychiatrists and the College of Problems on Drug Dependence. She received the R. Brinkley Smithers Distinguished Scientist Award from the American Society of Addiction Medicine and, from HMS, the A. Clifford Barger Award for Excellence in Mentoring, the Stuart A. Hauser Award for Mentoring from the Department of Psychiatry, and the Dean's Community Service Award for McLean Hospital's Outreach Program with the Indian Health Service in New Mexico. Dr. Greenfield is a co-author of Chapter 12, "Substance Use Disorders in Global Mental Health Delivery and Training."

James L. Griffith, MD, is a Professor of Psychiatry and past Chair of the Department of Psychiatry and Behavioral Sciences at the George Washington University School of Medicine and Health Sciences, Washington, DC (USA). As a psychiatric educator, Dr. Griffith developed a psychiatry residency program at George Washington University that has been distinguished for its curriculum in global mental health, cultural psychiatry, and psychiatric care for immigrants, refugees, and political torture survivors. He has received the Oskar Pfister Award from the American Psychiatric Association for his contributions to the field of religion and psychiatry. Dr. Griffith is a co-author of Chapter 3, "Promoting Global Mental Health Equity in Training Programs: Establishing Ethical and Reciprocal Partnerships."

Jennifer Guo, MD, PhD, is a volunteer clinical professor in the Department of Psychiatry at the University of California, San Francisco (UCSF) and a psychiatrist in private practice, also in San Francisco, California (USA). She completed her MD and PhD in Neuroscience at Yale School of Medicine, as well as residency at UCSF. Her interest in global mental health started in medical school through her work in Possible, an NGO that helps deliver health care to under-resourced regions in Nepal. In her practice, she is particularly interested in using interventional psychiatric approaches including Transcranial Magnetic Stimulation (TMS) and esketamine for treatment-resistant depression. In addition, she serves as the Medical Director for Psychedelic Medicine in her clinic, where she provides direct patient care with esketamine-assisted psychotherapy and works to increase access to ketamine-based treatments for patients. She continues to teach and mentor residents through her position as a volunteer clinical professor in the Department of Psychiatry at UCSF. Dr. Guo is a co-author of Chapter 4, "Developing a Global Mental Health Training Curriculum."

Dristy Gurung, MSc, is a PhD student in the health services and population research department at King's College London (KCL) and a research coordinator at Transcultural Psychosocial Organization (TPO), Nepal. She completed her MSc in Global Mental Health from KCL and the London School of Hygiene and Tropical Medicine (LSHTM) and has a keen interest in understanding the lived experiences of service users and their roles in stigma reduction and strengthening mental health systems. Ms. Gurung began working in global mental health as program officer/translator in 2009, where she was involved in development, implementation, and evaluation of a community mental health promotion program in a post-conflict setting. Since then, she has been involved in research projects regarding the mental health status of trafficking survivors, evaluation of reintegration packages for child soldiers, situation analysis of psychosocial counseling in Nepal, child behavior problems in communities, and mass psychogenic illness in Nepal. She was country lead for a consortium-based research project (EMERALD) focused on evaluating barriers and facilitators to mental health systems strengthening in six low- and middle-income countries. She was Co-Investigator for National Institutes of Health (NIH)-funded research projects focusing on reduction of health workers' stigma through service user involvement. She is currently a country lead for INDIGO, a project aiming to develop an anti-stigma package at community, primary care, and specialist levels through the involvement of service users. She is also focused on reducing structural levels of discrimination and stigma in mental health and other areas of global health. Ms. Gurung is a co-author of Chapter 5, "Mentorship in Global Mental Health."

Amruta Houde, MPH, MA, is the Mental Health Monitoring, Evaluation, and Learning Manager at Partners In Health (PIH), previously serving as PIH's Cross-Site Mental Health Program Coordinator. In her role, she collaborates with teams across 12 care delivery sites to strengthen data systems and integrate digital technology for routine monitoring and evaluation, quality improvement, and to demonstrate impact, as well as capacity-building through e-learning. Ms. Houde's interest in the field of global mental health stems from working closely alongside vulnerable communities in India, Sri Lanka, Brazil, and the United States to integrate community-based mental health programs and implementation science projects. She is passionate about advocating for mental health care as a human right throughout her work. Prior to PIH, Ms. Houde worked at the Columbia University Global Mental Health Program on research and advocacy projects, Sewa International in India on adolescent development programs, and interned with the Addictions Research Group at Sangath. She completed her Master of Public Health at Columbia University and Master's in Psychology from Boston University (BU). Ms. Houde is a co-author of Chapter 10, "Training for Humanitarian Crisis Response and Mental Health System Reform."

Xinran Hu, MD, MPH, is adjunct faculty at the Department of Psychiatry at Yale University in New Haven, Connecticut (USA) and a visiting scholar at the Mental Health Institute, Central South University, China. He has worked as a health literacy advisor for the World Health Organization's (WHO) Global Coordination Mechanism on noncommunicable diseases. Dr. Hu attended medical school at Vanderbilt University in Nashville, Tennessee, and Washington

University in St. Louis for the Master of Public Health and Global Health Fellowship. His interest in global health systems and health services in Chinese culture led him to collaborate with the World Health Organization on its Mental Health Literacy Demonstration Project, implementing programs across China to improve mental disorder recognition, management, and prevention. Dr. Hu is currently pursuing board certification in Public Health and General Preventive Medicine, as well as Occupational Medicine, and his current interests include global health service delivery with a focus on caregiving and the physician-patient relationship. Dr. Hu is a co-author of Chapter 7, "Educational Partnerships: Addressing Challenges in Meeting Trainee Goals with Established or New Global Mental Health Educational Programs."

Erick Hung, MD, is a Professor of Clinical Psychiatry in the University of California, San Francisco (UCSF) Department of Psychiatry and Behavioral Sciences and is a member of the UCSF Academy of Medical Educators in San Francisco, California (USA). He is the Associate Dean for Students in the UCSF School of Medicine. Prior to joining the Dean's team, he served as the Program Director of the Adult Psychiatry Residency Training Program from 2012 to 2022 and the Director of Curricular Affairs for GME for the UCSF School of Medicine from 2015 to 2022. He completed his medical school, psychiatry residency, and forensic psychiatry fellowship training at the University of California, San Francisco and joined the faculty at UCSF in 2009. He actively teaches in the areas of risk assessment, medical education, forensic psychiatry, leadership, and ethics. His interests include primary care and mental health integration, the interface between mental health and the legal system, inter-professional collaboration and training, HIV psychiatry, LGBTQ mental health, and medical education. His educational scholarship interests include competency-based assessment, faculty development, and near-peer learning in the workplace setting. He was a medical volunteer for the Himalayan Rescue Association in Nepal, wherein he helped a medical team set up the first Himalayan Rescue Association–sponsored clinic at Everest base camp in 2003. He has conducted global mental health research in Nepal on high altitude disorders, exploring the effectiveness of acetazolamide and ginkgo biloba on the prevention of acute mountain sickness. Dr. Hung is a co-author of Chapter 4, "Developing a Global Mental Health Training Curriculum."

Matias Irarrazaval, MD, MPH, is the Advisor on Mental Health and Substance Use at the Pan American Health Organization/World Health Organization. He is the former Director of Mental Health at the Ministry of Health of Chile and is also a child and adolescent psychiatrist. Dr. Irarrazaval started collaborating as a research assistant on the NIMH-Columbia University project RedeAmericas, and this experience inspired him to pursue his MPH in Global Health at Harvard University. He is working at the Millennium Institute for Research in Depression and Personality in several research projects on diminishing stigma, building mental health system treatment and research capacity, implementing prevention programs, and establishing sustainable scale-up of public health systems to improve access to mental health treatment in Chile and the Americas. Dr. Irarrazaval received the Paramjit Toor Joshi International Award from the American Academy of Child and Adolescent Psychiatry for his contributions in Global Mental Health. Dr. Irarrazaval is a co-author of Chapter 8, "Mobilizing a Range of Resources to Advance Research and Service in Global Mental Health Training."

Samah Jabr, MD, is a Palestinian psychiatrist and Clinical Associate Professor of Psychiatry at the George Washington University School of Medicine and Health Sciences, Washington, DC (USA). For three decades, Dr. Jabr has served in Israel, West Bank Palestine, and Jordan as a major consultant on clinical issues, training, mental health policy, and program development for psychiatric illnesses and mental health problems in Palestinian populations. Recognized internationally as a human rights advocate, she has provided a voice for the mental health needs of the Palestinian people, while also working collaboratively with Israeli mental health professionals and members of the US Jewish community to build mental health services for the Palestinian population. She has trained and mentored scores of mental health professionals who now practice in public and private mental health sectors in the West Bank. Dr. Jabr is a co-author of Chapter 3, "Promoting Global Mental Health Equity in Training Programs: Establishing Ethical and Reciprocal Partnerships."

Helen Jack, MD, is on the faculty at University of Washington in Seattle, Washington (USA), where she divides her time between primary care practice in a prison in rural Washington State and global mental health research. After completing Internal Medicine residency at the University of Washington in 2021, Dr. Jack is now an early-career primary care physician and researcher. Dr. Jack's research focuses on the integration of mental health and substance use treatment into primary health care in low-resource settings in both the United States and Zimbabwe. Dr. Jack has been doing research and research capacity-building in Zimbabwe since 2013, and she is the Co-Director of Kushinga, a Zimbabwean mental health research and advocacy organization that works to generate locally relevant research on mental health policy and systems. After graduating from Yale University, she completed a second BA in Philosophy, Politics, and Economics at Oxford University as a Rhodes Scholar. Dr. Jack received her MD from Harvard Medical School in 2018. Dr. Jack is a co-author of Chapter 9, "Student Engagement in Global Mental Health: Perspectives on Curricular, Extracurricular, and Advocacy Opportunities."

Bonnie N. Kaiser, PhD, MPH, is an Associate Professor at University of California, San Diego (UCSD) in La Jolla, California (USA), jointly appointed in the Department of Anthropology and Global Health Program. She conducts rigorous mixed-methods studies with multidisciplinary engagement, drawing on her training as an anthropologist (PhD), epidemiologist (MPH), and global health implementation scientist. Dr. Kaiser came to global mental health via anthropology, by leading an interdisciplinary research team exploring mental health in Haiti during her graduate training. Her scholarship balances critical and constructive engagement with the field of global mental health, advancing both theory in psychological anthropology and practice in global mental health. Her research focuses on elucidating cultural models of mental health and illness and exploring their connections to care-seeking; developing and adapting measurement tools for cross-cultural research and interventions; improving cultural adaptation of global mental health interventions; and critically exploring concepts of trauma, risk, and resilience. Her research balances deep ethnographic engagement in her primary field sites of Haiti and Kenya with mixed-methods and multi-sited research in other global regions, including in Nepal, Ethiopia, and Nigeria. Mentorship and capacity-building are central to her work in all these sites, particularly training scholars and professionals from low- and middle-income countries in anthropology and global health research skills. Dr. Kaiser is a co-author of Chapter 5, "Mentorship in Global Mental Health."

Christopher Kemp, PhD MPH, is an Assistant Scientist in the Department of International Health at Johns Hopkins University in Baltimore, Maryland (USA). He is co-director of the Implementation Strategies branch within the Johns Hopkins Center for AIDS Research Implementation Science Core and core faculty with the Johns Hopkins Center for Indigenous Health. He is an implementation scientist focused on supporting integrated approaches to mental health, HIV, and other chronic disease-related care in low-resource settings. Christopher has been involved in program implementation and research with the World Health Organization, UNICEF, NIH Fogarty Center, Wellcome Trust, I-TECH, PATH, and the University of KwaZulu-Natal. He holds an MPH and PhD from the University of Washington School of Public Health. His published works can be found at https://www.ncbi .nlm.nih.gov/myncbi/christopher.kemp.1/bibliography/public/. Dr. Kemp is a co-author of Chapter 6, "Implementation of Integrated Care Models: Lessons for Training and Practice in Low-Resource Settings."

Arthur Kleinman, MD, is Rabb Professor of Anthropology and Professor of Global Health and Social Medicine and Psychiatry at Harvard University in Cambridge and Boston, Massachusetts (USA). Professor Kleinman holds a BA and MD from Stanford University and an MA in Anthropology from Harvard. He has conducted cross-cultural research on depression and other mental health problems in Chinese society beginning in 1969. He directed the first World Mental Health Report (Oxford University, 1995) and the first mental health project of The World Bank (*Out of the Shadows*, 2016). He is a distinguished lifetime fellow of the American Psychiatric Association and a Member of the National Academy of Medicine and the American Academy of Arts and Sciences. He is the author of *Rethinking Psychiatry* (1988) and co-editor of *Reimagining Global Health* (2013). Dr. Kleinman is co-author of Chapter 2, "Resocializing Global Mental Health: What Anthropological Perspectives Offer to Learners, Educators, and Practitioners."

Brandon A. Kohrt, MD, PhD, is the Charles and Sonia Akman Professor in Global Psychiatry and Professor of Psychiatry and Behavioral Sciences, Global Health, and Anthropology at George Washington University in Washington, DC (USA). Dr. Kohrt began working in global mental health when apprenticing at a traditional healing temple in southwestern Nepal in 1996. He spent much of the next decade conducting medical anthropology and mental health research in Nepal. When he wasn't in Nepal, Dr. Kohrt was working at a group home for persons with mental illness in Los Angeles, developing a program in Atlanta for torture survivors seeking political asylum, or studying culture-bound syndromes in Mongolia. After completing a PhD in medical anthropology and psychiatry residency training, Dr. Kohrt has consulted with the World Health Organization (WHO), United Nations Children's Fund (UNICEF), The Carter Center Mental Health Program in Liberia, and Transcultural Psychosocial Organization (TPO) in Nepal. Dr. Kohrt's primary interest is in increasing availability of culturally grounded mental health services in settings affected by humanitarian crises and in low- and middle-income countries. Dr. Kohrt and his collaborators have developed innovative approaches to partnering with mental health services users to reduce stigma among non-specialists taking on mental health service delivery roles. Dr. Kohrt has had a long list of mentors who have made all this possible, and over the past decade, he has had the privilege of providing mentorship for global mental health students from around the world. Dr. Kohrt is a co-author of Chapter 5, "Mentorship in Global Mental Health."

Eve Lasswell, PsyD, is an Assistant Professor of Psychiatry at University of California, San Diego (UCSD) in San Diego, California (USA). She is a clinical psychologist who treats individuals struggling with substance use disorders and trauma. She completed her doctorate at Indiana State University in Terre Haute, Indiana, where she studied the relationship between mutual help group involvement and overall well-being. She completed her post-doctoral fellowship in Addiction Psychology at the Veterans Affairs Salt Lake City Health Care System before joining the UCSD Substance Treatment and Recovery Program in La Jolla, California. Dr. Lasswell is a co-author of Chapter 7, "Educational Partnerships: Addressing Challenges in Meeting Trainee Goals with Established or New Global Mental Health Educational Programs."

Victoria Leonard, BA, is a doctoral candidate in clinical health psychology at the University of San Francisco (USA) and former Program Coordinator at the Columbia University–WHO

Center for Global Mental Health. Her work centers on mental health systems strengthening with a focus on boosting access for women and girls in underserved settings. After receiving her BA in Politics and Religion from Brown University, Ms. Leonard developed and implemented health education initiatives for Universal Promise in Addo, South Africa. She was then awarded a Princeton in Africa Fellowship at Comprehensive Community Based Rehabilitation in Tanzania, where she served on the Maternal Health Capacity Building team and discovered her passion for psychology. In this role, Ms. Leonard collaborated with clinicians, patients, and government partners to collect and disseminate data on improving health outcomes in primary and perinatal care. She is currently treating people with cancer and their loved ones and developing mental health programs for women with an obstetric fistula and clinicians who treat them. Ms. Leonard is a co-author of Chapter 8, "Mobilizing a Range of Resources to Advance Research and Service in Global Mental Health Training."

Zhening Liu, MD, PhD, is currently a Professor and Deputy Director at the Institute of Mental Health of Second Xiangya Hospital, Central South University, China. He was a visiting scholar at Yale University in New Haven, Connecticut, and the Chinese University of Hong Kong. Dr. Liu received his master's degree in Hunan Medical University and his PhD degree from Central South University in Changsha, Hunan, China. He is currently a member of the Pacific Rim College of Psychiatrists, Asian College of Schizophrenia Research, Chinese Medical Association, and Chinese Psychological Association. His areas of interest are psychiatry education, neurocognition, neurogenetics, and computational psychiatry in psychotic disorders. Dr. Liu is a co-author of Chapter 7, "Educational Partnerships: Addressing Challenges in Meeting Trainee Goals with Established or New Global Mental Health Educational Programs."

Liza Magill, BA, is a MD/MPH student at the Icahn School of Medicine at Mount Sinai in New York, New York (USA). Her research and clinical experience focus on cross-cultural psychiatry and global implementation of evidence-based psychological treatment methods. Ms. Magill first became interested in mental health after learning about the comorbidity of mental health disorders among juveniles in the US criminal justice system, and she had the opportunity to apply this interest globally on Partners In Health's mental health team. After studying International Studies with a focus in global health at Boston College (BC), Ms. Magill was selected as a Global Health Corps fellow and supported development of a psychosocial intervention for adolescent mothers in Rakai District, Uganda. She joined the Columbia-WHO team to support a variety of scientific writing and research initiatives related to global mental health. Ms. Magill is a co-author of Chapter 8, "Mobilizing a Range of Resources to Advance Research and Service in Global Mental Health Training."

Carla Marienfeld, MD, is a Clinical Professor of Psychiatry at the University of California, San Diego (UCSD) in San Diego, California (USA), as well as an addiction psychiatrist. She founded and led the Yale Global Mental Health Program (YGMHP). The YGMHP resulted in significant increases in the number of core and elective didactic sessions, resident international health experiences, mentored scholarly projects completed by residents, funding sources for experiences, and GMH scholarly projects. The YGMHP significantly affected recruitment to the residency. Dr. Marienfeld's first global mental health project in medical school looked at behavioral effects of iron-deficiency anemia of infancy in Chile, followed by residency projects in China on access to mental health care and projects in Nigeria looking at medical and nursing student attitudes about mental health. She worked with the Wuhan, China Centers for Disease Control on the development, expansion, and quality improvement for methadone treatment for opioid use disorder in China and did some work evaluating training of allied professionals in resource-poor settings. She attended Baylor College of Medicine in Houston,

Texas, where she completed the International Health Track. She is the Program Director of the UCSD Addiction Psychiatry Fellowship, and the Medical Director of the UCSD Substance Treatment and Recovery (STAR) Program in La Jolla, California. Dr. Marienfeld is a co-author of Chapter 7, "Educational Partnerships: Addressing Challenges in Meeting Trainee Goals with Established or New Global Mental Health Educational Programs."

R. Kathryn McHugh, PhD, is the Chief of Psychology and Director of the Stress, Anxiety and Substance Use Lab at McLean Hospital and an associate professor in the Department of Psychiatry at Harvard Medical School (HMS) in Boston, Massachusetts (USA). She received her BA from Harvard College and her PhD from Boston University. Dr. McHugh's research focuses on understanding the nature and treatment of anxiety, substance use, and related disorders. In addition, Dr. McHugh conducts research on the dissemination and implementation of behavioral therapies. She has published over 160 articles and book chapters and an edited book spanning these research areas. Her research is currently funded by several grants from the National Institute on Drug Abuse (NIDA), focused on mechanisms linking stress and pain to outcomes in people with opioid use disorder. She is also a Co-Investigator of the New England Consortium Node of the NIDA Clinical Trials Network. Dr. McHugh is a recipient of several national awards, such as the David Shakow Early Career Award for Distinguished Scientific Contributions to Clinical Psychology from the American Psychological Association (APA). She recently co-chaired the APA Taskforce on Clinical Responses to the Opioid Crisis and is a member of the National Academies Forum on Mental Health and Substance Use Disorders. She is a member of several journal editorial boards and an Associate Editor of *Psychology of Addictive Behaviors* and *Cognitive Therapy and Research*. Dr. McHugh is also a practicing clinical psychologist and regular provider of continuing education, with a focus on behavior therapy. Dr. McHugh is a co-author of Chapter 12, "Substance Use Disorders in Global Mental Health Delivery and Training."

Georgina Miguel Esponda, PhD, is a Strategic Information and Impact Manager at Compañeros En Salud (CES), a not-for-profit organization working to strengthen health systems in rural Mexico. She is also a consultant at Ember Mental Health, a project that aims to support mental health initiatives in the Global South to achieve sustainability. Previously, she was a Postdoctoral Research Associate at King's College London (KCL) where she collaborated in the INTernational REsearch programme on Psychoses In Diverse settings (INTREPID II), which explored the epidemiology and impact of psychotic disorders in Trinidad, Nigeria, and India. Prior to this, she completed a PhD in Epidemiology and Population Health at the London School of Hygiene and Tropical Medicine (LSHTM). She also completed an MSc in Global Mental Health at KCL and the LSHTM and an undergraduate degree in Psychology at the Universidad Iberoamericana. She hopes to continue collaborating in projects that contribute to the improvement of population mental health through co-production, community mobilization, and tackling the social determinants of mental health. Dr. Miguel Esponda is a co-author of Chapter 9, "Student Engagement in Global Mental Health: Perspectives on Curricular, Extracurricular, and Advocacy Opportunities."

Michael Morse, MD, MPA, is a child, adolescent, and adult psychiatrist and Assistant Professor of Clinical Psychiatry in the Georgetown University School of Medicine in Washington, DC (USA), where his clinical focus has been the treatment of attention deficit disorder across the lifespan and increasing access to treatment for women with attention deficit disorder. For nearly two decades, Dr. Morse has collaborated with academic and non-profit humanitarian organizations to expand clinical training and development of mental health services in West Bank Palestine and in West Africa. Dr. Morse is a co-author of Chapter 3, "Promoting

Global Mental Health Equity in Training Programs: Establishing Ethical and Reciprocal Partnerships."

Byamah B. Mutamba, MBChB, MMED, MPH, PhD, is a Senior Consultant Psychiatrist at Butabika National Referral Mental Hospital in Kampala, Uganda, where he practices general adult psychiatry, and is the clinical head of the Alcohol and Drug Unit. He is also a co-founder and technical director at YouBelong Uganda, a locally registered NGO working to transition institutionalized and/or abandoned individuals back to family and community. Dr. Mutamba has dual expertise in public health and mental health. He has been involved with various mental health implementation research projects including piloting the Mental Health Gap Action Programme (mhGAP) in Uganda, the Mental Health Beyond Facilities (mhBeF), the Family Based Interpersonal Therapy for Caregivers of Children with Nodding Syndrome to Improve the Mental Health of Both (GCC/IPT-F), and the Curtailing Hospital Readmissions of Persons with Severe Mental Illness in Africa (ChaRiSMA), which sought to determine which patients with severe mental illness are most likely to be readmitted to Butabika hospital, as well as generate evidence on the feasibility, acceptability, and appropriateness of a community mental health model (the YouBelongHOME intervention) in low-resourced settings. He is currently the principal investigator (PI) on the Strengthening CAre in collaboration with People with lived Experience of psychosis in Uganda (SCAPE-U). For the past 15 years, his work at the hospital in Uganda and with community health worker initiatives, highlights the need for a public mental health approach to his practice. This experience and interest in the development of culturally appropriate, non-specialist led (public mental health) interventions in low-resourced health systems, informs his participation in the global mental health field. Dr. Mutamba is a co-author of Chapter 5, "Mentorship in Global Mental Health."

Victoria Mutiso, PhD, is a clinical psychologist at Africa Mental Health Research and Training Foundation (Kenya). Her involvement in global mental health evolved out of her interaction with underserved and marginalized populations in Kenya both in urban and rural settings. Her experience in navigating the political and bureaucratic terrains motivated her to be a "voice for the voiceless" and she found herself working very closely with service users and engaging them in her work. This exposure propelled Dr. Mutiso into the global mental health field. She has served as Principal Investigator (PI) and Co-PI for Kenyan published clinical and community epidemiological studies on mental health and substance abuse. Dr. Mutiso is a co-author of Chapter 8, "Mobilizing a Range of Resources to Advance Research and Service in Global Mental Health Training."

David M. Ndetei, DSc, MD, MBChB, is a Professor of Psychiatry at the University of Nairobi (Kenya) and the Founding Director of Africa Mental Health Research and Training Foundation. He has served as the Principal Investigator (PI) or Co-PI for most Kenyan published clinical and community epidemiological studies on mental health and substance abuse. He has 400 scholarly publications and is currently finalizing his latest book, *African Textbook of Psychiatry and Mental Health: Integrated Clinical and Public Health Approaches*, which brings together multidisciplinary contributors from Africa and beyond. He is a member of various professional bodies and honorary official of various academic institutions and associations globally. Dr. Ndetei is a co-author of Chapter 8, "Mobilizing a Range of Resources to Advance Research and Service in Global Mental Health Training."

Brian Neff, MA, MALD, is a doctoral candidate in clinical psychology at the City College of New York (USA) and a resident therapist at the Manhattan School of Music Counseling Center. He currently conducts psychotherapy process-outcome research in LGBTQ+ populations with a focus on minority stress processes. He holds a Bachelor of Arts (BA) in history from Yale University and a Master of Arts (MA) in Law and Diplomacy from the Fletcher School at Tufts University, where he first became interested in global mental health research-ing the efficacy of psychosocial interventions for mental health outcomes in refugee popula-tions. Mr. Neff has served as a political affairs consultant for the United Nations Mission in Sudan and the US Chief Executive for London-based conflict resolution NGO Peace Direct. He has also contributed to a wide range of research and programmatic efforts at Columbia University's Global Mental Health Program, including the World Health Organization's (WHO) 11th revision of the International Classification of Diseases. Mr. Neff is a co-author of Chapter 8, "Mobilizing a Range of Resources to Advance Research and Service in Global Mental Health Training."

Inge Petersen, PhD, is a research professor in the field of public mental health and Director of the Centre for Rural Health (CRH) in the College of Health Sciences at the University of KwaZulu-Natal, South Africa. She initially trained as a counseling psychologist and her ini-tial work in community psychology in South Africa provided the foundation for her work in global mental health. Over the past 20 years, she has played a leading role in several collabora-tive global mental health research consortia in low- and middle-income countries (LMICs) across Asia and Sub-Saharan Africa. This work has spanned using participatory implementa-tion research to build the evidence for task-sharing of psychosocial counseling interventions for adults, and mental health promotion for children and adolescents to her more recent work on strengthening of health systems to be enabling of the integration of mental health care into routine health services, particularly at the primary healthcare and community levels of care. She has also authored a number of international texts on the evidence base for mental health promotion and prevention of mental disorders in LMICs. Her publications can be found on ORCID https://orcid.org/0000-0002-3573-4229. Dr. Petersen is a co-author of Chapter 6, "Implementation of Integrated Care Models: Lessons for Training and Practice in Low-Resource Settings."

Kathleen M. Pike, PhD, is a Professor of Psychology in the Departments of Psychiatry and Epidemiology at Columbia University Medical Center in New York City, New York (USA). She is Director of the World Health Organization (WHO) Collaborating Centre for Capacity Building and Training in Global Mental Health and Chair of the Faculty Steering Committee for the Global Mental Health Programs at Columbia University. She held a Faculty Fulbright Award in Japan where she was Associate Dean at Temple University Japan and Visiting Professor at Keio University. She is a global expert on eating disorders and has conducted pioneering work on their risk factors and the development and dissemination of evidence-based treatments. Dr. Pike came to global mental health through studying international rela-tions and psychology. Her passions for public policy, arts advocacy, and teaching intersect in the field of global mental health. Dr. Pike is a co-author of Chapter 8, "Mobilizing a Range of Resources to Advance Research and Service in Global Mental Health Training."

LeShawndra N. Price, PhD, is Director of the Office of Research Training and Special Programs within the National Institute of Allergy and Infectious Diseases (NIAID) at the US National Institutes of Health (NIH), where she supports capacity-building for early career researchers and physician scientists and implements international outreach and compliance programs. Prior to joining NIAID, Dr. Price served as a Program Official at the National Institute of Mental Health (NIMH) where she was Project Scientist for a multi-million-dollar initiative involving eight distinct clinical trials designed to improve treatments and expand access to mental health care in more than 20 low- and middle-income countries. A graduate school field course in Brazil on cross-cultural child development sparked Dr. Price's interest in global health. She then realized the similarities between global health research in low- and middle-income countries and health equity research on populations in the United States and has focused on these areas throughout her career. Dr. Price is a co-author of Chapter 8, "Mobilizing a Range of Resources to Advance Research and Service in Global Mental Health Training."

Sauharda Rai, MA, PhD, is a research scientist at the Division of Global Mental Health, School of Medicine and Health Sciences at the George Washington University in Washington, DC (USA). He has been working in the field of global mental health focused on stigma, migration, and post-conflict societies for over a decade. Dr. Rai has also been working extensively on capacity-building of researchers and institutions in his home country Nepal through various trainings, workshops, and mentorships. Through his work, he aims toward the decolonization of global mental health and bringing more emic-indigenous perspectives and methods to the field. Dr. Rai is a co-author of Chapter 3, "Promoting Global Mental Health Equity in Training Programs: Establishing Ethical and Reciprocal Partnerships."

Deepa Rao, PhD, is a Professor in the Departments of Global Health and Psychiatry and Behavioral Sciences at the University of Washington in Seattle, Washington (USA). She is a licensed clinical psychologist, and her professional interests are to implement effective interventions to improve mental health and reduce stigma for people with various conditions such as breast and cervical cancer, HIV, diabetes, and depression. Prior to her work as faculty at the University of Washington, she trained at the National Institute of Mental Health and Neurosciences in Bangalore, India. She currently works in the United States on stigma reduction efforts, in South Africa on building mental health research capacity, and in India with pregnant women with depressive symptoms and experiences of domestic violence. She is the Associate Director of the Center for AIDS Research Behavioral Science Core, Associate Director of Global Mental Health, and the Associate Director of the MPH program in Global Health at the University of Washington. Her research publications can be found at http://www.ncbi.nlm.nih.gov/sites/myncbi/deepa.rao.1/bibliography/41143522/public/?sort=date&direction= descending. Dr. Rao is a co-author of Chapter 6, "Implementation of Integrated Care Models: Lessons for Training and Practice in Low-Resource Settings."

Giuseppe Raviola, MD, MPH, is the Co-Director of Mental Health at Partners In Health (PIH), Associate Director of The Chester M. Pierce Division of Global Psychiatry at Massachusetts General Hospital (MGH), Director of the Program in Global Mental Health and Social Change in the Harvard Medical School (HMS) Department of Global Health and Social Medicine, and assistant professor in psychiatry and global health and social medicine at HMS in Boston, Massachusetts (USA). In 2002, he published the first study examining physician mental health in Sub-Saharan Africa, in the context of HIV/AIDS. Since 2009, Dr. Raviola has been engaged in global mental health program building in Haiti, Peru, Mexico, Rwanda, Liberia, Sierra Leone, Malawi, Lesotho, Russia, and Kazakhstan, building site-based teams delivering mental health services to meet the significant burden of illness. In his role with PIH, Dr. Raviola supports local team leadership on strategic planning related to mental healthcare delivery. Since 2016 PIH has delivered more than a quarter million mental health care visits across twelve global sites. At Harvard, he works to advance efforts related to training and education, and research, promoting excellence in global mental healthcare delivery. Dr. Raviola is a co-author of Chapter 10, "Training for Humanitarian Crisis Response and Mental Health System Reform."

Tahilia J. Rebello, PhD, is an Assistant Professor in the Department of Psychiatry and Program Manager of the World Health Organization (WHO) Collaborating Centre for Research and Training in Global Mental Health at Columbia University in New York City, New York

(USA). She also serves on the Steering Committee for the consortium of Global Mental Health Programs at Columbia and serves as the Project Coordinator for WHO's Global Clinical Practice Network. Her work focuses on the development of studies and trainings on the WHO's diagnostic guidelines for mental and behavioral disorders as part of the ICD-11, suicide and migration, and multisectoral scale-up of community-based mental health care by engaging non-specialists. Though she is trained as a neuroscientist, she transitioned into the global mental health field following a post-doctoral internship with the World Health Organization, where she applied her scientific training to various mental health initiatives around the world. Dr. Rebello is a co-author of Chapter 8, "Mobilizing a Range of Resources to Advance Research and Service in Global Mental Health Training."

Meghan E. Reilly, BA, is a medical student at University of Massachusetts (UMass) Chan Medical School in Worcester, Massachusetts (USA). Ms. Reilly received her BA in Psychology at Clark University and formerly worked as a clinical research assistant in the Alcohol and Drug Abuse Treatment Program at McLean Hospital in Belmont, Massachusetts. In this role, she assisted in coordinating studies that examined gender-responsive care for women with substance use disorders, as well as assisting in the review of literature for the chapter she co-authored in this book. It was during this time that Ms. Reilly saw the efficacy of medication-assisted treatment for both substance use and other mental health disorders, which led her to consider a future in medicine. As a future physician, Ms. Reilly hopes to deliver quality, compassionate care for disenfranchised and stigmatized patient populations in the United States and in global contexts. Ms. Reilly is a co-author of Chapter 12, "Substance Use Disorders in Global Mental Health Delivery and Training."

Pragya Rimal is a current PhD student at the Fielding School of Public Health in the Health Policy and Management Program at the University of California, Los Angeles (UCLA) in Los Angeles, California (USA). As the former Senior Mental Health Research Analyst at Possible, she is driven to ensure that the most underserved communities in remote locations have access to high-quality mental healthcare services. In her role at Possible, Ms. Rimal led a two-year-long research project on integrated mental health care. The project entailed training mid-level practitioners and non-specialist clinicians to provide high-quality mental health services. She implemented two National Institutes of Health (NIH)-funded research studies to adapt and develop a motivational interviewing tool to assist community health workers engage with patients who are non-adherent to treatment. Ms. Rimal feels fortunate to have found great mentors early in her career who support her to not just build mental health programs but also to navigate through complex social structures, guiding her career trajectory. Ms. Rimal is a co-author of Chapter 5, "Mentorship in Global Mental Health."

Robert M. Rohrbaugh, MD, is a Professor of Psychiatry, Associate Dean for Global Health Education, and Deputy Dean for Professionalism and Leadership Development in the Yale School of Medicine (YSM) Office of Academic & Professional Development (OAPD) at Yale School of Medicine in New Haven, Connecticut (USA). He is the former Yale Department of Psychiatry Deputy Chair for Education and Career Development and adult psychiatry residency program director. Collaborating with colleagues at the Xiangya School of Medicine in Changsha PRC and at Yale and the Yale-China Association, Dr. Rohrbaugh consulted on the development of a competency-based model for residency training for all medical disciplines; significant components of that model have been utilized by the Ministries of Health and Education in developing the national model for residency training for all of China. Dr. Rohrbaugh and colleagues are working to promote primary care at the local level in Township-level hospitals in rural China. Recognizing that global health educators in low- and middle-income countries are often excluded from academic discussions of global health education, Dr. Rohrbaugh cofounded the Bellagio Global Health Education Initiative in which educators from low-, middle-, and high-income countries collaborate to develop equitable bilateral relationships, curriculum, and educational policy recommendations that promote global health education. Dr. Rohrbaugh is a co-author of Chapter 7, "Educational Partnerships: Addressing Challenges in Meeting Trainee Goals with Established or New Global Mental Health Educational Programs."

Jonathan Sadowsky, PhD, is the Theodore J. Castele Professor of the History of Medicine, History Department Chair, and Associate Director of the Program in Medicine, Society, and Culture at Case Western Reserve University in Cleveland, Ohio (USA). He holds secondary appointments in the Departments of Bioethics and Medical Humanities, and Psychiatry. He holds degrees in History from Wesleyan (BA), Stanford (MA), and Johns Hopkins University (PhD), and studied psychiatric epidemiology at Columbia. He is the author of *Imperial Bedlam: Institutions of Madness and Colonialism in Southwest Nigeria* (University of California Press, 1999); *Electroconvulsive Therapy in America: The Anatomy of a Medical Controversy* (Routledge, 2016); and *The Empire of Depression: A New History* (Polity Books, 2020). His articles have appeared in journals including *Culture, Medicine and Psychiatry, The Journal of the History of Medicine and Allied Sciences, Harvard Review of Psychiatry, Bulletin of the History of Medicine*, and *History of Psychiatry*. He is the co-editor of the six-volume *Cultural History of Madness*, forthcoming from Bloomsbury Press. Dr. Sadowsky is co-author of Chapter 1, "The Colonial and Postcolonial Roots of Global Mental Health Efforts."

André Fiks Salem, BA, is a student at Faculdade de Ciências da Saúde Albert Einstein (FICSAE) medical school in São Paulo, Brazil. He received a BA in Neuroscience and Behavior from Columbia University in 2019. Mr. Fiks Salem supported adaptation and translation of evidence-based practices from high-income countries to Portuguese-speaking low-income settings in Mozambique and designed questionnaire-based algorithms for psychiatric medication management for Professor Milton Wainberg's scale-up and research capacity-building grants on global mental health and implementation science. As an undergraduate international student from Brazil, Mr. Fiks Salem entered the field of mental health already with a global mentality, contributing initially as a translator in US-funded projects, and now, as a local researcher in Brazil. Mr. Fiks Salem is a co-author of Chapter 8, "Mobilizing a Range of Resources to Advance Research and Service in Global Mental Health Training."

Manaswi Sangraula, PhD, MPH, is currently working as the Assistant Director of Research at the Trauma and Global Mental Health Lab at the New School for Social Science Research (NSSR) in New York City, New York (USA). Her work is focused on increasing access to mental health care and equity for migrants and displaced populations and various communities in New York City, using task-sharing and scalable interventions. Prior to her current role, she coordinated a cluster randomized controlled trial on Group Program Management Plus (PM+), a World Health Organization (WHO) task-shifting psychological intervention for humanitarian settings in Nepal. Her primary interests in global mental health include cultural adaptation of psychological treatments, group therapy interventions and community/social support, and gender and mental health. Dr. Sangraula received her PhD from the University of Amsterdam and her MPH from Columbia University. Dr. Sangraula is a co-author of Chapter 5, "Mentorship in Global Mental Health."

Pamela Scorza, ScD, MPH, is an Assistant Professor in the Department of Obstetrics and Gynecology at Columbia University in New York City, New York (USA). Dr. Scorza studies intergenerational processes in the transmission of risk for poor mental health, with a focus on using biomarkers to test the effects of perinatal mental health interventions in populations exposed to adversities. Dr. Scorza holds a Master of Public Health (MPH) degree from the University of Ghana in West Africa and a Doctor of Science degree from the Harvard T.H. Chan School of Public Health. Dr. Scorza has conducted Global Mental Health implementation research in Rwanda, Burundi, and Peru. Her interest in global mental health grew through studying medical anthropology as an undergraduate in Ecuador and Ghana and then studying public health at the University of Ghana. Dr. Scorza is a co-author of Chapter 8, "Mobilizing a Range of Resources to Advance Research and Service in Global Mental Health Training."

Nick Seymour, AB, is the Associate Director of Grassroots Strategy at Partners In Health (PIH) in Boston, Massachusetts (USA). In this role, he works with the Global Policy and Partnerships department, the US-based volunteer Network Leadership Team of coach-organizers, as well as Socios En Salud and Compañeros En Salud leadership to organize over 80 local teams building the right to health movement. Mr. Seymour graduated from Harvard College in 2019, where he studied Social Anthropology and Global Health and Health Policy. His senior honors thesis, advised by Professor Arthur Kleinman, was on intern physicians' influence on state-society relations in Chiapas, Mexico. Previously, Mr. Seymour volunteered with and supported several research projects at Compañeros En Salud. Having learned from and been inspired by peers, professors, advisors, and colleagues who have made global mental health central to their professional lives, Mr. Seymour hopes to incorporate global mental health practice into a career as a primary care clinician and through advocacy for global mental health as indispensable to universal health care. Mr. Seymour is a co-author of Chapter 9, "Student Engagement in Global Mental Health: Perspectives on Curricular, Extracurricular, and Advocacy Opportunities."

Sonya Shin, MD, MPH, is an Associate Professor at Harvard Medical School (HMS) in Boston, Massachusetts (USA), associate physician at the Division of Global Health Equity at Brigham and Women's Hospital, and a practicing infectious diseases physician at Gallup Indian Medical Center in Gallup, New Mexico. Dr. Shin received her BA at Yale University, and her MD and MPH at Harvard. She trained in Internal Medicine at Brigham and Women's Hospital and in Infectious Diseases in the Longwood Program at Harvard. She has worked for over 20 years with Partners In Health (PIH) to develop and evaluate community-based programs addressing chronic diseases in populations facing significant barriers to healthcare access. In Tomsk, Russia, Dr. Shin worked with healthcare providers to integrate delivery of interventions addressing alcohol use disorders into routine care for tuberculosis patients. In Peru, she has developed and studied interventions addressing a variety of behaviors through community health worker models of care, including adherence to antiretroviral therapy and parenting behaviors to promote early child development. In Navajo Nation, she has worked since 2009 to collaborate with tribal leadership and health services to strengthen healthcare delivery by enhancing integration of community health worker outreach and addressing food security. She served as the founding Director of a non-profit organization, Community Outreach and Patient Empowerment (COPE), which is dedicated to improving health outcomes in Native communities. Dr. Shin is a co-author of Chapter 12, "Substance Use Disorders in Global Mental Health Delivery and Training."

Sarah Singer, MPH, works for Partners In Health (PIH) as the Cross-Site Mental Health Program Manager. Together with a cross-national team, she provides program management and technical advisement to mental health service delivery development across 12 PIH care delivery sites. Her experience in global mental health has focused on grants and financial management, operations, strategic planning, capacity-building, training, and knowledge sharing. Mrs. Singer came to the global mental health field through an interest in implementing social justice-oriented community-based programs and volunteering in India, Israel, and local communities in the United States. Prior to her work at PIH, Mrs. Singer worked at Massachusetts General Hospital (MGH) in the Benson-Henry Institute of Mind-Body Medicine, conducted mental health research at Boston University (BU), and interned at the World Health Organization (WHO) in Geneva, Switzerland. She received her Master of Public Health at BU in Social/Behavioral Sciences and Health Policy/Management. Mrs. Singer is a co-author of Chapter 10, "Training for Humanitarian Crisis Response and Mental Health System Reform."

Stephanie L. Smith, MD, is Co-Director of Mental Health at the global non-profit Partners In Health (PIH), and Director of the new Program in Global Mental Health Equity at the Brigham and Women's Hospital in Boston, Massachusetts (USA). She is also an affiliate in the Department of Global Health and Social Medicine at Harvard Medical School. Dr. Smith was the inaugural Dr. Mario Pagenel Fellow in Global Mental Health Delivery with Partners In Health in Rwanda. Dr. Smith's expertise and scholarly contributions are in innovative program design, implementation, and evaluation of mental health services in resource-limited settings. She has supported the development of community-based mental health service delivery platforms, and the establishment of a cross-site learning collaborative in mental healthcare delivery, across all PIH's global sites (Haiti, Kazakhstan, Lesotho, Liberia, Malawi, Mexico, Navajo Nation, Peru, Russia, Rwanda, and Sierra Leone). Dr. Smith continues her clinical practice as a consult-liaison psychiatrist on the Medical Psychiatry service at the Brigham and Women's Hospital, and actively teaches and mentors psychiatry residents and fellows, medical students, and other allied health professionals in the principles of public and global mental health. Dr. Smith is the co-author of Chapter 10, "Training for Humanitarian Crisis Response and Mental Health System Reform."

Markos Tesfaye, MD, PhD, is a general psychiatrist working at the Department of Psychiatry, St Paul's Hospital Millennium Medical College in Addis Ababa, Ethiopia. Dr. Tesfaye began working in global mental health in 2007 as head of the Department of Psychiatry at Jimma University in Ethiopia. As the primary care centers in the region did not provide mental health services, his first project aimed to assess the mental health knowledge, attitudes, and practice of nurses working in those health facilities. He has been involved in developing training programs for mid-level mental health specialists and psychiatrists. In addition, Dr. Tesfaye has been teaching psychiatry for medical students and health science undergraduate students, and mentors graduates in their endeavors to set up psychiatric services as well as in mental health research. Dr. Tesfaye has supervised several graduate students' mental health research projects contributing toward the improvement of person power in global mental health research. Dr. Tesfaye is a co-author of Chapter 5, "Mentorship in Global Mental Health."

Jürgen Unützer, MD, MPH, is Chair of the Department of Psychiatry and Behavioral Sciences at the University of Washington in Seattle, Washington (USA). He also directs the Garvey Institute for Brain Health Solutions at University of Washington School of Medicine and holds adjunct appointments as Professor in the School of Public Health in the Departments of Health Services and Global Health. Dr. Unützer is an internationally recognized psychiatrist and health services researcher. His work focuses on innovative models that integrate mental health and general medical services and on translating research on evidence-based behavioral health interventions into effective clinical and public health practice. He has over 300 scientific publications and is the recipient of numerous federal and foundation grants and awards for his research to improve the health and mental health of populations through patient-centered integrated mental health services. Dr. Unützer trained in Medicine (MD, Vanderbilt University), Public Policy (MA, University of Chicago), and Public Health/Health Services (MPH, University of Washington). Dr. Unützer has served as Senior Scientific Advisor to the World Health Organization (WHO) and as an advisor to the President's New Freedom Commission on Mental Health. He works with national and international organizations to improve behavioral health care for diverse populations. Dr. Unützer founded the AIMS Center (Advancing Integrated Mental Health Solutions) and the IMPACT Program, which support national and international dissemination of evidence-based collaborative care programs for depression and other common behavioral health problems in primary care and other general medical settings. Dr. Unützer is a co-author of Chapter 6, "Implementation of Integrated Care Models: Lessons for Training and Practice in Low-Resource Settings."

Craig Van Dyke, MD, is currently Professor and Chair Emeritus of the Department of Psychiatry at the University of California, San Francisco (USCF) (USA) and High-Level Foreign Professor, Institute of Disaster Management and Reconstruction, Sichuan University. Dr. Van Dyke was the Chair of the Department of Psychiatry at UCSF from 1994 to 2008. After stepping down, he established the Department's Global Mental Health (GMH) Program. Later in 2008, the Director of the National Institute of Mental Health (NIMH) appointed him as a Special Advisor to assist in establishing the Institute's GMH Program. That same year, Dr. Van Dyke was part of the University of California delegation to Sichuan Provence, led by Professor Gretchen Kalonji, following the Wenchuan earthquake. The delegation provided advice to the national government's recovery efforts. Because of this work, Dr. Van Dyke was invited to work on the recovery effort in Japan following the 2011 earthquake, tsunami, and nuclear power plant disaster in Fukushima. In 2014–2015, he was a visiting professor at Jikei University in Tokyo. Since 2017, he has been collaborating with faculty members of the Institute of Disaster Management and Reconstruction at Sichuan University in Chengdu, China. The work focuses on a series of projects addressing mental health problems in victims of the 2008 earthquake. Currently, he is starting a new project examining stigma toward health workers and people associated with the COVID-19 epidemic in China. Dr. Van Dyke received his BS and his MD from the University of Washington and completed his residency at Yale University. Dr. Van Dyke is a co-author of Chapter 4, "Developing a Global Mental Health Training Curriculum."

Bradley H. Wagenaar, PhD, MPH, is an Associate Professor in the Department of Global Health (DGH) at the University of Washington in Seattle, Washington (USA), and an adjunct associate professor in the Department of Epidemiology. Trained as an epidemiologist, his work focuses on using innovative implementation science methods to answer pressing questions around improving public-sector health systems and health policies globally. He has particular interests in improving the prevention and treatment of mental illness in low-resource settings in the United States and globally. In addition, he is passionate about the use of quasi-experimental designs and routine health information systems data to optimize the scale-up of complex health systems approaches globally. He is currently the Principal Investigator or Co-Investigator on various mental health implementation science projects in Mozambique, Guatemala, and India. As faculty in the DGH, he teaches the Advanced Global Health Evaluation Methods course (GH537) offered each spring focused on quasi-experimental designs and analyses. He has also worked to develop innovative online distance learning courses in implementation science that have, to date, trained over 1000 students from more than 30 countries. Dr. Wagenaar is a co-author of Chapter 6, "Implementation of Integrated Care Models: Lessons for Training and Practice in Low-Resource Settings."

Milton L. Wainberg, MD, is a Professor of Clinical Psychiatry in the Department of Psychiatry at Columbia University in New York City, New York (USA). He has been principal or co-investigator of NIMH, NIAAA, NIDA, and CDC studies addressing the intersection of mental illness, substance use, and HIV, and several scale-up comprehensive mental health implementation projects worldwide aiming to decrease the global mental health burden and treatment gap. He is the Founding Chair of the Caucus of Global Mental Health and Psychiatry of the American Psychiatric Association. He is Director of four NIH-funded mental health implementation science research capacity-building programs in the United States, Sub-Saharan Africa, and South Asia, mentoring over 50 post-doctoral fellows. As a Latino psychiatrist with roots in Venezuela and Brazil, Dr. Wainberg has always seen mental health through a global lens, which, combined with an interest in health systems and a goal to improve access to health among people, led him to enter the Global Mental Health field. Dr. Wainberg is the director of the Columbia Psychiatry Mental Wellness Equity Center that brings evidence learned in low- and middle-income countries to inform scale-up of mental health services in the United States in partnership with the New York State Office of Mental Health. Dr. Wainberg is a co-author of Chapter 8, "Mobilizing a Range of Resources to Advance Research and Service in Global Mental Health Training."

Yang Yang, MPH, is the former Deputy Director of Health Programs at the Yale-China Association, responsible for executing and developing health program activities, including fellowship training, medical and nursing education collaborations, and community health initiatives in Hunan, China. Ms. Yang holds a BS in Biochemistry from UCLA and an MPH in Epidemiology from Yale University. Ms. Yang previously spent six years at the Los Angeles Immunization Program, conducting monitoring and evaluation of the immunization information system for the greater Los Angeles region. Ms. Yang has also conducted research on rural health insurance in Guizhou Province and HIV/AIDS anti-retroviral therapy at the Yale AIDS Program. Ms. Yang is a co-author of Chapter 7, "Educational Partnerships: Addressing Challenges in Meeting Trainee Goals with Established or New Global Mental Health Educational Programs."

Research Assistants/Project Managers
Louisa Fresquez Hudson
Anne J. Lheem
Pragya Rimal

Foreword

About half a century ago, psychiatry (and, in due course, other mental health disciplines) took a radical new direction in the hope of transforming our understanding of mental health problems and discovering new cures that could dramatically improve the outcomes of persons living with these problems. Leaders of the field were convinced that we needed to abandon the prevailing approaches, which were characterized by vague and imprecise categories of mental health problems and care models dominated by insight-oriented psychotherapies for common mental health problems or social interventions for severe mental health problems, and embrace the medical model that had served the cause of other health problems so well. In doing so, the implicit assumption was that, even if social, cultural, life-course and inter-personal factors were robust influences on mental health, mental health problems themselves were, like other medical conditions that are also influenced by such external determinants, essentially the result of biological dysfunctions of the brain. Sadly, those hopes have dimmed considerably.

The last five decades of research and practice, built on the narrow biomedical foundation of an algorithm-based diagnostic approach to mental health problems (because we did not then, or now, have any objective biomarkers for any of these diagnoses), led to the privileging of medical models of mental disorder, narrowly defined medical treatments (increasingly dominated by pharmaceuticals), the practitioners of these medical models (in particular, psychiatrists who were the sole mental health professional cadre licensed to prescribe psychotropic drugs), and biological paradigms for research. But, to paraphrase the words of one of the champions of this approach, Thomas Insel, a psychiatrist who led the US National Institute for Mental Health for over a decade in the new millennium, while over $20 billion was spent under his watch, the lion's share guided by this biomedical foundation, every single metric reflecting the mental health of the population has worsened in the United States over this period, from rising suicide mortality to the number of persons with mental illness who are incarcerated. Moreover, if the practical solution to mental health problems involved the deployment of highly trained mental health professionals and specialized clinical facilities, the United States was an outstanding example of the limitations of this approach: not only did the United States enjoy more mental health resources per capita than almost any country in the world, but it spent more on mental health care than for any other category of health conditions. From a purely clinical perspective, we still do not have a single biological finding of note for any mental health problem, nor a single new therapeutic agent or target for prevention. From a population perspective, there seems to be little correlation between the density of mental health professionals and facilities and the prevalence or incidence of mental health problems.

It is in this context that the field of global mental health is, arguably, the most exciting scientific and practical endeavor in the past two decades to invigorate the diverse disciplines concerned with mental health care and population mental health more broadly. Global mental health has offered, through a systematic process of interdisciplinary knowledge generation, encompassing such diverse fields as anthropology, epidemiology, psychology, clinical trials, and implementation science, new hope that we may find novel approaches. Such approaches will be built not only on science but also on a foundational commitment to empowering communities and widely available human resources, which are both deeply contextual but also generalizable. They will also embrace the new opportunities offered by digital technologies, to address the despondency about whether the world will ever be able to shift the needle on the burden of suffering related to mental health problems.

My own personal journey into this discipline began back in 1992 when, straight after completing my psychiatric residency at the world-renowned Maudsley Hospital, I found myself working in a western suburb of Sydney, the magnificent Australian city which, like much of the country in those days, hoped that the tragic history of genocidal dispossession of the aboriginal peoples, who had made that country their home for over 40,000 years, would not soil the image of a prosperous white country, teeming with modernity and progressive values. But I was posted as a psychiatrist serving a community located in a neighborhood called, not accidentally, Blacktown. The area of today's Blacktown was inhabited by different groups of the Darug people, the majority of whom died of diseases introduced by the arrival of the British in the late eighteenth century. When I started working in that community, I quickly discovered how its brutal history, mired in a century of structural violence, racism, and poverty, conspired to contribute to high rates of substance abuse, self-harm, mental illness, and interpersonal violence. It was my first introduction to global mental health (which, of course, did not exist as a specific discipline back then), and it remains one of the most important reminders to me that the values, principles, and approaches that define global mental health are just as relevant in wealthy countries as in less-resourced countries.

Soon after, I found myself working in Harare, the salubrious capital of Zimbabwe, itself a postcolonial country that had only a decade earlier ejected the British from its land. Here, I found myself in a country of nearly ten million people with fewer than ten psychiatrists, most of whom (like myself) were foreigners, unable to speak any local language and, therefore, unable to conduct the most essential technique in mental health care: interview a patient and offer information about their illness and the ways they can deal with the distressing symptoms and consequences of the illness. I realized very quickly that almost everything I had learned in my training, which was dominated by the biomedical model, was extremely limited in relevance and set about a journey to learn about health problems through an interdisciplinary lens, informed by medical anthropology (and, in particular the work of Kleinman, one of the authors in this book), epidemiology, and the emerging field of global health (which was being birthed in the tragic circumstances of the HIV pandemic decimating the communities of southern Africa).

But mental health was very far from being accepted as a legitimate area of concern in global health back then. A number of challenging attitudes prevailed at that time, some of which I myself harbored, fresh from being trained in a highly critical form of medical anthropology that viewed mental health problems as a signal of the failure of the "western" system and entirely socially constructed. These attitudes led to notions that mental health problems were not a concern for brown and Black people (or, more generally, for poor people or poor countries), that they were primarily the result of social suffering, and their solutions lay in dismantling structural factors that contributed to their social determinants. In any event, even if the latter were not sufficient, "western" psychiatry had failed to address mental health problems in wealthy countries and had little to offer, apart from expensive and inaccessible care models, to the less privileged.

Global mental health as the discipline we know it today, and which is beautifully covered in this book, was born out of this historic and social context. While some of its origins can be traced much further back (as has been rightly described by Sadowsky and Greene), for example the colonial origins of global psychiatry, the intellectual lodestar of the field was the publication, in 1995, of *World Mental Health* (whose editors included several distinguished colleagues of Anne Becker, one of the editors of this volume), which presented mental health problems through a complex prism of social, cultural, and political determinants, demanding responses that eschewed a dogmatic disciplinary ideology and sought to recognize and alleviate suffering through methods that borrowed from both indigenous traditions and the global health and clinical sciences. This was the need that a new generation of global mental health researchers and practitioners sought to address, with some radical departures from the research which preceded it, not least the inclusion of a much more diverse range of disciplines, often working together in a mutually respectful way, and much greater voice to, and leadership by, researchers who were from, and worked in, low-resource contexts.

My own work, much of it in India, the country of my birth to which I returned in 1996 after two years in Zimbabwe, and that of the many colleagues I have had the privilege of collaborating with, has led to a number of key observations. Mental illnesses are universal health experiences with similar "core" features and responses to interventions, but this does not imply that psychiatric diagnoses travel across cultures; in fact, they have limited validity everywhere. An individual's mental health problems cannot be addressed solely through a cookie-cutter approach beginning with the application of poorly validated diagnostic systems because mental health is inseparable from one's personal life history and socioeconomic conditions. This, in turn, implies that a one-size-fits-all approach has limited effectiveness and mental health care must embrace a diversity of approaches, in particular those that address a person's psychological skills and social environments, acknowledge the cultural influences on mental health experiences, and leverage providers who are widely available and live in the same context as the communities they serve. Above all, people with lived experience must be central to all aspects of mental health care, from identifying the priorities of the care system to holding it accountable.

Along the way, this body of knowledge has also offered a fresh light on many of the dilemmas, and false dichotomies, that have bedeviled the discourse regarding mental health problems in the global context. The observation that mental health problems were profoundly influenced by a person's lived experience from the earliest years of life did not mean that people with mental health problems could not be supported in their recovery journey by clinical interventions. Relatedly, the fact that medications had limited impact on mental health outcomes did not mean that they had no place in the armamentarium of effective interventions; instead, health systems needed to ensure the availability of a comprehensive set of interventions, including psychological and social interventions, to tailor care to be aligned with the person's needs. The delivery of care, therefore, must always include diverse providers, in particular community health workers who could "accompany" a patient (an evocative term coined by Paul Farmer) on their journey to recovery, offering a range of interventions, including psychological treatments. This can be achieved through a balanced care model, where both specialist care and community-based non-specialist care are available and delivered through collaboration among various providers (a topic covered thoroughly by Kemp and others in this volume). Further, just because social determinants were important, this did not mean that biological factors had no role to play; after all, the final substrate of a mental health experience had to lie within the brain. The large unmet needs for care did not diminish the importance of investment in research; as the history of the field has shown, it is research in resource-limited contexts that has led to the most scalable and contextually acceptable interventions. Finally, global mental health research was truly "global" in its scope and relevance. Thus, knowledge derived from global mental health could be relevant to diverse contexts, including in wealthy countries that had their own problems of mental health disparities and, as quoted earlier, the failure to impact the population burden of suffering.

These observations, and many more, have served as the basis for not only the emergence and establishment of global mental health as a unique discipline in the pantheon of global health, but also in the training of frontline and primary care providers, and of mental health professionals. This book offers a superb introduction and orientation to global mental health training and practice for the next generation of learners and educators, offering content that will be useful for learners who are relatively new to the field and are looking for a way to explore or deepen their interest. Further, the editors have adopted an inclusive definition of learners to encompass prospective students, current trainees, and early—even mid-career—mental health providers who are exploring a career in global mental health. Moreover, its coverage of the issues related to the history, principles, values, methods, and practices of global mental health are unique and make this volume an essential *vademecum* for any student of this discipline. The volume admirably demonstrates how global mental health must be truly global, for the knowledge generated by the field can derive from and be applied to populations in diverse contexts. The solutions for personalized care, a favored concept in the clinical world these days, must consider personal life stories, illness narratives, and social contexts. While knowledge of brain processes must continue to be studied, for now at least, it is the former that will have greater, indeed the only, practical utility in the clinical encounter.

While the editors have rightly acknowledged the limitations of the material, in particular the dominance of the Global North in the authorship and the target readership, this is surely testimony to the historic asymmetries in research capacity and resources in global mental health that I have personally witnessed being dramatically rebalanced in the past decade. I expect that future editions of this book will have far greater voice of authors, and case studies, from the Global South. In the meantime, I hope that some of the readers from the Global North will seek to implement the lessons of global mental health in their own backyard and the material in this book could easily be repurposed by institutions and practitioners in all contexts. As I once advised a medical student who wondered which country she should go to in order to gain experience in global mental health, she need not have gone much further than cross the tram line opposite my office, for there were vast disparities and suffering right in the shadows of the world's best medical school.

Furthermore, this volume also provides a clarion call for those who are studying, and practicing, global mental health to ensure that the work they do, which will continue to be influenced by persisting global inequities in resources, will squarely address these very inequities. Several authors of this volume rightly call for a concerted effort to repair the inequity that pervades the field (and this is true of all disciplines of global health and medicine) and one strategy to realize this goal is for privileged institutions, such as those of the editors and this author, to forge long-standing, mutually rewarding, sustainable, and equitable partnerships with institutions in low- and middle-income countries and historically disadvantaged institutions in wealthy countries. There is no place in global health for those who wish to bungee-jump into (and out of) contexts, like tourists pursuing a hobby. Incorporating training in these values and principles of global mental health is needed in all countries. These are ideals that my colleagues and I are committed to.

Both editors, and the over 60 authors of individual chapters, bring immense and diverse experience in service, research, and education in global mental health, working in academic and non-profit organizational settings and building collaborations to advance global mental health both in low-resource contexts in the Global South and the Global North. The case studies in Sections II and III offer a first-person account of training in the discipline and on additional areas that have often been marginalized, notably the care of persons with neurological or substance use problems and the needs of populations affected by humanitarian contexts. The latter strikes me as particularly relevant, for our present moment in history is fraught with great uncertainties around the threat of climate change on human prosperity and, importantly, its impact on the sustainability of human settlements around the world. While the editors are right to acknowledge the limitation that there are no chapters written from the perspective of the lived experience of mental health problems, the inclusion of a chapter written by students is the equivalent for a book that is focused on training.

In closing, I must acknowledge that this foreword was originally intended to be jointly authored with Paul Farmer. Much has been written, and much will be written, about Paul Farmer whose sudden passing at the age of 62 left legions of people around the world bereft. There are many scholars of global health who may have spent a few months, a few years even, with the less privileged in less-resourced environments. But there are very few who have spent significant periods of their lives in those environments, not only conducting research but serving as a doctor, an educator, and a builder of institutions whose legacies will outlive us all. Paul transformed global health from a highly academic subject, typically taught in wealthy countries about the less-fortunate peoples of the world by scholars whose lives are disconnected from those peoples, into a subject suffused with rights, equity, dignity, inclusion, compassion, and, most of all, outrage at the structural forces that had created and perpetuated poverty, inequality, violence, and injustice, where entirely preventable suffering continued to prevail even as a handful of countries and peoples with historic power and gunpowder created a world polluted by their greed, which in turn now threatens the very existence of our civilization. These high-minded ideals permeate many themes of this book, which stands out as one more example of the incredible intellectual legacy of Paul Farmer.

Vikram Patel, MBBS, MSc, PhD
Department of Global Health and Social Medicine
Harvard Medical School
September 2022

Introduction

Why an Orientation to Global Mental Health Training and Practice for Learners and Educators?

Bibhav Acharya and Anne E. Becker

The field of global mental health (GMH), the study and practice of improving mental health equity worldwide, has progressively developed into a multidisciplinary, specialized field over the past several decades. Whereas it shares a rather long history with the broader field of global health and its precursors, advances in mental health have lagged behind those for other health conditions in the global arena, where the primary focus and activity have been directed toward infectious diseases and maternal and child health. As global mental health emerges as a distinct discipline, it continues to contend with competing priorities for resource allocation. Worldwide, there is a stark asymmetry between the large health burden associated with mental disorders (encompassing psychiatric, neurological, and substance use problems) and the resource capacities to provide adequate access to high-quality prevention and treatment services for these ailments.[1] Despite the substantial health, economic, and social burdens associated with mental disorders, an enormous treatment gap persists between the associated needs and available services to meet them.[2] This gap, in turn, is underwritten by shortfalls in financial, scientific, and human resources that are especially marked in low- and middle-income countries (LMICs)—sometimes referred to collectively as the Global South—and also persist in high-income countries (HICs), or the Global North.[3,4] Many of these challenges were elaborated and brought into greater public and scientific visibility in a landmark series in the journal, *The Lancet,* in 2007,[5] further addressed in another series in 2011,[6] and in the 2018 *Lancet* Commission report on global mental health and sustainable development goals[7] as well as in numerous other subsequent publications in the context of the COVID-19 pandemic.[8–11]

Notwithstanding remarkable progress in the availability of evidence-based approaches for the effective treatment of mental disorders, a vast majority of people living with mental health problems are still unable to access high-quality care that meets their needs and preferences.[7] There continues to be an urgent need to develop both local and collaborative capacities to generate and share knowledge that can expand access to quality mental health services, while simultaneously addressing social drivers of poor mental health.[7] Closing this persistent gap will ultimately depend on training a health workforce that can develop, evaluate, and implement effective mental health treatment and prevention and generate scientific knowledge about effectiveness across diverse local contexts while also advancing a globalizing strategy for delivering evidence-based treatment and preventive approaches at scale.[12]

Among the most critical resource constraints that shape needs in global mental health, is a shortage of health professionals with specialized mental health expertise. Although this workforce shortage is global, it is especially pressing in low-resource settings. As a result of the shortfall in psychiatrists in LMICs, the conventional model of specialist-centered mental healthcare delivery familiar to most high-income country psychiatry trainees cannot meet the current full need for care delivery in low-resource settings. Training mental health professionals in LMIC settings is therefore an urgent necessity; that being said, the pipeline of mental health professional trainees

DOI: 10.4324/9781315160597-1

in most low-income settings will likely be inadequate to build the workforce that is needed in the near term.[13-15] Hence, in addition to in-country educational and training opportunities for mental health professionals to support expansion of this sector of the health workforce, other strategies to meet mental health treatment needs must be deployed in tandem. Meeting mental health treatment needs will require approaches that can leverage relatively scarce specialty expertise, for example, by integrating specialist and non-specialist roles in care delivery through task-sharing. In other words, adequate expansion of mental health delivery capacity will require not just training more mental health professionals but also a reimagination of the care delivery system that, fundamentally, will need to rely on supporting generalist healthcare workers (such as community health workers and primary care providers) and other professionals at the frontline (such as teachers), reorganizing care systems using integrated and collaborative care models, implementing preventive and self-help approaches, and utilizing specialists for highly specialized tasks requiring advanced knowledge or experience that cannot be delegated to others. Whereas both a greater number of mental health professionals and innovation in delivery models are needed in the Global North and the Global South, the needs are more exigent in the latter. In this respect, HIC–LMIC (or North–South) partnerships across training programs that link academic medical centers and research universities with counterpart institutions, as well as with local community-based service providers, can contribute to efforts to advance the quality and effectiveness of care delivery alongside in-country programming and South-South partnerships.

Despite the imperative to meet these enormous mental health delivery needs and despite rapid growth in political will, funding, and available empirically supported therapies, the global mental health field still lacks a strong framework for orienting future and current mental health professionals to educational and career paths for advancing the field of global mental health. This book's purpose is to respond to this need by providing such an introduction to the field for learners who seek to explore their interest in global mental health as well as for students, trainees, educators, and early career health professionals who seek to build upon their foundational training in order to advance the objectives of global mental health.

Who is this book for?

The field of global mental health has plural constituencies. The field also offers a big tent for learners. Whereas much of the material in this book is explicitly tailored to the interests of trainees, in the conventional sense of the word, we also intend for the book to be useful to learners at any stage of educational path or career, whether they are new to exploring the field of global mental health or are continuing to develop and deepen their engagement within it. The diverse range of career interests, perspectives, and prior life experiences learners bring to GMH shape how their engagement with the field will begin and where priorities will eventually steer them. Regardless of the vast array of points of entry and career paths in this field, new learners and seasoned practitioners broadly share an interest in and commitment to advancing mental health equity and access to quality care, while drawing from and contributing to the broader discipline of global mental health. Whereas the most visible actors in academic global health are often investigators and practitioners engaged in research and implementation aimed at generating data that can be applied across regions, many practitioners—often those working in low-resource settings in LMICs or HICs—are already practicing global mental health by directly addressing health inequities at a local level. Teaching and supervision geared toward understanding and overcoming clinical care delivery challenges in low-resource settings are, of course, at the heart of global mental health training. Also integral to training is developing the sensibility and skill set to work effectively *across* resource gradients. Such resource gradients exist in both HICs (e.g., a university-based trainee delivering care in a low-income urban neighborhood or working with an indigenous population) and also in LMICs (e.g., a trainee from the capital city working in a rural region of the same country). Global mental health trainees across all regional settings are likely to encounter these disparities and will need to navigate them as they also work to mitigate their adverse impacts; that being said, these gradients are likely to be steeper for learners situated in the Global North. Although this book's contributors share insights that generally have wide applicability, Global North trainees are most likely to find this volume's content useful in augmenting their training to prepare them for global mental health engagement.

There has been a proliferation of programming on global health in higher education.[16] This is a welcome development, but we highlight thoughtful critiques that illuminate how such learning opportunities can be linked to a pro-equity agenda and to responsible use.[16–18] The great majority of these programs are situated in the Global North[17] and, as such, primarily serve learners also situated in the Global North,[19] albeit with notable exceptions.[20–22] We join the chorus of others who have rightly insisted that such programming be mirrored, made accessible and affordable, and/or complemented in ways that are useful to global health learners and needs in the Global South.[16–19] These responsibilities fall on the shoulders of both educational institutions and their leadership as well as of funders and policymakers. Students, trainees, and other learners in the Global North, however, bear a different sort of responsibility in their global health engagement. But surely these very same learners, if contemplating careers through which they might contribute to global health, are invested in understanding how they can best serve a health equity agenda. Thus, our intention in presenting this orientational framework for current trainees—and prospective learners of all kinds—is to provide an introduction to the ideas, theories, and global mental health literature that can furnish the building blocks for their engagement with global mental health.

Next, we write for GMH educators situated in the Global North. Similar to our broad definition of learners in this book, we also intend for our usage of the term "educators" to be understood as inclusive. We mean for educators to encompass those who are engaged in the work of teaching, mentorship, supervision, and training for learners embarking on exploration or career paths in the global mental health space. We all have a role in interrogating the ways in which our academic work may replicate and reinforce inequities—however paradoxical this may seem and however unintended this may be. And, likewise, we all have opportunities to reflect on, reimagine, and reconfigure our academic engagements in global health toward the goal of reform to achieve equity. An awareness of these responsibilities and opportunities—and certainly also the challenges in rising to them—motivates the organization of this book so that we begin with chapters examining the historical context of global mental health, the social antecedents of poor mental health, and the ethics of engagement across gradients of resources and privilege.

The field of global mental health continues to develop and refine its collective aspirations to achieve health equity, alleviate suffering of those living with mental illness, and promote mental well-being for and within communities who share these goals. As the constituencies comprising the field look forward, we must also recognize and undo colonial and related legacies that continue to cast their long shadow on the present-day field of global mental health.

Toward this end, we would like to remind our readers in the Global North that success in eliminating health inequities will also entail the eradication of North–South disparities in academic opportunities. There is an inequitable distribution of academic capital that accrues disproportionately to academics in the Global North, even while value is extracted from human and other resources in the Global South in advancing the scholarly work. Indeed, this direction of flow and accrual of academic capital recapitulates the social dynamics set into motion in the colonial era. We join critics of global health and global mental health who have decried the structural dynamics that perpetuate academic and high-income region privilege in setting the agenda, participation in knowledge-making, and reaping many of the rewards (academic and financial) of their social position in academic global health. Access to funding, the privilege of opportunities to interpret data—and by extension, to influence the research agenda—begets greater access to both academic capital and financial supports and, arguably, imposes and reinforces a kind of hegemonic point of view. Critics writing against this unjust distribution of opportunity rightly point out that the research and higher education institutions in high-income regions have created incentives that serve the objectives of these institutions well, but that unfortunately have also resulted in perverse incentives for academic participation. These are fundamentally incompatible with the principles of equity that animate the field. Whereas root causes have been elucidated and remedies have been proposed, some of these dynamics are deeply embedded in conventions of academia and will not be straightforward to reverse and correct. We consider some of this important literature here to render more visible the dynamics that structure the flow of knowledge, prioritization of knowledge, funding, and publication. We all have a part in undoing these and thus begin by laying them out.

We, as the editors, want to invite learners and educators—and especially call on those in the Global North—to engage in global mental health in ways that tear down and remake the persisting hierarchies of knowledge and power that are legacies of the colonial era[19] to reject any engagement framed as "charity or saviourism" and, instead, occupy roles as "allies and enablers"[23(p.1628)] toward learning and practice that are inclusive and respectful of their colleagues' expertise and priorities. Structural reforms that have been proposed to rebalance power dynamics in global health range from how research funding resources are allocated and distributed,[24] to how educational and training resources are made accessible[17] and optimized for local needs.[25] Other considerations—such as how and which research topics are chosen, what knowledge or deliverables are sought, and how these will be shared[26]—will be more immediately relevant to learners as they prepare for collaboration. Research topics must reflect the priorities of the local community so that the benefits of their effort in knowledge generation are directed back to serve these communities. Investigators should seek publication venues—such as in open access platforms and local journals—that will be accessible to health practitioners, academics, and policy-makers in the region.[27] Health research publications emanating from North–South global health collaborations in sub-Saharan Africa, for example, reflect that local authors are underrepresented in prime authorship positions.[28] Students and supervisors must, therefore, work to integrate plans for equitable opportunities and representation of local authorship into their engagement with collaborators.[29] These efforts, furthermore, should be accompanied by curricular offerings that support reflexivity about how the dynamics of power and privilege play out in North–South global mental health collaborations and "research ecosystems."[18,29] Mentorship must provide clear guidance on how to avoid so-called "parachute" and "parasitic" research,[30] how to eschew "epistemic injustices,"[31, 32] and more importantly, how partnerships and other collaborations can be successful and equitable.

Program directors and supervisors and, indeed, all academics in the Global North must provide mentorship and oversight to guide equitable distribution of opportunities for authorship; beyond this, they should consider how resource use at LMIC host institutions by their students and trainees can be offset and fairly compensated as well as how investment in local capacity-building to enable research grant writing and productivity can be ensured.[19] Such actions are oriented toward inclusion, capacity-building, and bidirectional learning, consistent with an approach to global health partnerships that the late Paul Farmer has framed as "accompaniment."[16] This approach not only enhances fairness and advances the goals of health and academic equity, but also sets the stage for generativity by elevating the perspectives and contributions of local experts and the communities they serve. Much more has been written about related topics such as: Who sets a research agenda? How are ideas sourced and how are they credited? How is academic culture structured in ways that reproduce the very inequities that the field of global health seeks to dismantle? How do we reflect on these and form intentions, commitments, and actions to do better? How do students, trainees, learners, and their mentors in the Global North engage with global mental health in ways that promote equity in the broadest sense of the word as well as generativity through reciprocity, bidirectional learning, and inclusion that will advance the field and quality of mental health care?

No one book on global mental health could offer all that a learner or educator would wish to learn. These lacunae are a matter of both content and perspective. With respect to the former, there are also already many excellent resources available to GMH trainees and practitioners to draw from as key references in their work. We encourage readers to use this book's introductory framework both as a launch point for interfacing with global mental health and also in conjunction with other sources for foundational knowledge from both their own respective professional fields and from the mental health literature and other related resources. For example, readers can access guidance on clinical therapeutics from the World Health Organization (WHO) mental health Gap Access Program (mhGAP), which publishes clinical protocols that incorporate both pharmacological and non-pharmacological therapeutics for low-resource settings.[33-35] While the authors in this volume present several examples of successful programs and training approaches, these are intended as a starting point to illustrate the underlying themes that comprise this introductory framework. As such, readers seeking a broader selection of innovative programs in GMH are encouraged to consult additional resources, such as the catalog of a variety of innovative approaches in GMH at the Mental Health Innovation Network.[36]

As we have indicated, there are also diverse perspectives among GMH investigators and practitioners that, while often complementary, continue to highlight unresolved differences of opinion. Another critical resource in the practice of GMH is the perspective of mental health service users. Their experiences and perspectives are diverse: frustration with the challenges in accessing care; descriptions of human rights violations while receiving care; or transformative, positive experiences. Unified advocacy from service users and their allies was a major driver for changes in attitudes, funding, and access to care for HIV treatments and is a key means for integrating the preferences and perspectives of those with lived experience into policies and resources. Similar efforts are building among mental health service users who are advocating for principles of recovery, person-centered care, reduction in stigma to access mental health support, ability to freely choose among several therapeutic options, service intensity that matches the severity of the problem, maintenance of the users' right to refuse care, and use of psychiatric advance directives for situations when the service user may have diminished capacity for decision-making in the context of imminent harm to self or others.[37-39] In training and practice, however, service users are often at a high risk of losing these choices. It is therefore important for training and practice settings to establish mechanisms for user perspectives to be heard and to inform GMH practice. Indeed, some of the most inspiring and transfromative lessons we, ourselves, have had in our training and practice were learned from people with lived experience in mental health, who exercised their autonomy and shared their perspectives. This book lacks a chapter by individuals with lived experience of mental illness to have an opportunity to address how the service user and caregiver perspective can be better integrated into global mental health training and service delivery. Although discussion of user perspectives is beyond the scope of this book, we encourage readers to seek out these perspectives (e.g., through available literature such as Stein and colleagues' recent book that includes perspectives of individuals living with psychosocial disabilities and caregivers[40]) to incorporate experiences that facilitate mutual respect and empathy for users throughout training and practice, and to become attuned to opportunities to promote mental health through advocacy for social, clinical, and policy reform. Additional resources for user perspectives to advocate for dignified and stigma-free achievement of mental health can be found in the Global Mental Health Peer Network,[41] Convention on the Rights of Persons with

Disabilities (CRPD),[42] and the National Alliance on Mental Illness.[43] Other volumes in GMH have further incorporated these diverse voices, including criticisms, of GMH.[44–47] Furthermore, we recommend that learners seek out one of many excellent ethnographies that engage with the lived experience of mental illness and many of the frustrations and indignities individuals describe in their interactions with the health system, such as those by Brodwin[48] and Sue,[49] and a collection edited by Luhrmann and Marrow.[50] Finally, we recommend that learners foster an openness to listen to the perspectives of those who are experts on their own lived experience, and to incorporate such views in developing both individual treatment plans and large-scale interventions.

Global mental health is a field that is enriched by its diverse and many vantage points and no single one point of view can encapsulate, illuminate, or advance the field in a way that is either complete or even enough; nor will any one approach be equal to the enormity of need the field seeks to redress. We believe that fact makes it not just wise, but rather also essential, to consider how multiple approaches and perspectives can be layered for the fullest range of understanding and the most effective complement of actions to advance the goals of global mental health equity. This is a key reason that we urge readers to be attentive to the positionality of the perspectives and supervisors from which and whom they learn. The same is true for our positionality as editors—and, likewise, is the case for the authors who have contributed to this volume. In that same spirit, we begin with a short statement about our own coordinates in the field; this is to acknowledge how our own perspectives are informed and, in many ways, limited. As editors of this book, we recognize that our selection of content for this volume is shaped by perspectives forged within our own experiences and backgrounds—one of us having grown up in the Global South and one of us in the Global North—as well as our opportunities to train and interface with the field. Since each of us is a psychiatrist who has trained in the United States, we would be remiss if we did not acknowledge how the privilege of training at a major academic medical center in a high-resource setting also informs and, in some ways, limits our professional experience. In this respect, we also benefit from understanding the limits of US psychiatry residency training for trainees who seek to engage in global mental health. And we hasten to acknowledge that our perspective is incomplete for students working in other disciplines, for learners training within other high-income regions outside of the United States, and that it is also comparatively less informative for trainees in low-income settings. That being said, we each bring expertise and experience that we feel is valuable, even if incomplete.

As we bring this book to completion, we also note the historical moment that has marked increasing engagement in an important dialog on decolonizing global health. This dialog is the backdrop and subtext for some of the discussions in this book. And we note another anchor in the positionality of this book: the majority of the contributing authors hail from the Global North whereas authors from the Global South are less well represented. Although we worked toward more robust representation of scholars, practitioners, and learners from the Global South, we want to be clear that we did not succeed in accomplishing our goal. An asymmetry reckoned by this uneven regional distribution of contributors undoubtedly translates to an unbalanced representation of ideas put forth. This is not just a deficiency in the content of the book, but also speaks to a shortcoming—and, of course, an opportunity—in the field. We are optimistic that the next generation of students and trainees in global mental health will overcome the fallout from coloniality and entrenched structural inequality. We cannot work toward health equity and social justice without also addressing the many pernicious ways inequities persist, even in academia and even in our own field. The issues that have been raised are numerous, but all touch on equity, justice, and representation: goals that are consonant with the aspirations of the field. The points raised are complex to resolve and foreground a tension between the ideal and pragmatic. But they also serve as a checkpoint for academic hubris regarding which knowledge counts and in which direction it flows. And this is our primary reason for underscoring that this book's introductory framework may be especially useful to learners and educators in the Global North. It is a primer to ideas, disciplines, and perspectives that should arrive at the beginning of their work, and not as an afterthought.

Organization and overview of this book

This book provides an orientational framework—an introduction to the field—for prospective learners, current trainees, and their mentors in reflecting and responding to questions like the ones posed above and also in seeking an entry point for their engagement with global mental health. In doing so, it builds both upon existing transdisciplinary and interprofessional approaches to global health while also introducing learners to the unique challenges attendant to mental health in low-resource settings.[51] Global mental health trainees comprise a number of diverse constituencies beyond the North–South spectrum that we have mentioned. These range from students to established professionals and also encompass those exploring an educational or career path in the health sector to learners in public policy, architecture, and beyond. Students include those in pre-professional programs (high school or college students) and in professional training (public health, medicine, nursing, clinical psychology, psychiatry, sociology, anthropology, and social work). Those who have already entered their professional career may be seeking direction to engage with global mental health as an additional dimension of their work, either as practitioners or as educators. Other professionals may already have had field-based experiences with care delivery or teaching and now may be seeking a more comprehensive, ethical, and effective approach to provide training and conduct practice in global mental health. Seasoned educators may be seeking support in response to the increasing trainee demand for approaches to reduce health inequities, both within HICs and LMICs.

Such a diverse readership warrants an orientation to the field that is flexible enough to accommodate students and prospective trainees with varying levels of experience as well as plans for integrating global mental health into their educational and career paths. Therefore, rather than being prescriptive, this orienting framework offers approaches, core principles, strategies, evidence-based models, and ethical considerations, and also raises thought-provoking questions about values, that can inform development and deployment of global mental health training and practice flexibly across a range of settings. The book details, critiques, and outlines best practices based on the growing empirical base to circumvent specialist mental health personnel shortages.[33,52–55] These include, and build upon, proven strategies in the field of global health writ large: integrated care models, task-sharing, and a variety of models for capacity-building, that include institutional twinning, field-based mentored research, bedside teaching, and remote supervision.[56] The book emphasizes, moreover, that engagement with and integration of local knowledge and expertise are foundational to the co-creation of knowledge and development of a workforce that is authentically global in representation.[57] This integration, moreover, provides the empirical base that can both inform application and generalization across diverse regions and also assist local actors in drawing from lessons in other regions to solve the challenges they face in their own communities. These are critical components of a training and practice approach that will allow LMICs and HICs to develop a workforce capable of addressing the large burden of mental illness in low-resource settings worldwide. Whereas we provide illustrations of how aspects of this introduction can be implemented in certain contexts, our goal for readers is that they find the book's content useful and adaptable across diverse social settings and health system capacities as they embark upon and develop their work in global mental health.

In order to provide this breadth of orientation, this book is organized into three sections: (1) Social and Historical Contextualization of Global Mental Health; (2) Strategies for Training in Global Mental Health; and (3) Additional Areas for Special Focus in Global Mental Health

Training. In other words, this book offers an introduction and entry point as well as a view into the scope of opportunities for engagement and enrichment. As a result, we anticipate that some readers may already be familiar with some of the ideas presented, depending on their prior training and experience, but we also expect that the various approaches described will introduce new concepts and approaches for a range of learners interested in global mental health.

Section I: Social and Historical Contextualization of Global Mental Health

In order to be effective in delivering on its aspirations, the field of global mental health must draw knowledge from many disciplines, including from the clinically relevant social sciences and humanities. The sobering lessons from the COVID-19 pandemic serve as a reminder that a narrow focus on health technology will not equip health systems and practitioners to meet all of the socially and clinically complex challenges of health delivery. An approach to advancing health delivery and health equity must, therefore, draw from clinically relevant and adjacent social sciences disciplines to illuminate and respond to this complexity. Chapters 1–3 focus on the social, cultural, and historical contexts of poor mental health and associated inequities as well as relevant relational dimensions to approaching and elevating health equity in global mental health training and care delivery. The resocializing sub-disciplines, history of medicine and medical anthropology (discussed in Chapters 1 and 2, respectively), offer avenues for a critical understanding of the historical grounding of global mental health as well as the through line to its present core tenets. These chapters, along with Chapter 3, which examines approaches to establish ethical partnerships in global mental health, (re)situate global mental health engagement in the historical and social contextual underpinnings of practice and research.

In their call to reimagine global health teaching in high-income countries, Atkins and colleagues suggest that "decolonising pedagogy in global health" can start with incorporation of the historical roots of the persisting dynamics of coloniality.[18(p.3)] We agree that this content is essential to an introduction and thus begin the book with "The Colonial and Postcolonial Roots of Global Mental Health Efforts," as Chapter 1. In this chapter, Sadowsky and Greene situate contemporary global mental health practices in a historical tapestry of colonialism, institutionalization, psychoanalysis, local understandings of the mind and mental illness, postcolonial evolution, and deinstitutionalization. This historical context is critical to understand the current manifestation of the field of global mental health and to guide learners and practitioners on a path that attempts to address and avoid the mistakes of the past. The authors use a fictional story to illustrate a common point of contention in GMH: how much of mental suffering is an "illness" and how much is an expected consequence of life situations that can be remedied by a more just society? The authors then unpack another question that has historically dogged the field: are mental illnesses universal or relative? The authors weave the history of colonial psychiatry, decolonization movements, and ethnographic inquiry into mental disorders to bring us to the twenty-first century, where GMH has *seemingly* emerged as a new discipline. However, the authors' primary goal is not to try to settle long-standing debates but rather to direct the attention of global mental health learners and practitioners to the colonial legacies of global health. These legacies illuminate an unequivocally oppressive, racist past while efforts for independence and decolonization have led to a more diverse mosaic of our collective understanding of the mind. The authors encourage an approach to global mental health not as a brand-new movement but as a field that has deep roots in history; further, they advise learners and practitioners to become familiar with this important history for its relevance to informing contemporary global mental health engagements.

A biosocial framework for global mental health training—one that integrates social and biomedical dimensions—informs an approach to health delivery that encompasses social determinants of poor mental health and is, thereby, more likely to be effective and equitable. In Chapter 2, "Resocializing Global Mental Health: What Anthropological Perspectives Offer to Learners, Educators, and Practitioners," Becker and Kleinman draw from their experience in teaching a large undergraduate course on global health—that includes a substantial focus on mental health—in presenting key social theories as tools to unpack the biosocial complexities of the global distribution, visibility, and associated health and social burdens of mental disorders. In addition, they discuss applications to clinical practice and implementation that can enhance understanding of lived experience as it relates to suffering, medicalization, and help-seeking. They also examine impacts of structural violence on the mental health burden as a launch point for informing approaches for redressing the social determinants of poor mental health and designing effective health delivery. There is striking phenomenological variation in the presentation of mental distress across diverse social and cultural contexts compared with other clinical domains comprising global health, and yet the premise for advancing health and mental health care delivery across diverse regions within a global health framework partly rests on a universalizing framework for nosology. The authors acknowledge some misalignment between universalizing and local categories of experience but reject this as an argument against promoting the tools, resources, and access to quality mental health care to alleviate suffering caused by mental illness across the globe. Instead, they encourage global mental health practitioners and trainees to learn from local experience and perspectives and to integrate these into the development of local educational, clinical, and research programming that responds to local needs, values, and preferences. Moreover, the authors demonstrate how concepts and approaches informed by the resocializing disciplines, such as anthropology, deepen a contextualized understanding of local needs and enable applications aimed both toward improved mental health care delivery as well as eradication of structural drivers of poor health and health inequities. They conclude by advocating for *accompaniment* as an invaluable approach and the re-centering of *care* in mental health delivery.

This section concludes with Chapter 3, "Promoting Global Mental Health Equity in Training Programs: Establishing Ethical and Reciprocal Partnerships," by Griffith and colleagues. Drawing from the fields of ethics and philosophy, the authors generate lessons for navigating partnerships in global mental health training, research, and practice, and consider applications of both procedural ethics and an ethics of alterity in GMH contexts. Based on theoretical underpinnings from ethics, the chapter addresses the complex challenge of working collaboratively across hierarchies that are often characterized by asymmetric access to resources and sometimes by competing priorities. The authors focus on the importance of building trust and mutual respect as priorities for ethical and productive GMH collaborations. Finally, the authors caution about the risk for moral distress to emerge as trainees encounter their own limitations in addressing mental health needs in conditions of extreme poverty and resource constraints, and discuss how mentors can anticipate and mitigate demoralization. The authors convincingly advocate for ethics in GMH practice to be a core component of every global mental health training curriculum.

Section II: Strategies for Training in Global Mental Health

The second section of the volume addresses a range of considerations for developing curricula, providing effective mentorship, building local capacity, fostering institutional collaborations, addressing research and service needs, and involving students in global mental health training. Many of the principles that undergird development of health professional education and training are applicable to global mental health, too, of course; these chapters address additional considerations that are more specific to global mental health training. These chapters have particular salience for programs, training directors, and trainees that are situated in relatively well-resourced academic centers and plan to work across resources gradients.

Chapter 4, "Developing a Global Mental Health Training Curriculum," by Acharya and colleagues, describes a theoretical framework that can be fruitfully applied toward the systematic development of a global mental health training curriculum and illustrates an application of this framework for the University of California San Francisco (UCSF) Psychiatry HEAL Fellowship in Global Mental Health as an in-depth case study. The authors present their experience with Kern's six-step process for developing a medical curriculum.[58] The authors' case study in developing the UCSF Fellowship, currently in its sixth year of training learners from UCSF, Navajo Nation, Nepal, and Mexico, provides examples of how each of the six steps can be operationalized to develop a robust GMH curriculum. The authors argue that a structured approach for curriculum development has numerous benefits because it purposefully seeks out learners' needs and capacities and then guides the educators toward teaching strategies that are most likely to be successful in meeting goals associated with specific competencies. This strategy can be used for pedagogic approaches for educational programs, such as a fellowship, and also for practitioners who may need to be re-trained to deliver mental health services (e.g., primary care providers who may need a mental health curriculum for a task-sharing intervention).[59] The chapter advises that, although this framework can provide a roadmap for developing educational materials, potential contextual factors, such as stigma against mental illness and mental health providers and challenges in obtaining institutional support, need to be anticipated to increase the likelihood of successful implementation and sustainability of GMH training programs. Moreover, strategies to finance the training program and the development of reciprocal training approaches to ensure learners from both high- and low-resource settings have equitable access to opportunities are integral to program success.

In Chapter 5, "Mentorship in Global Mental Health," Kohrt and colleagues provide an in-depth discussion of the role of mentorship as a cornerstone of training and capacity-building in global mental health. The chapter addresses a range of relevant roles for mentorship, including as a formal component of an academic degree program, as central to research and other capacity-building in LMICs, and as a means of supporting local leadership in building national organizations. The authors discuss kinds of mentorship that are important but often overlooked in this domain, such as peer mentorship and mentorship of organizations (whereby HIC-based institutions can support the growth and independence of LMIC-based organizations). The authors also discuss practices for structuring ongoing mentorship within organizations. Given that the vast majority of health workers in the world are women while those in leadership positions are mostly men, the authors consider some strategies to overcome gender-specific challenges in fostering mentorship for women in GMH. The authors make a compelling case for focusing mentorship in GMH on promoting equity and access to high-quality mental health services. This is a refreshing contrast to conceptualizing mentorship as designed solely around goals for professional growth. The framework for mentorship emphasizes development of characteristics such as humility and reflexivity. Finally, the authors present a detailed case for improving communication systems and meeting practices to enhance mentorship and coaching in LMICs. Such structured systems have also been shown to be helpful in promoting equity, since unstructured systems continue to favor the status quo and, in this case, demographics that are more empowered.

When it comes to mental health, all countries in the world struggle to meet the clinical needs. In response, task-sharing, the practice of distributing clinical tasks among specialists (e.g., psychiatrists) and non-specialists (e.g., primary care providers) to expand access to care, has been a staple of GMH practice. Integrated care models have been developed to use task-sharing in non-mental health systems to bolster GMH care delivery. However, training programs, especially those focused on specialists, often lack dedicated focus on these models of care. In Chapter 6, "Implementation of Integrated Care Models: Lessons for Training and Practice in Low-Resource Settings," Kemp and colleagues address the question: what do trainees and practitioners need to know about models for integrating mental health into existing care delivery platforms? This chapter identifies common challenges in the implementation of task-sharing for mental healthcare delivery and provides evidence-based recommendations to mitigate risks, particularly to quality of care, in such models. As task-sharing becomes a routinely used strategy in LMICs, there is a potential trade-off in achieving greater coverage with the quality of mental health care provided by newly trained non-specialists. Chapter 6 provides two strategies for integrating mental health services into existing platforms in low-resource settings, while squarely focusing on the quality of care delivered in task-sharing models. The first strategy they describe is the Collaborative Care Model (CoCM),[60] which has substantial demonstrated evidence for improving outcomes for common mental disorders. This model leverages the rare (and expensive) psychiatrist to focus on ensuring that the care is of high quality. By moving the psychiatrist from directly evaluating and treating patients to the role of overseeing the treatment plan for a large panel of patients, CoCM helps attain the triple aims of access, cost, and quality. The second strategy, the Apprenticeship Model,[61] provides a framework for training healthcare workers on their jobs to progressively enhance their clinical skills. Because much of GMH training for task-sharing models occurs outside of professional programs (i.e., in a clinic that is implementing CoCM rather than in a medical school curriculum), the Apprenticeship Model provides a valuable strategy for such settings where healthcare workers will learn clinical skills while they are delivering care.

In Chapter 7, "Educational Partnerships: Addressing Challenges in Meeting Trainee Goals with Established or New Global Mental Health Educational Programs," Marienfeld and colleagues provide guidance on a common dilemma faced by educators: is it preferable to establish long-term partnerships between institutions or better to give learners the freedom to seek out and pursue their own one-off collaborations? The authors argue that whereas long-term partnerships are invaluable, one-off collaborations are also feasible. The case studies focus on the long-standing relationship that Yale has developed across the Yale-China Association, the Xiangya-Yale medical school partnerships, and the Yale Global Mental Health educational program. The authors share their experiences in developing a complex, long-standing partnership that facilitates reciprocal travel and learning for trainees from both Yale and China, while engaging in ethical and well-structured educational experiences. The authors supplement this type of enduring engagement with a variety of additional opportunities for short-term collaborations in other settings that allow trainees at Yale to leverage their skills, experiences, and career aspirations to build new partnerships. The chapter describes the processes through which such new partnerships can continue to be fostered and developed into longer-term partnerships. It shares generalizable lessons for LMIC- and HIC-based institutions to navigate the landscape of the range of partnerships to provide high-quality educational experiences for their trainees.

A long-standing tension in GMH (and global health) engagement reveals the competing priorities between exigent healthcare delivery needs and the very real scarcity of GMH practitioners, especially in LMICs, that constrain their capacity to devote time to conducting research. In Chapter 8, "Mobilizing a Range of Resources to Advance Research and Service in Global Mental Health Training," Scorza and colleagues provide case examples to argue against what is often a false choice between GMH research and service delivery. By integrating perspectives from academics, practitioners, and researchers, the authors explore and demonstrate strategies to achieve success in both conducting research and delivering services in low-resource settings. The authors make a case that research is an essential component of closing the global mental health treatment gap. They argue, moreover, that LMIC-HIC collaboration in research capacity-building not only supports this need but, when effective in allocating resources, also complements and enhances the capacity for clinical care.

This section concludes with a chapter written by students and trainees addressed to their peers exploring an interest in global mental health as well as to prospective GMH mentors: "Student Engagement in Global Mental Health: Perspectives on Curricular, Extra-curricular, and Advocacy Opportunities." In Chapter 9, Eappen and colleagues position students as strong advocates for GMH and as the future of the mental health workforce. While students early in their career may not have the requisite clinical or public health skills for GMH practice, the authors describe other pathways for students to engage in promoting a GMH equity agenda. This chapter highlights the role of learners not just as recipients of knowledge but as important agents of change. The authors, all of whom were current or recent students at the time of writing, point out that in recent years, students have become more open about discussing mental health problems that they or their loved ones have experienced. Moreover, they explain how this awareness and courage can be a powerful tool in reducing stigma attached to mental illness and, with the right mentorship and support, can be mobilized for advocacy, support for clinical teams, and can enhance preparation for a career in GMH. The authors highlight the historic pivotal importance of student advocacy in the HIV/AIDS movement to demonstrate the potential that learners have in tackling issues in GMH. They also caution that, given the lack of established career pathways in the field of global mental health, many students who may have been inclined to pursue a career in global mental health may miss the opportunity to explore their interest in the field. They encourage prospective mentors to find ways to inspire and creatively engage the students.

Section III: Additional Areas for Special Focus in Global Mental Health Training

The three chapters comprising the final section of the book address important content for global mental health trainees that nonetheless may not always be comprehensively covered in specialty mental health training: the intersection of mental health delivery with humanitarian crisis response, neurological disorders, and substance use disorders. In this regard, this section addresses an imperative for global mental health training that may require augmentation of conventional curricula. Humanitarian crises are more common in LMICs—and with the impact of climate change, are becoming more frequent worldwide—and yet many training programs do not prepare trainees to address them. In addition, most experiences in such settings are focused on acute service delivery rather than on long-term reforms. Epidemiological studies in GMH[1] frequently include data from the burden of neurological and substance use disorders when describing the overall burden of "mental disorders." Similarly, clinical guidelines from the World Health Organization (such as mhGAP) include protocols for some neurological and substance use disorders in the mhGAP intervention guide (mhGAP-IG)[34] and the mhGAP humanitarian intervention guide (mhGAP-HIG).[35] However, in many training programs and in practice, these two categories of disorders may not receive as much attention as common affective disorders or severe mental illness, such as psychotic disorders. Furthermore, although LMIC-based mental health practitioners are expected to routinely deliver services for neurological and substance use disorders, such training in neurology or sub-specialized mental health may not be commensurate to—or adequate to meet the needs for—the overall burden imposed by these conditions.

Global mental health trainees and practitioners may encounter communities that have acute mental health needs in the aftermath of a humanitarian crisis; moreover, these acute needs may be superimposed on chronic mental health needs. It is not uncommon for such a crisis to raise the visibility of mental health needs and serve as an impetus for additional investment in mental health services, especially in regions where services had been inadequate to meet local mental health needs. In Chapter 10, "Training for Humanitarian Crisis Response and Mental Health System Reform," Raviola and colleagues describe approaches and resources as well as requisite foundational knowledge and competencies for GMH trainees and practitioners responding to a humanitarian crisis. They advocate, moreover, for linking this response to efforts to build on and strengthen existing mental health services toward mental health system reform that can be sustained beyond the immediate crisis response. Drawing on case examples from work conducted with the non-governmental organization (NGO) Partners In Health and from the Ministry of Public Health of Lebanon, the authors describe approaches to training and health system design to build a better and stronger mental health system that can be integrated into the response to a humanitarian crisis. This chapter describes key considerations and available resources for trainees and practitioners who find themselves working in global mental health settings during and after a humanitarian crisis. The authors make an argument that, in addition to the imperative to respond to acute mental health needs in a humanitarian crisis, this crisis response can be strategically coupled with long-term mental health system reform.

In Chapter 11, "Neurology in Global Mental Health Delivery and Training," Fils-Aimé and Berkowitz provide their high-level perspective on the importance of addressing neurological disorders in global mental health training and practice. In outlining the compelling reasons to augment routine clinical training on neurological disease in preparation for mental healthcare delivery and research in low-resource settings, they begin by describing the substantial contribution of neurological disorders to the global burden of disease, juxtaposing it with the relative shortage of clinicians specialized in the care of neurologic disease in low-resource settings, and posing the following questions: What is the role of a mental health practitioner in addressing this burden of disease in settings where there may be no neurologists? How can neurological services be delivered within existing care delivery platforms? Given the comorbidity between neurologic and psychiatric disorders, some phenomenological overlap of symptom presentation, and the potential for neurological symptoms to be attributed to mental illness, the authors point out that GMH clinicians are likely to encounter individuals presenting with primary neurological illness in their work. Moreover, they discuss that GMH clinicians and trainees should be prepared to redirect their care to a specialist, when available, or work with a consultant to manage the symptoms when appropriate. They use an in-depth exploration of epilepsy to illustrate a critical point that from the patient's perspective, the behavioral, emotional, and cognitive experiences from neurological or psychiatric illnesses may be indistinguishable, further increasing the importance of GMH practitioners who are adept at incorporating neurological care in their clinical management, when appropriate. In the course of their discussion, the authors consider approaches to the incorporation of neurological care into global mental health delivery. Drawing from their experience and knowledge of the work of the non-governmental organization, Zanmi Lasante, in Haiti, they outline strategies to integrate both neurological care and training into primary care systems, alongside other global mental health efforts in low-resource settings so that individuals presenting with common neurologic conditions receive high-quality care for their illness.

In Chapter 12, the final chapter of this book, "Substance Use Disorders in Global Mental Health Delivery and Training," Connery and colleagues build an argument for augmenting coverage of substance use disorders (SUDs) in the scope of GMH training and practice. The authors present data showing both the considerable global prevalence of substance use disorders, and the associated treatment gap resulting from unmet needs. Although alcohol use disorder (AUD) and other SUDs have global distribution, the authors point out that the impact of alcohol and substance use on disease burden varies across countries and across the economic spectrum.[62] They make a compelling case that despite a common perception that treatment for SUDs requires specialized centers and rare specialists, community-based treatment for SUDs is feasible and effective. Stigma against SUDs continues to exact a significant toll on individuals living with a SUD. The authors provide a brief overview of both behavioral and pharmacological interventions available for SUDs in low-resource settings. Many of the tenets for improving access to high-quality care for mental disorders in GMH settings are also highly relevant to care delivery for SUDs. In particular, the authors outline the value of addressing community-level and self-stigma; training peers and lay health workers for expanded access to treatment; delivering ongoing specialist supervision of care by non-specialist clinicians; integrating evidence-based practices into existing care delivery platforms; and shifting the focus on the implementation gap between what we know and what is done in practice.

Emerging issues for global mental health and the imperative for health equity

Although the 12 chapters in the volume introduce readers to many of the most pressing challenges in GMH training and practice, new challenges will continue to surface. As this volume is released, the impacts of the COVID-19 pandemic continue to reverberate around the world, having revealed not only our global interconnectedness but also unacceptable disparities in both access to preventive measures and risk for poor health outcomes from the illness. The pandemic has also highlighted shared vulnerabilities that included numerous associated social and health challenges, such as isolation and stress from sheltering in place prior to the rollout of effective vaccines and therapeutics, food and housing insecurity associated with economic impacts, and emotional distress and grief among caregivers and survivors. Another consequence of the public health measures taken to limit disease transmission during the pandemic is a rapid transition from in-person to remote visits in healthcare services, particularly for mental health. Virtual visits, either using only audio or both audio and video, had slowly been gaining acceptance in mental health care, but the pandemic accelerated uptake of this modality of care delivery in settings that have the requisite infrastructure. The capacity for remote care delivery provides a welcome opportunity to circumvent some structural barriers to mental health care—such as distance from centrally located clinical resources in the setting of inaccessible or unaffordable transportation or unacceptable opportunity costs—and, thereby, to extend the reach of care to underserved populations. That being said, such a transition also carries the risk of further disenfranchising marginalized communities who have been left behind by the digital revolution. In this respect, and in many others, the pandemic has served as a reminder not just that the tenets of global mental health are broadly applicable but also that health equity must be prioritized in GMH training and practice.

As the scope and possibilities for advancing mental health across all regions of the world continue to develop, it is inevitable that new challenges and priorities will emerge as well. On the one hand, discovery enabled by advances in genetics, neuroscience, big data, machine learning, and artificial intelligence bring the promise of novel therapeutics for reducing the burden of suffering associated with mental illness. On the other hand, the transformative potential for new health technologies cannot be realized without a commitment to supporting delivery of mental health services and to reaching the most vulnerable persons and communities. We must be mindful that sobering geopolitical challenges continue to escalate and arise. Climate change impacts on mental health, both direct and indirect—through catastrophic weather events, eco-anxiety, food insecurity, re-traumatization of vulnerable populations, and displacement, to name a few examples—are looming. Political violence, armed conflict, and economic fallout from the pandemic will exert migration pressure, imposing psychosocial stressors and disrupting access to mental health services. Current and future learners embarking on their professional development and exploring their own commitments to global mental health and avenues for identifying high impact solutions will need to rise to these challenges and navigate new ones. The common thread will be the continuing imperative to promote global health equity while advancing the evidence base and clinical, research, and educational capacities for improving mental health. This book, therefore, advocates for a broad and interdisciplinary educational foundation for learners that contextualizes their understanding of the distribution of mental health burdens within local historical, cultural, and social settings. We urge readers—prospective learners, current trainees, seasoned educators, and practitioners, alike—to interrogate the power dynamics that sometimes characterize North–South collaborations in global health research and treatment delivery and work toward partnerships that are bidirectional, mutually beneficial, and committed to the priorities of elevating local needs while advancing global mental health and health equity.

References

1. Becker AE, Kleinman A. Mental health and the global agenda. *The New England Journal of Medicine.* 2013;369(1):66–73.
2. Raviola G, Becker AE, Farmer P. A global scope for global health—Including mental health. *The Lancet.* 2011;378(9803):1613–15.
3. Demyttenaere K, Bruffaerts R, Posada-Villa J, Gasquet I, Kovess V, Lepine JP, et al. Prevalence, severity, and unmet need for treatment of mental disorders in the World Health Organization World Mental Health Surveys. *JAMA.* 2004;291(21):2581–90.
4. Saxena S, Thornicroft G, Knapp M, Whiteford H. Resources for mental health: scarcity, inequity, and inefficiency. *The Lancet.* 2007;370(9590):878–90.
5. Lancet Global Mental Health Group, Chisholm D, Flisher AJ, Lund C, Patel V, Saxena S, et al. Scale up services for mental disorders: a call for action. *The Lancet.* 2007;370(9594):1241–52.
6. Patel V, Boyce N, Collins PY, Saxena S, Horton R. A renewed agenda for global mental health. *The Lancet.* 2011;378(9801):1441–2.
7. Patel V, Saxena S, Lund C, Thornicroft G, Baingana F, Bolton P, Chisholm D, Collins PY, Cooper JL, Eaton J, Herrman H. The Lancet commission on global mental health and sustainable development. *The Lancet commission.* 2018;392(10157):1553–98.
8. Kola L, Kohrt BA, Hanlon C, Naslund JA, Sikander S, Balaji M, et al. COVID-19 mental health impact and responses in low-income and middle-income countries: reimagining global mental health. *The Lancet Psychiatry.* 2021;8(6):535–50.
9. Kola L, Kohrt BA, Acharya B, Mutamba BB, Kieling C, Kumar M, et al. The path to global equity in mental health care in the context of COVID-19. *The Lancet.* 2021;398(10312):1670–2.
10. Santomauro DF, Herrera AMM, Shadid J, Zheng P, Ashbaugh C, Pigott DM, et al. Global prevalence and burden of depressive and anxiety disorders in 204 countries and territories in 2020 due to the COVID-19 pandemic. *The Lancet.* 2021;398(10312):1700–12.
11. Campion J, Javed A, Lund C, Sartorius N, Saxena S, Marmot M, et al. Public mental health: required actions to address implementation failure in the context of COVID-19. *The Lancet Psychiatry.* 2022;9(2):169–82.
12. Becker AE, Kleinman A. An agenda for closing resource gaps in global mental health: innovation, capacity building, and partnerships. *Harvard Review of Psychiatry.* 2012;20(1):3–5.
13. Bruckner TA, Scheffler RM, Shen G, Yoon J, Chisholm D, Morris J, Fulton BD, Dal Poz MR, Saxena S. The mental health workforce gap in low-and middle-income countries: a needs-based approach. *Bulletin of the World Health Organization.* 2011;89:184–94.
14. World Health Organization. *Mental health atlas 2011.* Geneva: World Health Organization; 2011. 82 p.
15. World Health Organization. *Mental health atlas 2020.* Geneva: World Health Organization; 2021. 126 p.
16. Farmer PE. More than just a hobby: what Harvard can do to advance global health. *The Harvard Crimson.* 2011. Available from: https://www.thecrimson.com/article/2011/5/26/health-global-training-medical/

17. Svadzian A, Vasquez NA, Abimbola S, Pai M. Global health degrees: at what cost?. *BMJ Global Health*. 2020;5(8):e003310.
18. Atkins S, Banerjee AT, Bachynski K, Daftary A, Desai G, Gross A, Hedt-Gauthier B, Mendenhall E, Meier BM, Nixon SA, Nolan A. Using the COVID-19 pandemic to reimagine global health teaching in high-income countries. *BMJ Global Health*. 2021;6(4):e005649.
19. Binagwaho A, Allotey P, Sangano E, Ekström AM, Martin K. A call to action to reform academic global health partnerships. *BMJ*. 2021; 375:n2658.
20. Harvard Medical School. *Master in medical sciences in global health delivery*. Cambridge, MA: The President and Fellows of Harvard College; 2022. Available from: https://ghsm.hms.harvard.edu /education/master-medical-sciences-global-health-delivery. Accessed August 9, 2022.
21. Citrin D, Mehanni S, Acharya B, Wong L, Nirola I, Sherchan R, et al. Power, potential, and pitfalls in global health academic partnerships: review and reflections on an approach in Nepal. *Global Health Action*. 2017;10(1):1367161.
22. Sors TG, O'Brien RC, Scanlon ML, Bermel LY, Chikowe I, Gardner A, et al. Reciprocal innovation: a new approach to equitable and mutually beneficial global health partnerships. *Global Public Health*. 2022 Jul 25:1–13.
23. Abimbola S, Pai M. Will global health survive its decolonisation? *The Lancet*. 2020;396(10263):1627–8.
24. Khan M, Abimbola S, Aloudat T, Capobianco E, Hawkes S, Rahman-Shepherd A. Decolonising global health in 2021: a roadmap to move from rhetoric to reform. *BMJ Global Health*. 2021;6(3):e005604.
25. Cancedda C, Farmer PE, Kerry V, Nuthulaganti T, Scott KW, Goosby E, Binagwaho A. Maximizing the impact of training initiatives for health professionals in low-income countries: frameworks, challenges, and best practices. *PLoS Medicine*. 2015;12(6):e1001840.
26. Abimbola S. The uses of knowledge in global health. *BMJ Global Health*. 2021;6(4):e005802.
27. Abimbola S. The foreign gaze: authorship in academic global health. *BMJ Global Health*. 2019;4(5):e002068.
28. Hedt-Gauthier BL, Jeufack HM, Neufeld NH, Alem A, Sauer S, Odhiambo J, Boum Y, Shuchman M, Volmink J. Stuck in the middle: a systematic review of authorship in collaborative health research in Africa, 2014–2016. *BMJ Global Health*. 2019;4(5):e001853.
29. Morton B, Vercueil A, Masekela R, Heinz E, Reimer L, Saleh S, Kalinga C, Seekles M, Biccard B, Chakaya J, Abimbola S. Consensus statement on measures to promote equitable authorship in the publication of research from international partnerships. *Anaesthesia*. 2022;77(3):264–76.
30. Editors of the Lancet Global Health. Closing the door on parachutes and parasites. *The Lancet. Global Health*. 2018;6(6):e593.
31. Bhakuni H, Abimbola S. Epistemic injustice in academic global health. *The Lancet Global Health*. 2021;9(10):e1465–70.
32. Bemme D, Kirmayer LJ. Global mental health: interdisciplinary challenges for a field in motion. *Transcultural Psychiatry*. 2020;57(1):3–18.
33. World Health Organization. *Mental health gap action programme, World Health Organization. mhGAP intervention guide for mental, neurological and substance use disorders in non-specialized health settings: version 1.0*. Geneva: World Health Organization; 2010.
34. World Health Organization. *Mental health gap action programme. mhGAP intervention guide for mental, neurological and substance use disorders in non-specialized health settings: version 2.0*. Geneva: World Health Organization; 2016.
35. World Health Organization. *mhGAP humanitarian intervention guide (mhGAP-HIG) [Internet]*. Geneva: World Health Organization; 2015. [cited 2015 Aug 19]. Available from: http://www .who.int/mental_health/publications/mhgap_hig/en/
36. Mental Health Innovation Network. [Internet]. Available from: https://www.mhinnovation .net/. Accessed October 5, 2022.
37. World Health Organization. *Guidance on community mental health services: promoting person-centred and rights-based approaches*. Geneva, Switzerland: World Health Organization; 2021.

38. Fusar-Poli P, Estradé A, Stanghellini G, Venables J, Onwumere J, Messas G, et al. The lived experience of psychosis: a bottom-up review co written by experts by experience and academics. *World Psychiatry.* 2022;21(2):168–88.

39. Sunkel C, Saxena S. Rights-based mental health care. *The Lancet Psychiatry.* 2019;6(1):9–10.

40. Stein MA, Mahomed F, Patel V, Sunkel C, editors. *Mental health, legal capacity, and human rights.* Cambridge: Cambridge University Press; 2021. 412 p.

41. Global Mental Health Peer Network. [Internet]. Available from: https://www.gmhpn.org/. Accessed October 5, 2022.

42. United Nations Department of Economic and Social Affairs, Disability. [Internet]. https://www.un.org/development/desa/disabilities/convention-on-the-rights-of-persons-with-disabilities.html. Accessed October 5, 2022.

43. National Alliance on Mental Illness. [Internet]. Available from: https://www.nami.org. Accessed October 5, 2022.

44. Patel V, Minas H, Cohen A, Prince M, editors. *Global mental health: principles and practice.* Oxford, UK: Oxford University Press; 2013.

45. White RG, Jain S, Orr DMR, Read UM. *The Palgrave handbook of sociocultural perspectives on global mental health.* London: Palgrave Macmillan UK; 2018.

46. Kohrt B, Mendenhall E. *Global mental health: anthropological perspectives.* London: Routledge; 2016.

47. Stein DJ, Bass JK, Hofmann SG. *Global mental health and psychotherapy adapting psychotherapy for low- and middle-income countries.* London: Academic Press; 2019.

48. Brodwin P. *Everyday ethics: voices from the front line of community psychiatry.* Berkeley, CA: University of California Press; 2013. 233 p.

49. Sue K. *Getting wrecked: women, incarceration, and the American opioid crisis.* California Series in Public Anthropology. Berkeley, CA: University of California Press; 2019. 241 p.

50. Luhrmann TM, Marrow J, editors. *Our most troubling madness: case studies in schizophrenia across cultures.* Berkeley, CA: University of California Press; 2016. 286 p.

51. Farmer P, Basilico M, Kerry V, Ballard M, Becker AE, Bukhman G, Dahl O, Ellner A, Ivers L, Jones DS, Meara J, Mukherjee J, Sievers A, Yamamoto A. Global health priorities for the early twenty-first century. In: Farmer P, Kim JY, Kleinman A, Basilico M, editors. *Reimagining global health: an introduction.* Berkeley, CA: University of California Press; 2013. Pp. 302–39.

52. Patel V, Weiss HA, Chowdhary N, Naik S, Pednekar S, Chatterjee S, et al. Lay health worker led intervention for depressive and anxiety disorders in India: impact on clinical and disability outcomes over 12 months. *The British Journal of Psychiatry.* 2011;199(6):459–66.

53. Rahman A, Malik A, Sikander S, Roberts C, Creed F. Cognitive behaviour therapy-based intervention by community health workers for mothers with depression and their infants in rural Pakistan: a cluster-randomised controlled trial. *The Lancet.* 2008;372(9642):902–9.

54. Mendenhall E, De Silva MJ, Hanlon C, Petersen I, Shidhaye R, Jordans M, et al. Acceptability and feasibility of using non-specialist health workers to deliver mental health care: stakeholder perceptions from the PRIME district sites in Ethiopia, India, Nepal, South Africa, and Uganda. *Social Science & Medicine.* 2014;118:33–42.

55. van Ginneken N, Tharyan P, Lewin S, Rao GN, Meera S, Pian J, Chandrashekar S, Patel V. Non-specialist health worker interventions for the care of mental, neurological and substance-abuse disorders in low- and middle-income countries. *Cochrane database of systematic reviews.* 2013 Nov 19;(11):CD009149.

56. Fricchione GL, Borba CPC, Alem A, Shibre T, Carney JR, Henderson DC. Capacity building in global mental health: professional training. *Harvard Review of Psychiatry.* 2012;20(1):47–57.

57. Collins PY, Patel V, Joestl SS, March D, Insel TR, Daar AS, et al. Grand challenges in global mental health. *Nature.* 2011;475(7354):27–30.

58. Kern DE, Thomas PA, Hughes MT. *Curriculum development for medical education: a six-step approach.* Baltimore, MD: Johns Hopkins University Press; 2009.

59. Acharya B, Tenpa J, Basnet M, Hirachan S, Rimal P, Choudhury N, et al. Developing a scalable training model in global mental health: pilot study of a video-assisted training program for generalist clinicians in rural Nepal. *Global Mental Health.* 2017;4:e8.

60. Bower P, Gilbody S, Richards D, Fletcher J, Sutton A. Collaborative care for depression in primary care: making sense of a complex intervention: systematic review and meta-regression. *The British Journal of Psychiatry*. 2006;189(6):484–93. doi:10.1192/bjp.bp.106.023655

61. Murray LK, Dorsey S, Bolton P, et al. Building capacity in mental health interventions in low resource countries: an apprenticeship model for training local providers. *International Journal of Mental Health Systems*. 2011;5(1):30. doi:10.1186/1752-4458-5-30.

62. Degenhardt L, Charlson F, Ferrari A, Santomauro D, Erskine H, Mantilla-Herrara A, Whiteford H, Leung J, Naghavi M, Griswold M, Rehm J. The global burden of disease attributable to alcohol and drug use in 195 countries and territories, 1990–2016: a systematic analysis for the global burden of disease study 2016. *The Lancet Psychiatry*. 2018;5(12):987–1012.

Social and Historical Contextualization of Global Mental Health

Chapter 1

The Colonial and Postcolonial Roots of Global Mental Health Efforts

Jonathan Sadowsky and Jeremy A. Greene

Summary points

- The field of global mental health has deep historical roots in the colonial era, when psychiatric formulations reflected the agenda and ethnocentrism of the colonial regime. Empirically unsupported theories of racial difference and other racist attributions initially rationalized withholding psychiatric treatment to most colonial subjects, with attendant failure to recognize the pathogenic impacts of the suffering associated with colonialism.
- These colonial era interactions—which generally diminished and harmed the colonial subjects—also sowed the seeds of distrust for future interactions with foreign health interventions; global mental health trainees and practitioners benefit from understanding the historical context of present-day global mental health engagements.
- Global mental health trainees and practitioners benefit from understanding the relevance of colonial and postcolonial histories to contemporary questions in global mental health practice. For example, debates about the universality of mental illness versus its cultural relativism have been a longstanding and recurrent pattern in the history of global mental health and its precursors; trainees and practitioners should understand that the latter runs the risk of harmful stereotyping whereas the former risks missing clinically salient local variation. Trainees and practitioners should also understand from the histories of global mental health that delivering psychiatric treatment is not inherently a form of medical imperialism.
- Trainees and practitioners benefit from understanding the history of mental health innovation emanating from the Global South, for example Lambo's work at Aro Village.

Introduction: Ifemelu's critique

Imagine a young woman in the city of Philadelphia, attending college and living far from home for the first time. She finds herself wading through a long period of sadness that borders on despair. She feels isolated, and yet rejects any efforts others might make to include her in social events. She has become slovenly, lacking motivation to deal with the details of her life, letting her room get messier by the day. It doesn't take a psychiatrist to consider a diagnosis of clinical depression.

What if this particular woman, who grew up far from Philadelphia, rejects the label of depression when her physician aunt suggests it, on the grounds that it is a distinctly American way of naming her suffering, which is something she does not consider an illness at all? This is the situation in which we find Ifemelu, the Nigerian protagonist of Chimamanda Ngozi Adichie's novel *Americanah*.[1] Ifemelu believes her isolation and decline are not symptoms of a pathology, but signs of a normal reaction to her poverty, her undocumented immigrant status (which has made it hard for her to find employment), and her distance from loved ones. Ifemelu's aunt—another

DOI: 10.4324/9781315160597-3

Nigerian in Philadelphia—argues, by contrast, that depression is universally real, even if it is not recognized as such in Nigeria, and that her niece needs medical attention. Throughout the novel, as Ifemelu refuses to submit to this "Americanization" of her mind, she wryly observes that Americans have "a disease for everything." Her "symptoms" ultimately melt away without much comment once she finds a stable job and makes friends.

Ifemelu's predicament is fictional, but it renders in miniature two key problems for the field of global mental health. First, who is right—Ifemelu or her aunt? Is Ifemelu suffering from the universal pathology of major depressive disorder, or is the category a local American fetish to categorize all existential difficulties as disorders? Second, if Ifemelu does indeed have an illness, what are the gains and losses of approaching it using the categories of biomedical psychiatry, given that her situation is inflected by objective poverty and social hardship?[a,2]

A recent survey of the field of global health centers its critique on the frequent inattention to local culture in international interventions.[3] This criticism may apply to global health in general, but when it comes to the field of global mental health specifically, local culture has in fact long been a key dimension for understanding difference—sometimes excessively so. The presumption that cultural difference accounts for different patterns of mental illness in different parts of the world can lead to the extreme stance that mental illnesses are all, in effect, "culture-bound syndromes."[b,4] It can also lend itself to the more modest idea that any universal nosology of mental illness—be it the *Diagnostic and Statistical Manual of Mental Disorders* (DSM) or the *International Classification of Diseases* (ICD)—needs to be sensitive to local variations in presentation or course of illnesses. As the field of global mental health has developed in recent decades, these issues have been repeatedly identified as major challenges (see, for example, Opaku,[5] Fernando,[6] White and colleagues,[7] and Kohrt and Mendelhall[8]).

If global psychiatric tools like the DSM or major psychopharmaceuticals are too deeply rooted in their Euro-American origins to be of use in other contexts, then any efforts to apply them elsewhere amount to little more than psychiatric imperialism.[9,10] On the other hand, premature conclusions of cultural difference can also serve to rationalize withholding potentially helpful forms of medical assistance.[11] There are dangers in an over-emphasis or even a fetishization of cultural difference, with serious practical consequences. There are several instances of care being withheld for these reasons under European colonial rule in Africa. While most colonial states recognized, in principle, a responsibility to care for the mad[c,12]—especially when kin were unable to—they also used arguments about cultural difference to rationalize abdication of that responsibility on the grounds that European psychiatric solutions would be an imposition on the "African way of life."

Best practices in global mental health require a balanced "-emic" understanding of resources of local cultures, both material and intellectual, alongside the use of the best "-etic" understanding of global mental health frameworks. These problems point to fundamental concerns within the field of global mental health, and we will not be able to resolve them in this chapter. Rather, we will show these are not new problems, and that their history and development in colonial and early postcolonial contexts have immediate relevance to the practice of global mental health today. History provides vivid examples of how even well-intentioned efforts to use both "-emic" and

---

a   This section is adapted from J. Sadowsky, *The Empire of Depression: A New History*. London: Polity Books; 2020.

b   For a recent exploration of the continuing conceptual problems associated with the concept of culture-bound syndromes, see Catherine Mas, "'Falling-Out' in Miami and the History of Culture in American Medicine," *Bulletin of the History of Medicine* 96, 1 (Spring 2022) 102–134.

c   We use the terms "mad" and "madness," which have no clinical status, as social, not medical designations. This usage neither presumes nor precludes the judgment that those considered to be mad in their context were mentally ill. For a recent discussion of the pros and cons of this usage see Peter Beresford, "'Mad', Mad Studies and Advancing Inclusive Resistance," *Disability and Society* 35, 8 (2020) 1337–1342.

"-etic" approaches have led to excesses. If knowing this history does not resolve the -emic/-etic debate, there is still considerable value in understanding how perennial this debate has been and why both approaches are so deeply wedged and politically weighted. Too often, interventions in global mental health have unwittingly re-invented this debate by refusing to engage with its history. Our contribution to this volume is meant to help practitioners of all training levels see the relevance of this history in their current work.

History is often overlooked in discussions of global mental health for several reasons. First, historians have only recently begun to explore the archives of colonial and postcolonial psychiatry. Second, in the world of health sciences, where the latest research and publications receive the most attention, older publications are often considered obsolete or irrelevant, even though they often provide examples of pitfalls to avoid—and successes that can be replicated.

In global mental health, however, history is far from an inert background: it is present within the day-to-day challenges of the field. For example, distrust of foreign interventions in mental health is rooted in historical experience with feared and unhelpful institutions under colonialism. Casual generalizations of group psychologies can easily bleed into stereotyping, which also has an unfortunate colonial history. Consider the old notion that clinical depression was rare in traditional African cultures. The idea first emerged during the Atlantic slave trade, when slave owners and traders rationalized the inhumanity of slavery by portraying Africans as simple and untroubled people, who were not vulnerable to deep melancholy.[2] In this case, the dismissal of depression as a diagnostic possibility among Africans was rooted in a racist ideology. Ifemelu's rejection of the label, by contrast, can be read as a form of resistance to cultural assimilation and medical imperialism.

There is now a widespread consensus that mental illness contributes substantially to the global burden of disease.[13,14] If this consensus is new to the twenty-first century, the desire to study the international basis of mental health is not. That investigative impulse sprang from several sources during the twentieth century, including colonial psychiatry, decolonization movements, and ethnographic inquiry into the universality of mental disorders. From those sources emerged the central fault line of debate: Is it more appropriate to the postcolonial situation to assert that mental disorders are relative, or universal? This fault line renders all other inquiry unstable because every other question, whether epidemiological (How prevalent is depression, worldwide? How much does prevalence vary from one locale to another?) or therapeutic (Can the same treatments be applied across cultures?) requires us to recognize the dangers of excess in either direction.

While these dangers exist for any colonial encounter—whether in Asia, Oceania, North America, South America, or even Europe—our focus in this chapter is the relationship between colonial medicine and mental health in sub-Saharan Africa. African history does have a distinctive significance in this history because Europeans held Africa, above all, to represent a geography of incommensurably different minds. They also treated Africa as a site of substantial study as to how this incommensurability might be bridged.

One locale for this inquiry was, in fact, Ifemelu's region of origin. Ifemelu is of Igbo ethnicity, and grew up in Lagos, an approximately two-hour drive from the famed Aro Mental Hospital in Abeokuta. Aro was the site of some early and still-instructive efforts in what we now call global mental health in the late 1950s and early 1960s. These efforts grew directly out of a set of institutional and conceptual challenges that were themselves responses to colonialism, as we will explore in what follows. As we will see, the presumption of radical racial difference had important consequences for psychiatric thought and practice.

Colonial origins of global psychiatry

Ifemelu's critique of the medicalization of distress and the Americanization of the global psyche has been made by a number of prominent nonfiction authors, both inside and outside of the mental health field. Journalist Ethan Watters's 2010 *Crazy Like Us: The Globalization of the American Psyche*, for example, gave popular expression to a subject with which anthropologists have been grappling for decades.[15] Gananath Obeyesekere, meanwhile, offered a closer look at the problem of universalizing psychiatric epistemologies in his study of depression in Sri Lanka. If depression was not intelligible as an illness category to Sri Lankans because suffering is normative in Buddhist culture, why then were there people diagnosed with and subjectively experiencing depression in Sri Lankan hospitals? Obeyesekere attributed this phenomenon to the expanding global reach of Western psychiatry and its power to transform cultures far from its original ambit.[16] This notion that what is mental illness in one culture might be normal in another is such a hardy perennial of folk ethnopsychiatry that it might seem simply common sense to many. The presumption that cultural difference looms especially large in mental illness is salutary in some respects, but it is, we will show, also one with colonial origins, and these origins demand attention as much as cultural difference itself does.

Some evidence suggests that in precolonial contacts between Europeans and Africans, madness was a recognizable category across cultural frontiers. Though, as with other forms of illness, environments might make a difference, culture was not thought to pose any special problem of translation.[17] But in the nineteenth century, the gradual process of conquest and the creation of formal colonialism—as well as increasing mission activity—intensified scrutiny of cultural differences as an explanatory of other forms of difference.

In the late nineteenth and early twentieth centuries, European powers consolidated their rule over most of the African continent, creating new state structures that had little or no relation to precolonial political entities.[18,19] The policies and operations of these states caused massive social changes: increasing capitalization of the economies, a more mobile labor force, land dispossession, industry in some areas, and increased urbanization, for example. All these changes contributed to new epidemiological shifts, more visibly studied in epidemic diseases like tuberculosis and sleeping sickness, but visible across many categories of mental illnesses as well. With urbanization came new needs for social services, as people became increasingly distant from their familial centers of social support and social control. Written accounts of this period depict increasing numbers of "lunatics" on the streets of the urban centers. It was hard to determine whether there was a true rise in prevalence, or simply a growing visibility, but by the early twentieth century, the number of "lunatics" was acknowledged in much of colonial Africa as a significant social problem. Even colonial states, as oppressive as they were, could recognize some obligation to provide for social welfare, or at the very least maintain social order in the urban centers. They turned, naturally, to a European solution—one that was centuries old but becoming increasingly common in the West: the asylum.[20–22]

Colonial asylums generally had dismal physical conditions and served largely as custodial institutions, not therapeutic ones. The repertoire of treatments available in European and American asylums during this period was limited to the architecture of the asylum itself, so-called "moral" treatments that combined behavioral routines and attempts at rational persuasion, and physical application of therapeutic devices (including restraints, cold wraps, and straitjackets) that were confining as well as calming. In the early twentieth century, Western mental hospitals did offer rudimentary therapeutic services, such as hydrotherapy or early shock therapies—but these were often not available in the colonies, particularly not to African patients.[23]

Two factors inhibited the provision of therapeutic services in these colonial institutions. One was financial. Colonies were intended to be self-supporting, meaning they were supposed to provide at least enough revenue, usually by the export of primary resources, to cover the costs of their administration. Government spending on medicine of any kind jeopardized that mission. The other factor was ideological. Despite the massive social changes that colonialism necessarily caused, British administrators had a stated goal of preserving, to the extent possible, an "African way of life." British colonies followed a policy of Indirect Rule under which they sought to use local customary law, or in Muslim areas sharia law, rather than imposing British legal traditions. In principle, the colonial state then ruled through local chiefs, and the maintenance of African tradition was actively encouraged. Every aspect of this was, of course, rife with invented tradition—historians have shown at great length that the political, social, and cultural conditions that were maintained were in many ways fabrications of the colonial period itself, though not necessarily fabricated from whole cloth.

Indirect Rule was not simply a governance mechanism, but an ideology opposing cultural change. Some African elites who did assimilate by pursuing Western education or adopting European dress were promoted to positions of power. There was, though, a stress on the maintenance of African traditions, a condescending veneration of cultural difference, and a fetishization of the "primitive" that sought to preserve a museum-like way, and a disdain for the educated elite (for example, see Packard[24]). In this colonial mindset, an asylum for native Africans could be cast as a potentially disruptive imposition on traditional ways of life, and the provision of psychiatric therapy would be out of the question. The French followed a policy called *assimilation*, under which an equal disdain for African cultures sought not their preservation but the goal of becoming French, though in reality, opportunities for such assimilation were limited. When French colonial governments built asylums there was also little treatment offered to African patients for most of the colonial period.[22,25]

It is worth pausing to appreciate that while some critics now see the global delivery of Western psychiatric treatments as a form of medical imperialism, imperial thought during direct and indirect colonial rule often held a prejudice toward withholding Western psychiatric therapies from indigenous peoples considered unlikely or unable to benefit from them. They built asylums reluctantly as a way to confine people, but they offered little psychiatric treatment. They did, however, produce extensive psychiatric theory. Particularly in larger colonies, European psychiatric specialists—either working on site in asylums or as expert consultants—studied the asylums and their inmates and wrote reports. These reports were animated by two main questions: 1) Why was there an apparent increase in the numbers of "mad" people in the African colonies?; and 2) What factors characterized the so-called "African mind"?[17(pp.97–110), 26,27(pp.100–128)] These reports varied in quality, but few of them had much empirical substance. Medical personnel in colonial asylums virtually never spoke the first language of their non-European patients, and rarely did in-depth examinations. Their reports therefore were less the product of psychiatric research and more an expression of colonial ideology. As ideology, they were rationalizations for colonial rule, racially paternalistic at their best, and crudely reactionary at their worst.

As for the first question, according to colonial psychiatric theory, the purported rise of "lunatics" was caused by "deculturation."[27(pp.100–128)] The premise of this theory was that Africans were traveling from a primitive state of culture to modernity at a fast pace. With social change, Africans lost their cultural moorings and were rendered especially vulnerable to mental illness. The "tribal" group, in this conceptualization, was critical for the maintenance of African sanity. Colonial authors often viewed African cultures as fragile, and liable to collapse dramatically after even modest exposures to European influences.[28] In some versions, the rapid rise of literacy among colonial subjects was also viewed as pathogenic—a theory that was also invoked in speculations as to the origins of hysteria in Western women. Notably, in no versions of deculturation theory was colonial domination itself considered a possible source of ill health.[17(pp.97–110)]

Deculturation theory was a theory of unique African fragility. We can now see that increased migrancy and urbanization meant that more people were living far from close kin, and that these people were therefore more likely to come to the attention of colonial officials if they did exhibit signs of madness. Some people who were loudly critical of colonialism itself would come to the attention of officials, and if those people also showed behavior that might be seen as symptomatic of a disorder, they might be more likely to be placed in an asylum.[17(pp.65–73)]

As for the second question about whether there existed a typical "African mind," the answer formulated by the colonizers was an emphatic yes. These reports were replete with racist generalizations about the childlike, impulsive character of Africans.[21(p.229).] Researchers portrayed Africans as lacking the time horizon for long-term planning and lacking much capacity for reflection and introspection. A low level of intelligence was usually imputed.[26,27] Most of these authors acknowledged the diversity of African cultures, but it was a faint acknowledgment—one that was, in the end, dismissed more forcefully to reassert a uniform "African mind."

Despite all the assumptions of radical difference in African mentality or even physiology, Western psychiatric categories were used avidly. Every person admitted to a colonial asylum received a diagnosis derived from Western psychiatry. The belief in a radically different "African mind" was not thought to suggest that a different diagnostic vocabulary was needed. Similar contradictions can be found in other contexts as well. In colonial Vietnam, French psychiatrists insisted that differences in mentality and pathology between Europeans and Vietnamese were based on fundamental racial differences, but this led to no questioning of the relevance of European psychiatry for Vietnamese patients.[18] The question of whether there were illnesses specific to Africa or specific manifestations of universal illnesses received surprisingly little attention. Among the psychoanalytically inclined, there were occasional speculative forays into ways different family structures or age at weaning from breast-feeding might influence child development. Psychoanalytic influence was more widespread in anthropological than psychiatric writing, however. The psychiatric reports were written by psychiatric professionals who drew their data from people confined in asylums, but the theories of "the African mind" were primarily theories of "normal" African psychology, not psychopathology. This may be less surprising when we consider that little medical treatment was intended.

While colonial psychiatric thinking was an expression of colonial ideology and racial thought, the asylum was not the original or even most influential source of these ideas. Scientific racism and allied eugenic ideas had been on the rise since the late nineteenth century and were pervasive throughout the industrialized world. The political scientist Crawford Young has argued that the concurrence of the colonial period in Africa with the period of the most virulent racist thought—itself not a coincidence—was one of the reasons colonialism was so deeply harmful to Africa and left it facing especially deep challenges of development when independence came.[29] Stereotypes alleging the tendency to lie, sexual immorality, and drunkenness as aspects of African mentality were well developed in colonial thought long before there were any colonial psychiatric institutions or theory.[30–33]

While some contemporary anthropologists challenged these stereotypes, there were many others who gave them significant elaboration, such as the French ethnologist Lucien Lévy-Bruhl. Lévy-Bruhl had no direct research experience in Africa, yet his books on "primitive mentality" were read far more widely than those of any colonial psychiatrist. His ideas were also absorbed into European psychiatric thought through the psychoanalytic traditions. Lévy-Bruhl's work was read and admired by Carl Jung, who was deeply interested in what he regarded as racial differences in psychology.[34] This racial thinking was also present—albeit less pronounced—in the psychological theories of Sigmund Freud and his less apostate followers.[35] Freud and Jung differed on many points, of course, but their psychological theories both asserted the significance of individual psychology while retaining the belief that "races" had differences in psychological make-up. Like their European colleagues who worked in colonial settings, they combined aspirations to a universal science with the contradictory underlying assumption of deep racial difference. Neither Freud nor Jung was engaged directly with the colonial enterprise, but their careers coincided with the era of intense colonization and their views reflected the imperial assumptions common in Europe.

Psychoanalytic views received elaborate expression in the work of the colonial theorist Octavio Mannoni. Mannoni lived in the French colony of Madagascar from 1925 to 1947, where he worked as an ethnologist and government official. Upon returning to France, he underwent a psychoanalysis with Jacques Lacan.[26(p.99)] He brought his experiences with colonialism and psychoanalysis together in *Prospero and Caliban*, one of the most influential books on African mentality at the time.[36] *Prospero and Caliban* attempted to understand the Malagasy revolt against colonial rule that broke out around the time he left the colony. Though Mannoni shared the prevailing European attitude that anticolonial revolt was a puzzle requiring psychological explanation, he was unusual among his peers in considering the situation of colonial domination itself as a piece of the puzzle. Nonetheless, he did not develop a critique of colonialism on that basis. Instead, he resorted—like his colleagues—to broad ideas about African mentality, holding that African psychology was deeply shaped by feelings of dependency.

Africans, in Mannoni's view, were incapable of achieving individual initiative and personal independence. African psyches were protected by submersion in the collective without which they would be plunged into fear and insecurity, conditions he likened in Freudian terms to a castration complex. In fact, Mannoni held that colonialism itself was possible not so much because of military conquest, but rather more because of the African desire for dependence. Their unconscious welcomed the European colonizer as a protector, he posited. In a move that seems especially counterintuitive, he further argued that the anticolonial revolt was motivated by the fear that the colonizer would leave, not the desire for their departure. Not surprisingly, his views received sharp criticism from anticolonial theorists, most prominent among them the Martinique-born French psychiatrist Frantz Fanon.[26(pp.99–103),27(pp.114–115)]

Psychoanalytic views also circled their way back into anthropology through the American Culture and Personality school in the 1950s, which adapted a Freudian insistence on the importance of childhood experience in shaping character to the study of character formations held broadly within given cultures. The views expressed there came from a tradition associated with Franz Boas and others who ardently rejected racism and sought to sever the recognition of cultural difference from race. It nevertheless received critique for reifying cultural difference and for, at times, seeming to imply that cultures were bound and static entities.[37(p.21)] Among the contributors to this school was Ruth Benedict, a student of Boas's, who wrote one of the most important formulations of the idea that what was considered mad in one culture might be considered normal in another. Benedict gave examples of people acting in ways that would be considered abnormal in Western society, such as feeling good in a situation Westerners would consider a time of mourning. Conversely, she gave examples of people considered abnormal in their own society, whose behavior would be normative in the West. She concluded that some basic ethical standards might be human universals, but that "it is quite possible that...[w]hen data are available in psychiatry, this minimum definition of abnormal human tendencies will be probably quite unlike our culturally conditioned, highly elaborated psychoses such as those that are described, for instance, under the terms of schizophrenia and manic-depressive."[38(p.79)]

While, in retrospect, it is tempting to see in the post–World War II period an inevitable progressive arc of decolonization, this was not how it was experienced at the time of the end of the war. The postwar period saw an intensification of nationalist independence movements—many of them emboldened, perhaps, by the anti-colonialist terms of the Atlantic Charter between Franklin Delano Roosevelt and Churchill. India's achievement of independence in 1947 also inspired African nationalism. Yet in the early years of this period, most European officials in African colonies believed that colonialism would last for decades to come. As African demands for independence grew more visible and organized anticolonial movements gained strength, however, the increasing possibility of a rapid and total decolonization generated anxieties among colonial administrators and the medical personnel who served them. At the same time, colonial governments started to abandon the stance that interventionist government measures should be avoided. There was talk of a "New Deal" for Africa. This shift in attitude entailed renewed efforts to provide the social services that had always been part of the rationale for colonialism in the first place, but which had been continually deferred. This included, in some areas, mental health services designed to be therapeutic and not custodial. In Nigeria, for example, plans for a mental hospital at the Aro site in Abeokuta had been discussed since the 1930s. The colonial government continued for most of that time to cite budget constraints and fears about making "impositions" on the "African way of life" as reasons to postpone the project, which nevertheless finally came to fruition in the 1950s. Around the time the vision for Aro was finally realized, existing "asylums" were redescribed as "mental hospitals" to signal their new therapeutic emphasis.

These two developments—the stirrings of independence and the development of social services—form the backdrop to the strange concurrence in the 1950s of some of the most virulently racist psychiatric thought and some of the most creative innovations in mental health care. This movement—and our understanding of the profound violence done in the name of postwar international mental health—is best encapsulated in the career of J.C. Carothers. Carothers was a white South African who went to medical school in England. He served as a medical officer in Kenya and as a director of the Mathari Mental Hospital in Nairobi, though he had no formal psychiatric training. Most of his work was in Kenya, but he visited other colonies and wrote confidently about the field of mental health across the entire continent, if not the world. His work rehearsed the most derogatory themes expressed by other colonial psychiatrists. He described Africans as child-like and fragile, uniquely vulnerable to the stresses of modernity. Though he acknowledged that there were cultural differences within Africa, he denied they had much significance or that they had any relevance to psychopathology. One of his most disturbing and often-cited ideas was that normal Africans, with their purportedly childlike qualities, resembled lobotomized Europeans.[39] He further theorized that Africans had undeveloped frontal lobes. After Carothers, the phrase "frontal lobe defect" would echo in colonial psychiatry for decades.[27(p.111)]

Historians have subjected Carothers's views to severe and well-deserved critique. But two points deserve some continued emphasis. One is that his ideas were forged in the environment of the *Mau Mau* anticolonial uprising in the settler colony of Kenya. In most of Africa, European imperialism was what historians have called "true empire": places subjected to foreign rule and administration, but without a significant settler presence. Settler colonies—which also included South Africa, Southern Rhodesia (now Zimbabwe), and Algeria—were distinguished from true empire by historical traits like large-scale land appropriation and particularly violent paths to independence, as Africans fought to claim sovereignty and reclaim land, and settlers "dug in" to their privileged positions holding the best land and control over the government. In many ways, this distinction between settler colony and true empire had more practical significance than the differences characterizing the various European imperial powers. In Kenya, British settlers had seized much of the most arable land in the country, undermining the prosperity of Africans in the vicinity. This led to the *Mau Mau* uprising, a violent attack on colonial power—an uprising we might see as far from surprising. The settlers, however, were surprised, assured as they were that colonial dominion was justified by racial difference. They saw the uprising as a form of madness; it was, they believed, the result of primitive mentality, coupled with deculturation. Carothers gave this view the elaborate expression in his book *The Psychology of Mau Mau*. Thus, the most reactionary of colonial psychiatric thought derived from the most reactionary of settler milieus—one that was under siege on a level not seen on most of the continent.

The second point that bears emphasizing is that Carothers's views were reasonably consonant with mainstream European medical opinion at the time he was writing. The 1950s were post-Holocaust, and there had been several decades of scientific rebuttals to both racism and eugenics. But scientific racism was not undone by these proclamations: it remained a stubborn feature of the intellectual landscape, reappearing in every generation. Scientific racism—which maintains race must on some level be "real" (meaning, biologically based) and that these differences are clinically important—is so ingrained in racist culture that the science purporting to support it always receives some positive attention, despite devastating critique from the social and physical sciences. In short, it is a view that can be impervious to evidence that contradicts it.[40] Carothers himself included within his own work evidence that contradicted racial stereotyping, but he ignored it, unable to assimilate it into his core arguments. His work was published and read widely in prominent medical journals, and received much praise from contemporaries, and he was further commissioned to do work on Nigeria and to write his "diagnosis" of the problem of insanity in Africa more generally. In this connection, it is worth remembering that the researchers of the notorious and decades-long Tuskegee syphilis study also published their work in medical journals without arousing much attention, let alone censure. The study only became an index case of medical racism when it was exposed as such in mainstream media in the early 1970s.[41]

If Carothers's work was generally well received in Europe and North America (and among colonial administrators in Africa), it was not universally approved. At least two psychiatrists, both of them Black and from the colonized world, developed powerful critiques of Carothers and of colonial psychiatric thought generally at that time. One was the famous psychiatrist and anticolonial theorist Fanon, who himself wrote in the context of violent uprising in the French settler colony of Algeria.[22] Fanon was born in Martinique and studied medicine and psychiatry in France. He was strongly influenced by psychoanalytic thought, but also reacted against racist themes in it. During his medical residency he wrote his book *Black Skin, White Masks*, an enduring meditation on the complex interplay of race, sexuality, and power in colonial settings that was intended in part as a rebuke to Mannoni. He then went to work in a mental hospital in Algeria, in the midst of violent anticolonial war. This experience further radicalized him, ultimately leading him to join the resistance movement, as he came to think it was pointless to try to make people sane in manifestly insane circumstances. The result was another book, *The Wretched of the Earth*, which argued for the necessity of violent struggle against colonialism while also documenting the traumatizing effects of that struggle. *The Wretched of the Earth*, which included a sympathetic preface by Jean-Paul Sartre, was widely read in Europe and Africa, and later cited as a handbook of anticolonial liberation. Fanon took a position almost wholly avoided by colonial psychiatry: if there was indeed an increase in mental illness in colonial Africa, maybe the reason was colonialism itself, not innate traits of Africans, nor some vague effect of "modernization." Working in the midst of a traumatizing conflict—the psychic effects of which he witnessed first-hand while employed at an Algerian mental hospital—it is understandable that Fanon might trace the roots of the suffering he treated back to the pathogen of colonialism.

A different critique of Carothers came from the Nigerian Yoruba psychiatrist T.A. Lambo, who trained in the United Kingdom, and returned to West Africa in the 1950s with the opportunity to oversee the long-deferred creation of a therapeutic institution, the Aro Mental Hospital, in his hometown of Abeokuta. The Nigerian context differed from that of Kenya and Algeria. Kenya and Algeria were settler colonies, where large numbers of Europeans immigrated with their families and came to consider their new country their home. In "true empires" like Nigeria, the European presence largely consisted of colonial officials who intended to return to their country of origin after a term of service. In Nigeria, and other colonies without settlers, colonialism still caused significant social upheaval and led to a vigorous anticolonial nationalist movement. However, independence was negotiated relatively peacefully.

Unlike Carothers, Lambo did not locate the origins of mental illness in modernization or any stereotypes about the "African mind." Yet, unlike Fanon, he did not blame colonialism, either.

Instead, he and the other clinicians who worked at Aro in its founding years took a universalist view that mental illness was fundamentally the same everywhere and had the same basic causes. Lambo was deeply influenced by the Culture and Personality anthropologists and was interested in how variations in cultural difference could shape the presentation of underlying illness. But he rejected vehemently any suggestion that those differences could be drawn along racial lines, as most colonial psychiatric thought did, and he took Carothers to task on this point, stressing that African cultures were themselves highly diverse, that there was thus no single "African mind."[42]

By the time most sub-Saharan countries achieved independence, mental hospitals could no longer be dismissed as having little to offer to patients beyond social control, occupational therapy, and the often-dubious promise of refuge from the pressures of the outside world. In Europe and North America, insulin coma therapy and electroconvulsive therapy were showing demonstrable efficacy in wide use by the 1940s, and the "chemical revolution" of antipsychotic and antidepressant medications was well underway by the 1950s. Alongside somatic treatments, psychoanalysis held immense prestige, greatly expanding psychiatric outpatient practice and influencing hospitals. As the theoretical underpinning of colonial psychiatry was being questioned by Fanon, Lambo, and other decolonial theorists, mental health practitioners in decolonizing contexts faced the question of what kind of therapeutic practices they should adopt.

At Aro, Lambo and his colleagues began to offer biopsychiatric treatments that were state of the art in the industrialized world, including convulsive therapies and antipsychotic medications. This was a radical break from the custodial function of the colonial asylums. As one historian has put it, "Nigerian psychiatrists…sought to decouple the 'modern' from 'the Western.'"[43] Lambo became most celebrated, however, for the innovative village community he devised and spearheaded at Aro.[17(pp.26-47),43(pp.51-78),44,45] If there was one view Lambo shared with colonial officials, it was that a mental hospital would be a disorienting or alienating environment to Africans from rural settings. He instead used a village in the proximity of the hospital and housed the patients there, rather than in the hospital. The community that participated was rewarded with public health interventions like mosquito control. Though he insisted diagnostic and therapeutic models should follow a biomedical approach, Lambo enlisted traditional healers to work with him in the village as culture brokers and assure patients they were in a good and helpful place.[42] Lambo also had the insight to draw the healers from different Nigerian ethnicities. Although the country's three largest ethnicities (Yoruba, Igbo, and Hausa) are the best known, there are hundreds of ethnic groups in Nigeria with their own languages, histories, cosmologies, and concepts of health. Lambo's recognition of this in practice can itself be seen as a broadside against the concept of a singular "African mind."[17(pp.26-47)] It was also part of a burgeoning postwar global effort to promote the utilization of traditional healers.[46]

Aro can be compared to the Fann Clinic in the former French colony of Senegal. Senegal became independent in 1960, and its first President was Léopold Senghor, a major proponent of *Négritude*: a philosophy that emphasized specific African cultural attributes, but departed from colonial theories of difference by seeing African attributes as complementary to Western ones, not lower in a developmental hierarchy. It was in this context that the Fann was created in 1956. Its first director was a French military doctor, Henri Collomb, who had years of experience working in various parts of Africa. Collomb spearheaded what became known as the *L'École de Fann*, which sought to use psychiatric treatments developed in Western contexts and adapt them to an African milieu. Concrete steps included using traditional healers at the clinic and emphasizing group therapy, on the grounds that African culture was collective in orientation, which contrasted with the individualistic character of the West. Unlike Lambo, Collomb also sought to "demedicalize" psychiatry at the clinic by avoiding the use of somatic treatments. The main import from the West was psychoanalytic thought, which Collomb considered adaptable to the West African setting. Collomb's ideas and practices garnered high praise from Senghor himself.[47,48]

The approaches at Aro and Fann both sought to replace an inhumane and custodial colonial psychiatry with new models of postcolonial care. Both offered therapeutics, replacing the carceral approach that characterized colonial-era mental institutions. Both enlisted the help of traditional healers. Both developed theoretical critiques of psychiatric racism. However, they differed chiefly with respect to which forms of Western therapeutic techniques were best translated into mental hospitals in African contexts. Where Lambo sought to make state-of-the-art biopsychiatric treatments from Europe and North America available to Nigerian patients, Collomb worked to adapt psychoanalytic talk therapies specifically suited to a Senegalese social context.

The achievement of the Aro village experiment is worth dwelling on. "Community care" for the mentally ill quickly became a prominent topic of mental health research, fueling health policy efforts in the United States and elsewhere to move toward the widespread deinstitutionalization of the mentally ill. Yet the practicalities of this were all too rarely worked out in a thoughtful way. What would "the community" be? How would treatment follow-up be insured? What would be the community's response? Lambo devised a solution that could in many respects still be emulated: patients housed in the close ambit of the hospital, with careful attention to their specific cultural background, rather than referenced to an imagined uniform "African mind." If current advocates for the newness of global mental health distinguish the present field from colonial predecessors in its goals of collaboration, as opposed to paternalistic intervention, it is worth remembering that much of that ideal had already been realized a half-century earlier at Aro.[49]

In its time, Aro attracted international attention and became a magnet for researchers. In a sense, this had the effect of making "the Yoruba" into a "case" of its own: an ethnic group as a laboratory for the problem of cross-cultural psychiatry. One product of this was the landmark book *Psychiatric Disorder among the Yoruba*, co-authored by Lambo and an international research team, largely based at Cornell.[50] An extensive exploration of how psychopathology manifested in Yoruba culture, it sought an acute sensitivity to the particularities of Yoruba culture, while also attempting to show that the same mental illnesses known to the West were present. It thus sought to lay the groundwork for a future global psychiatric epidemiology, but also that field's ensuing category problems. The prevalence of depression among the Yoruba, for example, was a particularly fraught question. Lambo agreed at first with the colonial reports that found depression to be rare in Africa. A few years later, he began to wonder if it was prevalent, but being labeled "neurasthenia." The question was made challenging for him by the lack of a word in his own language, Yoruba, that translated exactly to depressive illness. The Cornell-Aro collaboration found many symptoms of depression listed as signs of mental distress, but often not considered to be clustered into a single illness category. Their general argument was that cultural difference had to be accounted for, but was not an insuperable barrier to diagnosis, when assessing the global prevalence of mental illnesses. This research became a key part of a historical inflection point, laying the groundwork for much future quantitative study of global mental health.

One of the Aro researchers, Jane Murphy, later made a powerful and influential argument for comparability of mental illnesses across cultures in the international journal *Science*.[51] Murphy's article "Psychiatric Labeling in Cross-Cultural Perspective," addressed "labeling theory," which holds that the genesis of mental disorder lies in the social process of labeling deviance as illness, after which the illness label becomes internalized as a part of the labeled person's identity.[52] Murphy reasoned that if social processes were indeed fundamental to the etiology of mental illness, mental disorders ought to vary across differing societies. Murphy put this hypothesis to an empirical test, which, she said, failed: similar mental disorders could, in fact, be found in widely divergent contexts. Murphy's research at Aro thus became an influential statement of the universalist approach to psychiatric illnesses. Where some may have thought that those called mad might be considered shamans or seers in other cultures, Murphy countered, her research in the Aro-Cornell group showed that cultures with shamans or seers also had people considered mad.

The mad living among Yoruba were not the same thing as shamans or seers; rather, the mad were considered mad for much the same reasons they were in the West. Benedict had wondered whether research on culture and psychiatry might, someday, show that culture-laden categories like schizophrenia and manic-depression would not have meaning outside of Western contexts. Murphy argued that the experience at Aro showed that in fact they did. Murphy's articulation of a universalist psychiatry, though, worked from a European baseline.

Conclusion

The emergence of Aro as a site for international and cross-cultural research into mental health and psychiatry helped lay the foundation for later global research on mental health. Once it was established that diagnostic labels could be applied cross-culturally, the World Health Organization (WHO) envisioned and implemented larger studies on the prevalence of schizophrenia as a universal category of mental illness. This work also set the stage for WHO's current declaration that depression is the single biggest contributor to the global health burden, with more than 300 million people worldwide living with depression, and an 18% increase between 2005 and 2015.[53]

But the matter is still far from settled. The schizophrenia studies, for example, have been criticized for not taking sufficient account of cultural difference—by, for example, treating the "developed world" and "underdeveloped world" as undifferentiated within themselves.[37,54,55] There continue to be more radical critiques arguing that the use of Western psychiatric labels represent a form of imperialism, or even calling for the eradication of psychiatric diagnosis altogether.[9,56]

As historians, we are less interested in resolving these debates than in drawing attention to their deeper historical context, and the repetitive patterns that continue to emerge. For more than a century now, the impulse to emphasize cultural difference has run the risk of reinforcing stereotypes. Attempts to emphasize the universality of illnesses have conversely risked downplaying the reality of social and political context. Neither conception is *inherently* more imperialist than the other, and the flaws—as well as the merits—of both approaches need to be acknowledged and worked through in specific clinical and epidemiological work. Awareness of the long, cyclical history of this conflict helps to make clear, we hope, why these issues are still so politically fraught—and remain unresolved—today.

In this overview of postcolonial global mental health's colonial origins—especially in the crucial contexts of East and West Africa—we have sought to show that debates over the extent and meaning of cultural differences, and the implications of those differences, have a long history. But we would like to conclude with another lesson from colonial medical history. It is no accident that dismal, oppressive institutions and racist psychiatric theory characterized the colonial period, whereas critique of that theory—and innovative therapeutic approaches—grew out of the movements for independence. Today's practitioners in global mental health who seek successful uptake and engagement with local communities need to understand that distrust of public health interventions today may come not from any particular resistance to Western medical approaches, but from a much longer history of mistrust in which the structures of colonialism, far from being located in the past, are understood to have been displaced on future generations.

References

1. Ngozi Adichie C. *Americanah*. London: HarperCollins; 2014. [See especially pages 150–58.]
2. Sadowsky J. *The empire of depression: a new history*. London: Polity Books; 2020. 224 p.
3. Packard R. *A history of global health*. Baltimore, MD: The Johns Hopkins University Press; 2016. 432 p.
4. Mas C. "Falling-out" in Miami and the history of culture in American medicine. *Bulletin of the History of Medicine*. 2022;96(1):102–34.

5. Okpaku S. *Essentials of global mental health.* Cambridge: Cambridge University Press; 2014. 465 p.

6. Fernando S. *Mental health worldwide.* London: Palgrave MacMillan; 2014. 222 p.

7. White R, Jain S, Orr D, Read U. *The Palgrave handbook of sociocultural perspectives on global mental health.* London: Palgrave MacMillan; 2017. 828 p.

8. Kohrt BA, Mendenhall E. *Global mental health: anthropological perspectives.* London: Routledge; 2016. 390 p.

9. Mills C. *Decolonizing global mental health: the psychiatrization of the majority world.* London: Routledge; 2014. 178 p.

10. Summerfield, D. Afterword: against "global mental health." *Transcultural Psychiatry.* 2012; 49 (3–4) 519–530.

11. Jenkins J, Kozelka E. Global mental health and psychopharmacology in precarious ecologies: anthropological considerations for engagement and efficacy. In: White R, Jain S, Orr D, Read U, editors. *The Palgrave handbook of sociocultural perspectives on global mental health.* London: Palgrave MacMillan; 2017. pp. 151–68.

12. Beresford P. 'Mad', mad studies and advancing inclusive resistance. *Disability & Society.* 2020;35(8):1337–42.

13. Murray CJL, Lopez AD. *The global burden of disease.* Cambridge, MA: Harvard University Press; 1996. 990 p.

14. Desjarlais R, Eisenberg L, Good B, Kleinman A. *World mental health: problems and priorities in low-income countries.* New York: Oxford University Press; 1995. 382 p.

15. Watters, E. *Crazy like us: the globalization of the American psyche.* New York: Free Press; 2010. 320 p.

16. Obeyesekere G. Buddhism, depression, and the work of culture in Sri Lanka. In: Kleinman A, Good BJ, Good B, editors. *Culture and depression: studies in the anthropology and cross-cultural psychiatry of affect and disorder.* Berkeley, CA: University of California Press; 1985. pp. 134–52.

17. Sadowsky J. *Imperial Bedlam.* Berkeley, CA and Baltimore, MD: The Johns Hopkins University Press; 1999. 188 p.

18. Edington CE. *Beyond the asylum: mental illness in French colonial Vietnam.* Ithaca, NY: Cornell University Press; 2019. 312 p.

19. Osei Quarshie N. *On "foreign lunatics": diversity, labor migration, and psychiatry in West Africa, 1930-present.* Ann Arbor, MI: University of Michigan; 2019.

20. Akyeampong E. A historical overview of psychiatry in Africa. In: Akyeampong, E, Hill, AG, Kleinman, A, editors. *The culture of mental illness and psychiatric practice in Africa.* Bloomington, IN: Indiana University Press; 2015. pp. 24–49.

21. Swartz S. Mad Africa. In: Eghigian G, editor. *The Routledge history of madness and mental health.* New York: Routledge; 2017. pp. 229–44.

22. Keller RC. *Colonial madness: psychiatry in French North Africa.* Chicago, IL: University of Chicago Press; 2008. 320 p.

23. Braslow, J. *Mental ills and bodily cures: psychiatric treatment in the first half of the twentieth century.* Berkeley, CA: University of California; 1997. 262 p.

24. Packard RM. The "healthy reserve" and the "dressed native": discourses on Black health and the language of legitimation in South Africa. *American Ethnologist.* 1989;16(4):686–703.

25. Kilroy-Marac K. *An impossible inheritance: postcolonial psychiatry and the work of memory in a West African clinic.* Berkeley, CA: University of California Press; 2019. 284 p.

26. McCulloch J. *Colonial psychiatry and 'the African mind'.* Cambridge: Cambridge University Press; 1995. 196 p.

27. Vaughan M. *Curing their ills: colonial power and African illness.* Stanford, CA: Stanford University Press; 1991. 224 p.

28. Carothers JC. *The psychology of Mau Mau.* Nairobi: Government Printer; 1954. p. 6.

29. Young C. *The African colonial state in comparative perspective.* New Haven, CT: Yale University Press; 1994. 368 p.

30. Comaroff, J. The diseased heart of Africa: medicine, colonialism, and the Black body. In: Lindenbaum S, Lock MM, editors. *Knowledge, power and practice: The anthropology of medicine and everyday life.* Berkeley, CA: University of California Press; 1993:305–329.

31. Ajayi, JFA. *Christian missions in Nigeria 1841–1891: the making of a new elite*. Essex: Longman; 1965. 261 p.
32. Curtin PD. *The image of Africa: British ideas and action, 1780–1850*. Madison, WI: University of Wisconsin Press; 1964. 304 p.
33. Cohen WB. *The French encounter with Africans: white response to blacks, 1530–1880*. Bloomington, IN: Indiana University Press; 1980. 382 p.
34. Bair, D. *Jung: a biography*. New York: Little, Brown and Company; 2003. 928 p.
35. Maddox B. *Freud's Wizard: Ernest Jones and the transformation of psychoanalysis*. Cambridge: Da Capo Press; 2006. 195 p.
36. Mannoni O. Prospero and Caliban: the psychology of colonization. P. Powesland, trans., New York: Fredrick A. Praeger; 1964. 217 p.
37. Kohrt BA, Mendenhall E, Brown PJ. Historical background: medical anthropology and global mental health. In: Kohrt BA, Mendenhall E, editors. *Global mental health: anthropological perspectives*. London: Routledge; 2016. pp. 19–36.
38. Benedict R. Anthropology and the abnormal. *Journal of General Psychology*. 1934;10(1):59–82.
39. Carothers JC. *The African mind in health and disease: a study in ethnopsychiatry*. Geneva: World Health Organization; 1953. 177 p.
40. Fields B, Fields K. *Racecraft: the soul of inequality in American life*. London: Verso Books; 2012. 311 p.
41. Reverby SM. *Examining Tuskegee: the infamous syphilis study and its legacy*. Chapel Hill, NC: University of North Carolina Press; 2009. 416 p.
42. Lambo TA. The role of cultural factors in paranoid psychosis among the Yoruba tribe. *Journal of Mental Science*. 1955;101(423):239–66.
43. Heaton, MM. *Black skin white coats: Nigerian psychiatrists, decolonization, and the globalization of psychiatry*. Athens, OH: Ohio University Press; 2013. p. 17.
44. Asuni T. Aro hospital in perspective. *American Journal of Psychiatry*. 1967;124(6):763–70.
45. Lambo TA. The village of Aro. *The Lancet*. 1964;2(7358):513–14.
46. Tilley H. Traditional medicine goes global: Pan-African precedents, cultural decolonization, and cold war rights/properties. *Osiris*. 2021;36(1):132–59.
47. Kilroy-Marac K. *An impossible inheritance: postcolonial psychiatry and the work of memory in a West African clinic*. Berkeley, CA: University of California Press; 2019. 284 p.
48. Collignon R. Some aspects of mental illness in French-speaking West Africa. In: Akyeampong E, Hill AG, Kleinman A, editors. *The culture of mental illness and psychiatric practice in Africa*. Bloomington, IN: Indiana University Press; 2015. pp. 163–85.
49. Bemme D, D'Souza N. Global mental health and its discontents [Internet]. *Somatosphere*. 2012. [cited 16 May 2017]. Available from: http://somatosphere.net/2012/07/global-mental-health-and-its-discontents.html
50. Leighton AH, Lambo TA, Hughes CC, Leighton DC, Murphy JM, Macklin DB. *Psychiatric disorder among the Yoruba*. Ithaca, NY: Cornell University; 1963. 413 p.
51. Murphy JM. Psychiatric labeling in cross-cultural perspective: similar kinds of disturbed behavior appear to be labeled abnormal in diverse cultures. *Science*. 1976;191(4231):1019–28.
52. Scheff TJ. *Being mentally ill: a sociological theory*, 2nd ed. Chicago, IL: Aldine de Gruyter; 1984. 220 p.
53. Chaib F, Brunier A. "Depression: let's talk" says WHO, as depression tops list of causes of ill health [Internet]. World Health Organization; 2017. [cited 7 July 2017]. Available from: http://www.who.int/mediacentre/news/releases/2017/world-health-day/en/
54. Edgerton RB, Cohen A. Culture and schizophrenia: the DOSMD challenge. *The British Journal of Psychiatry*. 1994;164(2):222–31.
55. Jablensky A, Sartorius N, Cooper JE, Anker M, Korten A, Bertelsen A. Culture and schizophrenia: criticisms of the WHO studies are answered. *The British Journal of Psychiatry*. 1994;165:434–36.
56. Timimi S. No more psychiatric labels: why formal psychiatric diagnostic systems should be abolished. *International Journal of Clinical and Health Psychology*. 2014;14(3):208–15.

Chapter 2

Resocializing Global Mental Health
What Anthropological Perspectives Offer to Learners, Educators, and Practitioners

Anne E. Becker and Arthur Kleinman

Summary points

- As an interpretative social science, anthropology offers a lens for a critical understanding of global mental health that illuminates both its limitations and avenues for improvement.
- Selected social theories offer an intellectual toolkit of conceptual approaches to global health that allows learners, educators, and practitioners to recognize and navigate challenges, uncertainties, and opportunities to advance the goals of global mental health.
- Students of global mental health should be aware of local cultural contexts that shape presentation and preferences in clinical care delivery and program implementation but, at the same time, avoid overly simplistic culturalist explanations for help-seeking behavior and the distribution of disease risk and outcomes. They should also develop an awareness and attunement to social structural determinants of health and constraints on personal agency.
- Students of global mental health should learn how to practice an approach to engaging cultural difference that integrates awareness of the history, social context, and other processes that shape illness experience, values, and possible constraints on health agency.
- Students should become familiar with the tenets and limitations of cultural competence; they should become familiar with approaches that highlight cultural humility, cultural safety, and structural competency. They should seek to integrate patient-centered and process-based approaches to understanding social identities in care delivery.
- Students should aspire to link their research and education to action and advocacy on behalf of the communities they seek to serve and collaborate with. They should consider the value of centering *care* in global mental health, developing their own capacity to redress social structural barriers to mental health and well-being, and practicing an accompaniment approach in their global mental health work.

Introduction

Global health is distinguished, in part, from its precursors, tropical medicine and international health, by the centrality of its commitment to health equity. The contemporary framework of global health, moreover, encompasses aspirations to ensure that high-quality care reaches the most vulnerable communities, can be delivered at scale across a full spectrum of clinical need, and redresses social structural inequities that contribute to the global burden of suffering from poor health. In contrast to its origins in colonial and tropical medicine, when the focus was largely on managing endemic infectious diseases that threatened the colonial enterprise, twenty-first-century global health encompasses a global clinical scope, including non-communicable diseases and global mental health.[1,2] The modern field of global health and concurrent advances in psychiatry have also made possible a reimagined era of global mental health. In the mid-twentieth century,

DOI: 10.4324/9781315160597-4

the emergence of a universalizing framework for mental disorders and cross-national studies on depression and schizophrenia shed new light on the global relevance of mental disorders.[3] In the 1990s, the Global Burden of Disease Study data first rendered visible the staggering health burdens associated with poor mental health.[4,5] Communications technology brought the global human toll of suffering associated with mental illness and its attendant stigma increasingly into view.[6] The convergence of advances in epidemiologic assessment and therapeutics, followed in rapid succession by heightened visibility of global mental health as critical to a broader public health agenda[7] and a Movement for Global Mental Health,[8] consolidated its centrality to the field of global health writ large. As global mental health advocates and practitioners continue to draw from and leverage lessons from key successes in the broader field of global health delivery, there have been steady gains in the visibility of need—and possibilities for responding—to serve those living with mental illness. The fruits of these efforts are evident in the appearance of mental and substance use disorders in the Sustainable Development Goals and the growing evidence base for effective interventions to alleviate the health, social, and economic burdens associated with poor mental health.[9]

Global health practitioners have increasingly understood disease distribution not just in terms of latitude, climate, and vectors but also in relation to structural violence, poverty, and geopolitical upheaval; in this respect, the understanding and redress of social determinants and drivers of poor health that heighten risk for disease, limit individual agency in engaging in health-promoting behaviors, and undermine care delivery have become central to a rights-based approach to global health.[10] The recognition that social determinants drive poor health has increasing purchase in mainstream US medical education[11] and health delivery[12] as well, and has been further highlighted by the visibility of health disparities in the course of the COVID-19 pandemic.[13] In this regard, the interpretative social sciences, including the disciplines of history of science and anthropology, have been instrumental in illuminating the drivers of health and social inequity and in critiquing the vestiges of coloniality and neoliberalism that continue to influence how global health delivery is conceived of and practiced. These *resocializing* disciplines also inform an understanding of mental health and mental healthcare delivery within a biosocial framework, toward the aims of optimizing effectiveness and promoting equity and, importantly, toward centering global mental health delivery around *care*. This chapter examines the foundational role and value of anthropology—as one of the resocializing disciplines—toward developing best practices in global mental health and global mental health training. In this chapter we draw from the interpretive social sciences, particularly anthropology, to present a set of theories and considerations that will be useful to global mental health trainees in reading the literature critically, navigating their experiences in collaboration and training, and strengthening their future development as investigators, implementers, and colleagues.

We begin with a brief introduction to how anthropological perspectives can inform an approach to global mental health. Next, we briefly review a selection of just a few social theories that can be useful for learners, educators, and practitioners of global mental health to draw on for an iterative and critical understanding of values, norms, and received wisdom that impact the quality and effectiveness of the programmatic work, capacity-building, bidirectional learning, and advancing health equity aims. We then consider how these approaches can help trainees to navigate dialectics between local and global perspectives on mental health and care delivery as well as cultural and social structural frameworks for understanding and responding to the burden of suffering associated with poor mental health. In addition, we will consider and comment on approaches to the engagement of cultural difference in clinical encounters, as well as in research programmatic design and service delivery in global mental health settings, and their overall relevance to conveying respect, promoting dignity, and fostering inclusiveness in these care delivery and global health contexts. We conclude by considering how practices centering care and accompaniment can humanize and enhance effectiveness of global mental health delivery.

Anthropological perspectives are useful to global mental health trainees, educators, and practitioners in several ways. First, they provide an intellectual framework for understanding and approaching the values, practices, and lived experience associated with illness presentation, help-seeking behavior, caregiving and therapeutic engagement, and health delivery across diverse cultural contexts. This framework anticipates challenging and perennial questions that arise in the real-world context of mental health delivery: How can students, clinicians, investigators, and policymakers engage effectively and collaboratively on a mutually agreed health agenda across cultural difference? And how can available universalizing frameworks for mental disorders, which are useful for estimating health burdens, diagnostic assessment, and deployment of effective therapeutics across geographies, also be thoughtfully integrated across a broad range of social contexts and local cultures for the maximum benefit of diverse populations and communities? Next, these anthropological perspectives furnish theoretical architecture for examining how social processes shape or drive dynamics of engagement, decision-making, organization and interpretation of clinical information, and epistemological premises. Anthropology also offers a distinctive methodologic approach—ethnography—that renders a more nuanced and experience-near understanding of illness and furnishes a complementary view of health and health care. Anthropological methods—and particularly ethnography and other qualitative data collection—are especially useful for navigating the dialectic between local and particular social contexts and universalizing frameworks. As such, anthropological perspectives and methods can illuminate dimensions of the lived experience, local norms, and values of patients and communities, which have direct bearing on health, well-being, and health delivery. Finally, anthropology offers a critical lens for evaluating the inherent assumptions, values, and power dynamics that shape and constrain mental health and health delivery as well as the global mental health agenda.

Trainees should understand that global mental health is, on the one hand, developed on the very premise of a universalizing nosology of mental disorders, such as described by the International Classification of Disease (ICD)[14] and the American Psychiatric Association's (APA) *Diagnostic and Statistical Manual of Mental Disorders* (DSM)[15] while, on the other hand, engaged with responding to mental health needs in local contexts. A vast body of literature in the fields of medical anthropology, cultural psychiatry, and psychiatric epidemiology presents evidence and a framework for approaching variation in phenomenology and risk for mental disorders across diverse social contexts. Within the last half of the twentieth century, these fields converged on a general acceptance of a universalizing framework for mental disorders.[3] Although this universalizing framework has limitations in its focus on commonalities across diverse cultural and social contexts rather than highlighting important phenomenological diversity, it has provided a means for both appreciating the global burden, reach, and impact of mental illness and also developing strategies for responding to the associated enormous unmet mental health needs. In other words, in identifying mental disorders across regions, this framework provided data that refuted earlier misconceptions that some populations were relatively free of mental illness. This framework also enabled the measurement of prevalence and distribution of mental disorders that illuminated the substantial aggregate burden of mental disorders globally, and thereby brought important attention and resources to bear on meeting associated mental health needs in low- and middle-income countries (LMICs).[4,5]

Although we acknowledge critiques of the validity of a universal nosology for mental health,[16] in this chapter we focus instead on the incontrovertible evidence of a substantial health burden of mental disorders across all regions of the world[17] and the enormous and pressing needs identified by unacceptable mental health treatment gaps. Nevertheless, we agree that a sophisticated understanding of the cultural patterning of the risk, lived experience, expression of, and help-seeking for mental distress and illness is essential to integrate into global mental health practice to ensure that programming is acceptable, fully responsive to local needs and priorities, effective, and equitable. We also acknowledge important limitations in global relevance of a universalizing criteria set for the diagnostic assessment of mental disorders when available empirical data are drawn disproportionately from high-income, industrialized settings.[18-22] In this chapter, we introduce social theory that can productively inform an approach to navigating these tensions in global mental health. We also advocate for the further integration of ethnography as a methodologic approach that complements quantitative data from epidemiologic approaches, clinical trials, and implementation research. Indeed, global mental health efforts are strengthened by the methods, theories, and other tools for critical thinking that anthropology offers.

An intellectual toolkit of social theory for global mental health trainees

For over a decade, the two of us have taught, with our physician-anthropologist colleagues, Salmaan Keshavjee and the late Paul Farmer, a large undergraduate course at Harvard focused on biosocial perspectives in global health.[23] In setting a framework for that course we have found it invaluable to introduce a selection of social theories as tools to think through case studies in global health.[24] In particular, these theories have been useful to our students as they toggle from the up-close perspective of on-the-ground logic in deployment of an intervention to the distanced view afforded by cross-site and historically contextualized comparison. We select just a few of these social theories that are most salient to the practice of global mental health to reference here. There are other social theories that are relevant and useful, of course, and we encourage trainees to draw from what we think of as an "intellectual toolkit"[25] of social theory in understanding and critiquing which research, educational, and clinical interventions, programming, and policies have—and have not—worked well to achieve their population health objectives. Such critical reflection will assist practitioners and trainees in formulating ideas, proposals, and actionable steps for adjustments in their work that can generalize to other settings and clinical problems in global mental health.

"Social construction of reality"

Berger and Luckmann articulated this theory to explain how knowledge is socially constructed and then naturalized.[26] This knowledge, in turn, informs a taken-for-granted reality that codifies and constrains behaviors; this socially constructed reality can also limit the possibilities that are imagined for resolving the most vexing challenges confronted in the field of global mental health. For example, social construction of knowledge in different geographies, conditions, and contexts gives rise to local perspectives on what counts as evidence and how to use it—including how to recognize and respond to disease. Local perspectives, in turn, are undergirded by their own histories and social contexts—also local and particular—and may vary in their alignment with other bodies of knowledge. Indeed, the failure to recognize and address differences between local and global views can surface as a tension in collaborations or misalignment of interventions with local needs and priorities; this, in turn, potentially undermines the acceptability and effectiveness of these interventions as they are developed, implemented, and scaled up. Importantly, students of global health should understand how some of the bedrock "truths" taught in institutions of higher education in high-income regions are also socially constructed. For example, Paul Farmer and his colleagues argued that resource constraints, which often drive decision-making for resource allocation, are frequently socially constructed as fixed.[27] Their critique frames this assumption as a kind of "socialization for scarcity" [28(p.272)] and has been used to urge global poli-cymakers and practitioners to re-imagine health resources as expandable rather than accepting them as inelastic.[28] Farmer and colleagues, moreover, reject that resource constraints reflect an immutable order.[29,30] Farmer has, in turn, been criticized for taking a position that is "resource-insensitive."[31(p.19)] Whereas critics point out the pragmatic value of priority-setting in allocation of limited health resources, Farmer and his colleagues argue, instead, that matching goals to needs is preferable and, indeed, essential to overturning a status quo that has been socially constructed and reified.[27]

Another example of social construction of reality highly relevant to global mental health is the reframing of behaviors and experiences as a mental disorder, in contrast to interpreting them as normative, socially deviant, or even socially valued; this type of social construction or interpre-tation of behavioral or experiential phenomena as pathological is referred to as *medicalization*. Examples include the reformulated understanding of alcohol misuse as a medical and psychiatric problem (i.e., formalized as a diagnosis of alcohol use disorder), rather than as personal failing or social deviance, as it previously had been.[32] In this respect, medicalization, or the social con-struction of alcohol misuse as a medical condition, could be viewed as having positive impacts in decriminalizing behavior and directing scientific and clinical resources toward therapeutic rather than punitive interventions. In contrast, another example of medicalization—the social construc-tion of post-combat experiences as post-traumatic stress disorder (PTSD)—has been critiqued as obscuring the social antecedents of suffering by casting it as psychopathology rather than as a common and predictable reaction to large-scale trauma.[33] Whereas the reframing of experiences as PTSD can, on the one hand, be viewed as mobilizing clinical and scientific resources intended to respond to the symptomatic experience of veterans—or others exposed to large-scale catastro-phes—social critics have argued that an atomistic focus on psychopathology afflicting individuals obscures the political and other social forces that drive the traumatic exposures. The framework of PTSD—viewed as a mental disorder, rather than as a manifestation of human suffering on a large scale—medicalizes suffering rather than framing it as a manifestation of injury due to social forces and consequently masking its root cause.[34] In this respect, medicalization situates the response to this kind of suffering in the domain of clinical therapeutic intervention as opposed to a political or social safety net intervention, for example. Understanding suffering as a collective phenomenon and a consequence of social events or dynamics is described as one form of *social suffering* below. Medicalization can also be contested or resisted by social actors deploying lan-guage that fits a counternarrative; an example of this is the term "neurodiverse," which reframes and extends the range of normative experiences to encompass individuals who may otherwise have been classified as manifesting a neuropathological condition.[35(p.108)]

Social suffering

The construct of social suffering has several dimensions, each of which anchors the antecedents and consequences of poor health within social contexts, which are contributory if not causal. Social suffering, for example, encompasses the far-ranging health impacts of *structural violence*. Structural violence refers to the adverse impacts of large-scale historical, political, and economic conditions—such as poverty, poor sanitation, or political oppression—that powerfully constrain agency to meet basic needs or to make choices and act in one's best interest.[36,37] With regard to health, constrained agency limits capabilities to achieve good health by undermining food security and access to safe housing, sanitation, and health care, among other basic needs.[38] The social conditions themselves comprise adversities that frequently have physical or mental con-sequences—and in this regard, some illness can be viewed as an embodiment of social adversi-ties.[39,40] This conceptualization of social suffering erases the distinction between health and social problems and formulates them as intrinsically inseparable. In this respect, the theoretical construct of social suffering is relevant to the practice of global mental health in fostering a critical stance toward health interventions that may be too narrowly focused on health per se, when economic, political, and other social factors must also be addressed to achieve desired goals. Another dimension of social suffering rejects the notion that suffering due to illness is wholly encapsulated in the affected individual. Rather, the scope of impact of illness encompasses others within an identified patient's social network who are affected by the illness—for instance, through their roles as family caregivers, in sharing a household and resources, or by extension of stigma. For example, when individuals living with dementia or other serious mental illness require family support for their safety and well-being, family caregivers may become exhausted, face economic challenges in arranging for appropriate care, or experience social exclusion. Finally, social suffering can refer to the compounding of suffering due to illness in the setting of errors or failures by social institutions.[41]

Social suffering is thus a useful lens in deconstructing how health-focused interventions may be inadequately effective in responding to mental illness when social privations imposing risk remain unrecognized and unmitigated. Returning to the above example of medicalizing trauma from exposure to mass casualty events or war as PTSD, the reformulation of widespread social suffering tied to a collective trauma (e.g., ongoing conflict, forced migration, political oppression) as psychopathology also renders the social causes opaque, even if there is arguably also value in alleviating symptoms such as hypervigilance, insomnia, and intrusive memories.[41] Students of global mental health will understand that redress of mental distress and social suffering is rarely an either/or choice; nonetheless, practitioners should bear these dimensions of etiology and suffering in mind to consider the best scope of intervention.

"The unintended consequences of purposive social action"

In his 1936 paper of the same title, sociologist Robert Merton elaborates on the limitations on anticipating outcomes that may diverge from those that were explicitly planned.[42] He underscores the limits of knowledge that cannot accurately anticipate outcomes emanating from complex factors. Error—in the assumptions underpinning a rationale—is a second source of mishaps that he describes. Next, bias ensuing from the "'imperious immediacy of interest'" preempts more considered action.[42(p.901)] And finally, adherence to particular values may privilege an emphasis on process over results. Merton's theory underscores the tension that can arise between the competing priorities of taking immediate action versus knowledge acquisition that can refine plans.[42] An important application of this theory to global mental health practice is balancing the imperative toward action that serves mental health delivery needs against the value of data collection and analyses that can enhance the effectiveness and efficiency of care delivery. For example, investigation ranging from community-based participatory research in needs assessment to a clinical trial for effectiveness may contribute to optimizing the validity of adapted and translated assessments, alignment with community preferences, or establishing superiority of one treatment over another. On the other hand, in the setting of enormous mental health need on the ground and the perception that available therapies are adequate, there may be reluctance to postpone implementation or divert time and attention away from care delivery. Merton's social theory thus illuminates how a short-term imperative for expeditious care delivery could drive decision-making that preempts consideration of the longer-term benefits of fine-tuning the approach. Relatedly, programs and initiatives intended to promote certain mental health goals may unfold in a nexus of competing priorities, which reflect institutional values or exigencies, and are also shaped within asymmetries of power. Moreover, tensions between priorities to advance knowledge, such as by devoting time and resources toward evaluation and monitoring of outcomes, versus a singular focus on care delivery can force difficult either/or decisions rather than allowing for both/and decisions in the setting of resource constraints.

Beginning a critical read of global health and global mental health

Global mental health engages with the challenges of understanding the health burdens, local priorities, and health delivery in low-resource settings and among socially vulnerable populations. Whereas there is intersection and synergy across the practice of global mental health and the fields comprising cultural psychiatry and medical anthropology, there are also points of debate that are instructive for students of global mental health to consider. As noted earlier in this chapter, a fundamental premise of global mental health is that available health metrics and a universalizing framework for recognizing mental disorders have acceptable validity as a departure point for measuring the distribution of disease burdens, identifying local needs, and deploying strategies for therapeutic management and tracking outcomes. These assumptions, in turn, buttress the rationale for a principal focus in global mental health as a problem of overcoming entrenched health inequities to meet mental health needs.

An anthropological perspective is largely complementary to this approach, but also raises important critiques of some of the assumptions inherent to the practice and field of global mental health. At one extreme pole of this range, some anthropologists reject the premise that the mental disorders identified within a biomedical nosology represent universal categories of illness and critique an approach that imposes an understanding of disease burden, diagnostic assessment, and therapeutic management that was developed by, for, and within populations of largely Anglo- and Euro-centric histories, cultures, norms, and values. Moreover, some who espouse this critique view global mental health as a form of cultural imperialism.[43,44] Others critique an epidemiologic framing of disease risk as being reductive and selective and, in doing so, eliding social context.[45,46] Whereas the former perspective rejects the premise and purposes of global mental health—a perspective with which we flatly disagree—the latter perspective alongside other critiques informed by social theory offers trainees and practitioners a vantage point from which to check their own assumptions and evaluate the quality, ethics, and appropriateness of their global mental health work.

There is also much room for critique about the limitations of our understanding of the causes and distribution of disease. Social scientists have called attention to the social construction of risk factors based on a biomedically Western understanding of medicine. For example, in his book *Epidemiologic Illusions*, Eugene Richardson points out how epidemiologic models construct disease attribution and risk through their selection (and exclusion) of variables to measure and model.[46] This selective omission has resulted in a distorted, and yet hegemonic, understanding of risk that fails to capture social determinants of disease adequately.[47] Other critiques call out the biased understanding of health burden that stems not from data, but the absence of it; such biases are then potentially reinforced and reified by country or health agency decisions not to collect data on such health conditions or through selection of which populations are represented in high-impact psychiatric journals.[18,19] Likewise, selective attention to some disease conditions may reflect biases that are informed by priorities by policymakers or other stakeholders.[48] Critiques of burden of disease metrics, such as the disability adjusted life year (DALY) or years lived with disability (YLD) have informed revisions of their underlying basis, by questioning assumptions and values reflected in age-discounting, setting the expected life span, and construction of disability weights.[49,50] These metrics have, consequently, been reformulated so as to encompass a more inclusive approach that decouples them from economic productivity and bases healthy years lost upon a lifespan set by the highest standard of health care. The latter is important so as not to naturalize and accept a shortened lifespan that is associated with local social, economic, and health conditions reflecting broader social inequities.[51,52]

The examples presented above are not intended to imply that anthropological and global mental health perspectives are necessarily mutually inconsistent. To the contrary, they can also be viewed as complementary. Anthropological approaches and critiques are useful in examining blind spots in global health delivery, such that the quality of care can be elevated—rather than constrained, or even undermined—by flawed logic or unfounded assumptions.[53] Moreover, ethnographic data on local cultural norms, values, and ways of knowing and responding to illness can also be crucial for the successful adaptation, application, and local utility of diagnostic and therapeutic approaches developed in biomedical settings.[54] To gain insight into how these approaches can be mutually informative, it is useful for students of global mental health to understand which empirical data, theories, contrasting values and approaches, and debates informed the modern foundation of global mental health as well as some persisting critiques.

Bridging the global to the local

A universalizing framework for mental disorders gained traction in the mid-twentieth century with the standardization of psychiatric diagnostic criteria through the publication of the first edition of the American Psychiatric Association's *Diagnostic and Statistical Manual for Mental Disorders* and efforts by the World Health Organization (WHO).[3,55] The operationalization of diagnostic criteria and the development of standardized assessments set the stage for several seminal cross-national epidemiologic studies of mental illness, including the Stirling County Study, the WHO International Pilot Study of Schizophrenia, and the WHO Collaborative Study on the Assessment of Depressive Disorders.[3,56–58] Although these studies provided evidence for the global reach of mental disorders, they did not initially attend to variation in how mental disorders are experienced, recognized, and patterned across diverse cultural and social contexts.[3] By contrast, ethnographic and other empirical data generated within the fields of cultural psychiatry and medical anthropology demonstrate striking cultural variation in the expression and local formulation of emotional distress and related symptoms.[59] Whereas some of these presentations share features with mental disorders within the Western biomedical nosology, there is great diversity of phenotypic expression of mental distress across social and cultural contexts.[60,61] In other words, even given the considerable overlap and convergence for some conditions, there are also local cultural expressions of distress that do not appear to correspond to any one mental disorder in the universalizing nosology.[62–64]

Symptom presentations regarded as unique to a particular setting are sometimes referred to as *culture-bound syndromes*. Whereas it is important for clinicians to be aware of and recognize local or culture-specific presentations of mental distress to understand how to proceed therapeutically, it is also helpful to understand such presentations as potentially fluid and dynamic. In other words, clinicians should avoid making assumptions about a patient's distress based solely on their cultural identity and, instead, engage the patient and/or their caregivers toward a contextualized understanding of their particular lived experience. There is also a risk for medicalizing, or pathologizing, expressions of distress when these actually might be culturally normative. In the DSM-5, the term "cultural concepts of distress" (CCD) was introduced as the term "culture-bound syndromes" was dropped in order to encompass a broader set of possibilities for how local cultural meanings relate to diagnostic categories in the DSM's nosologic framework.[65] Importantly, CCDs may describe context-specific presentations or even single symptoms that overlap with, but are not necessarily equivalent to recognized mental disorders.[65] A kind of CCD, an "idiom of distress," refers to a locally salient pattern of symptomatic manifestation or expression of distress.[66] Idioms of distress can reflect culturally legitimate available modes for expressing dissent, complaint, or an affective state and are not necessarily pathologized locally, although they can signify illness, too.[67] Although such idioms of distress may be well recognized in local contexts, they may not be readily recognized within, or shoehorned into, a nosologic framework developed within a body of empirical knowledge drawn from a very different social context (such as the Global North). Moreover, because an idiom of emotional distress may present as a blend of affective and—or even predominantly—somatic symptoms, the clinical interpretation and recommended therapy may not align well with the patient's needs if a clinician does not appreciate their local significance. Likewise, individuals may have locally patterned preferences for seeking care in clinical settings that reflect their concerns about stigma, level of trust in the clinicians, or understanding of their symptoms.

Health care and illness are experienced and enacted in social (interpersonal) spaces, characterized by values and routines that are local and particular, given that they are forged within their unique geopolitical histories and cultural rationales. In addition to shaping illness experience, local contexts also configure social responses to illness, including the values that shape social supports, stigma, and local moral worlds (where different things are at stake for the group and individuals).[68] Because global mental health typically operates within a globalizing framework that transcends regional locality, there are inevitable tensions that arise when a health delivery approach is misaligned with the local context of lived experience. Notwithstanding the good intentions of health professionals in their delivery of quality care, the mismatch between professional and lay understandings of illness can undermine care-seeking, valid diagnostic assessment, adherence, and a collaborative therapeutic alliance or, worse, lead to treatment that results in harm.[69]

The possibilities for divergence in understandings and expectations about illness have been elaborated in the conceptualization of *explanatory models.*[70] An explanatory model refers to an identified patient's or their family's understanding of symptoms, expectations about their course, and ideas about an optimal therapeutic approach. This explanatory model is informed by lived experience, cultural values, and prevailing social norms, as well as the local accessibility of folk or biomedical health resources and knowledge. An explanatory model may be implicit or explicit; it may also be fixed or evolving. Moreover, this explanatory model may align well with the biomedical explanatory model that a clinician has in mind, or there may be considerable divergence. When the latter is the case and the clinician is unaware of it, the patient's experience of the clinical encounter and interest in engaging in treatment may be adversely impacted. This is equally true in any clinical setting, and not just in settings where the clinician and identified patient do not share a language or culture. Of course, physicians and therapists also have explanatory models and critical self-awareness can be applied to practitioners' explanatory models, too, in order to detect implicit bias or influence of the culture of biomedicine and other healing systems.

The staunchest critiques of global mental health call into question the validity of a nosology for mental illness developed within a particular cultural (i.e., biomedical) framework when applied (or imposed) within a setting with a different understanding about the meaning and needs associated with various forms of lived experience and normative suffering.[16] The biomedical framework for mental illness, in other words, draws from epistemological traditions, relatively homogeneous study populations, and the results of deploying assessments, methods, and analytic approaches that prioritize particular ways of knowing about the world and embed values in a hierarchy of evidence and in formulating targets of intervention.[71] In this respect, what many regard as a universalizing framework for categorizing and understanding mental illness has also been critiqued as the hegemony of "but one among many ethnopsychiatries."[16(p.993)] Whereas that is not the position we are taking in this chapter, we see great value for global mental health practitioners, investigators, educators, and trainees to recognize that Western biomedical psychiatry encompasses a rather narrow framing of mental disorders and therapeutic approaches that may have limited acceptability and perceived benefits in some communities. As Kirmayer has pointed out, for example, some indigenous communities may have a broader agenda for healing that prioritizes the collective and social rather than the individual level.[71] Wholesale or uncritical importation of psychiatric nosology, assessments, and treatment priorities, without meaningful local engagement, it is argued, can risk not just disenfranchisement or poor uptake of interventions, but may also risk harm when assessments are inaccurate, result in stigma, disrupt local healing resources, or deflect attention from root causes that are social.[54,72,73] Whereas the most extreme critique of global mental health has been cynical, alleging that it "is a 'top-down' movement whose effect is to sell the products of the Western mental health industry to the non-Western world,"[74(p.407)] the critique of that knowledge exchange as being insufficiently bidirectional warrants serious consideration.[54] This underrepresentation of low- and middle-income country authors in global mental health research is not just a breach of academic equity,[75,76] but it also undermines opportunities to optimize interventions through the engagement of local expertise and community voices.[77,78]

Credibility gap and cultural congruence

Vikram Patel has framed the important critique of a "credibility gap" in global mental health delivery that stems from a fundamental risk for misalignment of biomedical diagnostic constructs with local experience of mental distress. In some cases, for example, this misalignment might lead to medicalization of normative experience in ways that do not necessarily resonate with local experience and to misclassification of emotional distress as a mental disorder. He argues that using biomedical diagnostic constructs may impose an artificially categorical—and thus, therapeutically narrow—framework on local illness experience. Sometimes termed an "etic" approach, Patel critiques "top-down" approaches to mental health delivery that fail to engage and integrate community-based perspectives.[79] Importantly, the perspectives of individuals living with psychosocial disability or difference are essential for promoting a mental health agenda that is inclusive of these views and is responsive to them.[80]

For example, therapeutic interventions based upon a biomedical conceptualization of mental distress and focused solely at an individual level may neither be well suited nor adequate for healing in American Indian communities, in which psychiatric illness and distress have sometimes been conceptualized as a manifestation of "historical unresolved grief" stemming from profound harms associated with the legacy of colonization.[81,82] Also conceptualized within this indigenous community as "historical trauma,"[82] this construct encompasses both psychological and social dimensions of distress. The injuries emanating from the brutality, forced assimilation, displacement, and other forms of oppression and sustained disenfranchisement associated with settler colonialism are a form of transgenerational social suffering. These impacts, moreover, have been theorized as injuries that have resulted in "social pathologies," [81] which are experienced as collective and intergenerational.[82] In this respect, so-called resurgent care intervention that can redress "the socio-psychological ravages of colonization" by reclaiming and enabling cultural participation has appeal and therapeutic traction.[82(p.683)] In fact, it is arguable that the failure of orthodox psychiatry to legitimize this unresolved historical grief may harm the indigenous community by further disenfranchisement and lack of "therapeutic congruence."[81]

How, then, can global mental health research and care delivery navigate beyond the legacy of colonialism and the arrogance of exclusively top-down approaches to narrow this credibility gap? The global mental health research agenda must, on principle, prioritize engagement of local knowledge in formulating research priorities and approaches.[83] In his critique of top-down approaches deployed in public health campaigns, historian Marcos Cueto describes the failure to learn lessons from a campaign to eradicate malaria in the 1950s that was ultimately unsuccessful; in his analysis, the approach leaned on "technological fixes" without integrating critical information from the social context that would have informed their local adaptation and implementation.[84] Likewise, anthropologist Vincanne Adams critiques rigid adherence to standard quantitative approaches favored by evidence-based medicine for global health research, given that these studies are designed to capture certain kinds of data to the exclusion of other data that are, nonetheless, essential to gaining local acceptance and traction.[85]

Ethnography as an invaluable methodological approach for global mental health

In contrast to epidemiologic and other quantitative approaches routinely deployed in the field of global health, the focus on social context and lived experience in ethnographic research provides an essential and complementary "counterknowledge of the people who are actually at the center of things" as the prospective end users of these interventions.[86(p.23)] Ethnographic research can, in turn, be integrated with other forms of community-based and local expert engagement to ensure that the formulation of research questions will yield scientifically valid and contextually relevant findings. For example, ethnographic data can inform adaptation of standardized psychiatric assessments to promote their sensitivity to identifying symptoms in the local context.[87] Likewise, research investigations can examine social determinants of poor mental health, including the lasting adverse impacts of settler colonialism, while centering local conceptualizations of these determinants.[88] We emphasize here the value of early engagement of local expertise and a broad range of stakeholders and collaborative integration of these perspectives in design of studies and interventions that will best serve the needs of the primary stakeholders: the patients and their community. This local engagement represents an imperative that is scientific, moral, and pragmatic.

Ethnography is a methodologic approach with unparalleled value for gaining a contextualized understanding of the lifeworld of individuals living with mental illness. Ethnographic interviews and observation can illuminate the priorities and concerns of caregivers, can examine how the meaning of symptoms or distress is made within their social networks, and can identify what resources in their community might enable them to manage well or even thrive. Beyond the pragmatic benefits of more sensible study design, more valid assessment, and more effective care delivery, an ethnographic approach provides learners and practitioners with a deeper understanding of how problems framed as mental illness in one context (the Western biomedical context, that is) are differently configured in another. Students and practitioners of global mental health will benefit from reading the ethnographic literature, even if they will not, themselves, be using this methodological approach. Such ethnographically based studies can certainly inform study design, enhance the validity of psychiatric assessment, and guide healthcare delivery planning to align with community priorities. Beyond this, ethnography also reveals how individuals manage their condition outside of the health sector (e.g., Hansen[89]), how the course of serious mental illness unfolds in particular social contexts (e.g., see Jenkins[90] and Luhrmann and Marrow[91]), and renders an up-close view of the frustrations and indignities that can be part of the lived experience of mental illness and interactions with services (e.g., Brodwin[92] and Sue[93]). The critical understanding generated by the ethnography of healthcare systems can also point out the problems with practitioners' attitudes and practice that undermine quality care and can, thereby, limit unintended consequences and improve care delivery.

Engaging with cultural difference in the global mental health encounter

To be effective, acceptable, and equitable, mental healthcare delivery must seek to be responsive to needs, preferences, and priorities in local settings. Social structural constraints, historical legacies, and cultural values—as well as the ecological and policy environment—contribute to the context of care delivery. Active engagement with cultural and social identities of patients and their communities is, of course, essential to effective and equitable health care in any health delivery setting. Health professional education in the United States now routinely addresses the critical importance of engagement and integration of social and cultural identities to care delivery. Whereas this preparation may be especially important to global mental health delivery—in settings where the lived experience, social norms, and values of the local community and healthcare providers may differ substantially—social and cultural identity, as well as cultural difference, must be examined and navigated in all health encounters.

Mental health trainees from many regions will likely have some familiarity with engaging with cultural difference, regardless of their interest in global health or health equity. In the United States, accreditation bodies for both undergraduate and postgraduate medical education introduced training requirements aimed toward developing competencies for healthcare delivery in multi-cultural settings in the early 2000s. In its landmark publication, *Unequal Treatment*, in 2001, the Institute of Medicine sounded a clarion call about the ethnic and racial health disparities in the United States across clinical conditions that required prioritization for their redress.[94] This sensitization to health inequities is thus foundational to undergraduate and graduate medical education in the United States. For psychiatrists practicing in US settings, the *American Psychiatric Association Practice Guidelines for the Psychiatric Evaluation of Adults* recommends assessment of cultural and linguistic factors related to the patient's illness presentation and treatment needs as part of the initial psychiatric evaluation in routine practice.[95] Embarking on global mental health research or care delivery not only requires skills and understanding of the value of engaging productively with cultural difference, but also benefits from a critical reading of the limitations of various approaches developed for this purpose.

Engaging across cultural difference: The evolution of cultural competence and related constructs in US health care and their salience to global mental health practice

The construct of cultural competence in clinical care emerged in the 1980s in response to evidence of ethnic and racial disparities in healthcare access and outcomes in the United States; this framework recognizes that illness and care-seeking are shaped by cultural context and, thus, healthcare delivery that is responsive to values, preferences, understandings, and needs within this context can be rendered more acceptable and more effective.[96] Notwithstanding limitations in how cultural competence has been understood and deployed in clinical settings, it can arguably be viewed as comprising tangible actions and values that embrace diversity, equity, and inclusion (DEI) in healthcare delivery settings in the United States. Cultural competence thus reflects both a commitment to reduce health disparities by improving access and effectiveness of quality care as well as an intention to promote respect, dignity, and belonging in clinical settings through concrete recommendations for clinical practice. In this respect, the imperative for healthcare providers to develop an understanding of healthcare needs and preferences in local populations helped to supplant an often paternalistic, "one-size-fits-all" approach to care delivery and, instead, aim to understand how a patient's particular lived experience and cultural identity shape a clinical encounter. Cultural competence is viewed as a means to inform and frame a response that is both effective and well received. The tenets of cultural competence have been recognized as requisite to US medical education through Liaison Committee for Medical Education (LCME) and Accreditation Council for Graduate Medical Education (ACGME) standards.[97,98] Likewise, institutional efforts to enhance the quality of patient experience by offering translation services, translated signage, and community-based access, and community representation in decision-making can be valuable forms of elevating cultural competence or responsiveness and signaling institutional values and commitments. Similarly, cultural competence can be manifest in therapeutic approaches that cater to cultural preferences and needs, through effective and respectful communication as well as an informed understanding of factors that perpetuate ethnic and racial disparities in health outcomes.[96,97,99] Although the attunement to understanding and responding to local cultural expression and experience of mental illness should likewise be a foundation of training and care delivery in global mental health settings, some critiques of cultural competence warrant consideration here. These critiques have suggested how the approach can be augmented for more effective and respectful engagement with cultural difference.

Despite its noble aim to elevate the quality of care within a multi-cultural population, the construct of cultural competence has limitations. In particular, its focus on building a clinician's knowledge base about characteristics relating to various socio-demographic groups has been critiqued for establishing assumptions about cultural identity that may be inaccurate, incomplete, or culturally essentializing. When cultures are taken to be monolithic, static, or siloed, a clinician's knowledge base risks being incomplete or reductive, or rapidly becoming obsolete.[100] Rather than serving the purpose of responding to a patient's needs, this content expertise-based approach may instead make a patient feel stereotyped and unheard.[99,100,101] In addition, the framework of cultural competence does not adequately emphasize opportunities for health professionals to reflect on the cultural and social identities they, themselves, bring to the clinical encounter, let alone reflect on the culture of biomedicine, and how practices and values associated with these cultures may interact with the patient's culture.[100] These interactions are not just academic, given how unexamined differences as well as implicit bias[102] can potentially undermine diagnostic accuracy or therapeutic engagement. Moreover, the construct of the biomedical practitioner's perspective as being a value-free reference point, against which a patient's or community's cultural difference is contrasted, obscures the very fact that clinicians and clinical settings are embedded in cultures, too.[103]

Kleinman and Benson acknowledge the indispensability of health professionals' understanding of the lifeworld of the patients and community they work among, but argue that the approach must be more centered on the process of engagement and understanding of what is "at stake for the patient."[100] This examination of what expectations, understanding, and agenda a patient brings to the clinical setting was framed as eliciting an "explanatory model" by Kleinman[70] and subsequently expanded to encompass an approach that would contextualize a patient's personal narrative.[32] Eliciting the explanatory model that a patient and his or her family hold about an illness episode is a tool for negotiating a common understanding that informs an effective response by the health professional.[32] Although the explanatory model approach can as easily be deployed for patients who share a culture or social demographic with their clinicians as for those who do not, it is especially useful in illuminating divergence between a patient's understanding and the biomedical conceptualization of illness. Given considerably diverse presentations of emotional distress across socio-cultural contexts, clinicians who are unfamiliar with the local context may not recognize the presence or qualities of symptoms adequately to arrive at an accurate diagnostic assessment. This misrecognition occurs even in contexts in which clinicians and those living with illness share common values and understanding of social norms for health and behavior. The opportunities for misrecognition are amplified, however, when clinicians and individuals living with illness do not share a common lexicon for affective states, cognitive experiences, or idioms for expressing distress.

Notwithstanding the value of clinical understanding of cultural and social contexts of a patient's illness experience, cultural competence is an inadequately broad framework to tap this dimension of patient experience for several reasons. First, cultures are neither static nor monolithic; history also matters because it speaks to how a community may have interacted with health professionals in ways where its members have either experienced disenfranchisement or developed trust. In other words, a working knowledge of local culture, history, and values is an important foundation, but requires additional tools and skills to optimize cultural engagement.

Alternative approaches to delivering care that is culturally acceptable and effective for a patient or broader community have built on the intentions of cultural competence. *Cultural safety*, for example, is an approach that improves upon cultural competence through engaging with and seeking to mitigate power differentials between healthcare providers and institutions and the communities they serve. As such, cultural safety is particularly focused on promoting health equity and redressing health disparities that are the legacy of social adversities. This concept was introduced and developed in New Zealand in the 1990s as a framework to respond to health inequities affecting the Māori community, through critical reflection and remediation of power differentials that persist in clinical settings and undermine equal access to and benefit from health care.[104] This approach has also seen uptake in Canada as a means of reducing the power differential between indigenous communities and healthcare providers.[96] It is especially germane to the development and delivery of mental health care in settings where colonial history and resource differentials of all types structure power dynamics that must be understood, reflected upon, made explicit, and dismantled when they have perpetuated social and health inequities.

Likewise, *cultural humility* is an approach first introduced by Tervalon and Murray-Garcia that encourages reflexivity on the part of clinicians toward recognizing and neutralizing the imbalance of power that frequently characterizes and undermines clinical encounters.[105] This approach contrasts with a focus on gaining mastery over content deemed relevant to a particular cultural identity or community to inform care delivery. The cultural humility approach instead emphasizes an ongoing commitment on the part of the healthcare provider to understand, respect, and value patient perspectives and experience in order to work collaboratively with patients and empower them in navigating their health care. In this respect, cultural humility builds on the cultural competence approach by extending the requisite knowledge beyond the culture of the patient toward a self-reflexive understanding of the culture of biomedical care delivery; this understanding includes how knowledge and power gradients and the history of a healthcare institution's local interactions within the community may impact a patient's experience.[105] This approach is highly relevant for individual, programmatic, and institutional global mental health delivery in encouraging ongoing evaluation of an ethos of inclusion and respect vis-à-vis the local community being served.[105] Moreover, a stance of cultural humility positions the mental health practitioner and the community as collaborators engaged in bidirectional learning. Furthermore, it also frames the community as a valued reservoir of expertise and a partner in developing and implementing interventions.[106]

Global mental health trainees and practitioners should understand from this overview that, although the construct of cultural competence is flawed insofar as no clinician or investigator can become truly culturally competent, cultural competence serves as an important heuristic for representing the ideal of manifesting respect, humility, and sensitivity to diversity while engaging across cultural difference.

The Cultural Formulation Interview: A tool for engaging patient social identities

The Cultural Formulation Interview (CFI)[107,108] was introduced with the DSM-5 to augment diagnostic assessment with structured questions aimed toward understanding and engaging a patient's perspective, experience, and preferences around dimensions of a patient's social identities. When introduced, the CFI was supplemented by 12 modules for more in-depth evaluation of dimensions of identity or experience that may be pertinent to understanding social and cultural factors important to diagnostic assessment and therapeutic engagement. These modules can be accessed online and include assessments of factors that impact a patient's understanding, resources, and preferences for addressing their illness, including their explanatory model, functioning, social network, stressors, role of spirituality, cultural identity, coping and help-seeking practices, and relevant experiences with other clinicians. Other modules are tailored to interviewing children and adolescents, older adults, immigrants and refugees, or caregivers.[109] An additional module on the cultural assessment of grief has subsequently been developed.[110] The CFI interview builds on the Outline for Cultural Formulation introduced in the DSM-IV[111] and structures a patient-centered approach to engaging aspects of these cultural and social identities without making assumptions about a patient's experience.[112] The CFI can be deployed after a very modest investment in training—as little as an hour—by psychiatrists and can elicit essential cultural information in 20 minutes or less.[113] In particular, the CFI allows for the likely possibility that an individual may have more than one dimension of their social identity that is salient to diagnostic assessment and therapeutic engagement. This process-oriented approach mitigates the risk that a clinician would draw from assumptions or clinical stereotypes[114] about a patient's presentation and, instead, promotes a more open-ended approach to understanding their experience of illness. The CFI has been developed as a tool to support the assessment of cultural factors in the setting of a psychiatric diagnostic interview and the majority of evidence supporting its utility to date comes from high-income regions.[115] However, the conceptual categories it encompasses around eliciting a patient's or family member's understanding of a mental health problem and perspective on treatment needs and goals have relevance and utility to global mental health delivery beyond individual clinical encounters. Given the CFI's patient-centered approach and the time required for the interview, more research on deployment in diverse settings, where clinical encounters may engage an entire family or unfold under extreme time pressure, will be helpful in assessing its utility in LMIC settings.[115] As a general principle of comprehensive training, however, all students of global mental health benefit from learning how to transcend a narrow biomedically-centric understanding of mental illness by engaging with cultural difference. The CFI offers an approach to operationalizing this understanding in clinical practice. Of course, global mental health approaches and practice also encompass underserved communities in high-income settings, including in the regions where students of global mental health train in the United States.

Structural competency

Structural competency augments approaches to engaging the lifeworld of the patient in a clinical encounter by foregrounding social determinants of poor health. In their seminal 2014 paper on the topic, Metzl and Hansen proposed that medical education should engage with health inequality through directing attention beyond cultural difference and individual level factors, toward social structural factors that drive poor health and health disparities.[116] Metzl and Hansen frame structural competency as the capacity to recognize the social structural precursors, such as poverty, exclusionary policies, and food insecurity, to embodied consequences and health outcomes. This framework not only positions health practitioners to recognize the limitations of promoting positive health solely through the practice of medicine but also to consider a broader set of interventions within policy, educational, and other social sectors. Metzl and Hansen propose structural competency as a tool for engaging health trainees in moving beyond healthcare delivery for individual patients to consider how macro-level interventions could complement conventional clinical care in targeting social determinants of poor health.[116] Structural competency also opens opportunities for mental health practitioners to engage in advocacy with other stakeholders toward policies and actions that promote health equity, rectify legacies of injustice, and otherwise mitigate the adverse impacts of social structural antecedents of poor mental health.[117] Both the Movement for Global Mental Health and cultural psychiatry have been critiqued for their inadequacies in addressing social structural determinants of poor mental health in LMICs.[118] In that respect, structural competency can complement approaches focused on quality and culturally responsive mental healthcare delivery by engaging with communities, advocates, and stakeholders in other government sectors to promote economic and food security, educational and economic opportunities, and social inclusion. In this way, global mental health trainees can be equipped to recognize structural determinants of poor mental health as a foundation for promoting health equity.[118]

Cultural humility[105] and structural competency[116] are especially useful concepts for global mental health trainees in situating them as learners, collaborators, and allies of community-based stakeholders with expertise based on local knowledge and experience.[118] These approaches focus on recognizing and repairing social inequities as central to the project of mental health delivery. In fact, a strong argument has been made that attention to social structural determinants of poor health is central—not peripheral—to healthcare delivery not just in the Global South, but in the Global North as well. Furthermore, when social structural determinants of poor health are not attended to, "we not only miss opportunities to improve outcomes, but we also may in fact fail at medicine's core responsibilities to diagnose and treat illness and to do no harm."[12(p.1083)]

We have provided this brief overview of the evolution of approaches to engaging cultural difference here to underscore that this kind of engagement should not be seen as commonsense, facile, or even finished. Moreover, engaging patients, caregivers, healthcare providers, communities, and other stakeholders across cultural difference in global mental health aims toward more than a symbolic courtesy or pragmatic exercise. Engagement is also premised upon a commitment to knowledge transfer that is bidirectional and generous in integrating complementary local knowledge, priorities, and needs with professional expertise and experience drawn from a simultaneously comparative and globalizing framework. We encourage learners, educators, and practitioners to further their understanding of cultural dimensions of mental health in the vast cultural psychiatry and medical anthropology literature that addresses idioms of distress, phenomenological diversity, and commonalities of mental distress and illness across diverse populations. Approaching cultural difference warrants care and reflexivity around sometimes taken-for-granted clinical truths that, in some cases, are nonetheless only partial in capturing important dimensions of illness presentation and experience. In this respect, the canon of medical knowledge—what is deemed salient, normative, and universal—can be understood as socially constructed in its framing. In 2021, the American Medical Association (AMA) and American Association of Medical Colleges (AAMC) released a guide providing suggestions for how medical practitioners can use language and understand narrative framing in a way that is respectful of difference, decenters whiteness as a norm, and promotes dignity and equity in healthcare delivery. As reflected in this document, there has been a shift in mainstream US healthcare delivery away from cultural competence toward structural competence, cultural safety, and cultural humility as approaches that can better serve pro-equity goals.[119] Clearly, these revisions and improvements will not be the last ones articulated, but the ongoing critiques of language and structures that characterize healthcare delivery in the United States also find their way into global health and global mental health delivery. This will be useful for global mental health practitioners and trainees to follow closely to reflect on their own practices and adjust them toward addressing the shortcomings of how mental healthcare delivery is formulated and implemented. In doing so, clinical trainees, educators, and practitioners can use such critical reflections to better serve the goals of supporting dignity, respect, and equity in the delivery of mental health care and, thereby, also raise the quality of care.

Conclusion: Resocializing global mental health

Anthropological perspectives illuminate several opportunities to advance the field of global mental health toward its goals. We have emphasized how essential it is—morally, scientifically, and pragmatically—for practitioners, investigators, and trainees to engage local perspectives and center the priorities of local collaborators in global mental health endeavors. This is particularly the case when those who have trained in a setting such as the United States, which relies on a universalizing diagnostic framework and empirical data largely drawn from populations residing in high-income regions, are collaborating in regions with distinctive historical and cultural contexts. As much as we have emphasized the value of understanding how illness is culturally and locally patterned, we also caution against relying on cultural explanations for health behaviors that overlook social structural drivers of poor health. Explanations that assume the primacy of cultural drivers, such as values or beliefs, to the exclusion of consideration of social structural constraints on health-related behavior have been critiqued by Paul Farmer as "culturalist."[39] In eclipsing competing explanatory factors, such culturalist explanations can attribute causality in ways that also obscure avenues toward effective social interventions. Farmer referred to the uncritical attribution of poor health outcomes to explanations based on cultural beliefs or behaviors as "immodest claims of causality" which, in turn, place unwarranted blame on individuals for "choosing" behaviors that elevate risk or undermine health, rather than understanding them as operating within the constraints of low health agency.[39] Accordingly, as essential as a culturally informed approach to illness is for recognizing and treating mental disorders, a pat reliance on superficial cultural explanations of help-seeking behavior or illness experience when social forces dominate the landscape of choice amounts to similar causal misattributions that can have the unintended effect of misguiding health interventions[10,39] In this respect, students of global mental health benefit from an approach to interpreting drivers of poor health that incorporates a broad set of considerations of both cultural and social factors that structure access to mental health resources and constrain personal agency. Likewise, we encourage such students to understand how social forces, events, or conditions—such as large-scale conflict, political violence, displacement, forced migration, and economic precarity—contribute to the risk and manifestation of poor health and illness, and we also encourage them to think broadly about interventions that can redress social determinants of poor mental health.

Pivoting to optimism, action, advocacy, care, and accompaniment

We encourage students, educators, and practitioners of global mental health to take the critiques offered by the resocializing disciplines—anthropology among them—as a call to do and be better in service of the aspirations to realize equity and quality mental health for all communities. We have demonstrated how social theories can be used to deconstruct and reconsider received wisdom, reject overly reductive explanations, and both better understand and also dismantle the health inequities derived from the legacy of colonialism. A sharpened awareness of the blind spots and constraints in global mental health delivery is also an opportunity to resolve and move beyond them with purpose toward promoting mental well-being and redressing mental health inequities. We close by examining not just the unresolved and vexing problems but also by recommending how two approaches can apply the lessons of anthropology as a resocializing discipline to serve the aims of global mental health. These are *accompaniment* and centering *care*.

Accompaniment

Accompaniment is a concept that emerged from liberation theology and was adapted by Paul Farmer for application as both an ideological and practical guide for global healthcare delivery.[120] As applied in the service delivery work of the non-governmental organization (NGO) Partners In Health (PIH) which Dr. Farmer co-founded, accompaniment augments standard approaches across several dimensions of global health delivery. First, in the most concrete way, this approach describes an enhancement of medical care delivery by also encompassing other kinds of essential social, economic, moral, and practical support. In other words, accompaniment provides whatever is needed to support a patient in getting well, which in communities besieged by poverty, likely extends beyond medicine and health information to include support for transportation, meeting basic needs, and overcoming other structural barriers to well-being. This approach reflects a moral stance—insofar as it recognizes and aims to redress the enormous burden of suffering when destitute poverty compounds illness—as well as an approach that is pragmatic in overcoming the structural barriers to quality care that have been imposed by extreme poverty. In addition to this patient-centered approach, the responsibility for adherence is shifted to the care team.[121] This approach encompasses a response to a host of psychosocial and economic adversities—such as housing insecurity, food insecurity, and lack of affordable transportation—that imperil engagement in care or well-being. Accompaniment has demonstrated effectiveness in providing complex care to individuals living in poverty with multi-drug resistant tuberculosis and HIV across diverse regional settings.[121–124] This approach recognizes the risk for poor healthcare access and distribution of health burdens as outcomes of structural violence; illuminating the social determinants of poor health identifies barriers to care delivery and thereby informs a therapeutic approach that can best overcome these barriers. Whereas its application to care delivery initially was developed to respond to infectious diseases, the approach is appropriate for addressing socially and medically complex delivery problems, including for mental health.[125]

Accompaniment also reflects a stance and set of values around centering a patient's needs, offering presence, listening with humility, and literally and figuratively walking alongside a patient. At another level, accompaniment is an orientation toward service that prioritizes health equity and social justice, and aims to eliminate the "outcome" gap between well-resourced communities and those who live in poverty.[120(p.22)] Accompaniment means collaboration with family, network, and community members. Indeed, some of the most impressive examples turn on training and working with community health workers. This omnibus concept stretches also to the intellectual and practical accompaniment of academic counterparts. As such, accompaniment helps expand the often too-narrow meaning of research capacity-building to signal and enact personal and institutional commitments to support academic careers—and academic equity more generally—in collaborations with local institutions. Indeed, students of global mental health should regard and draw upon accompaniment as a guide to effective engagement in partnerships to support health systems strengthening, policymaking, and local capacity-building to advance quality and equity in global mental healthcare delivery.

Centering care in global mental health delivery

One of us (AK) has written extensively about the striking marginalization of caregiving as a dimension of biomedical care delivery in the United States.[32,126,127] As medicine has become increasingly sub-specialized and medical care technologized, Kleinman has critiqued a shift in focus from care to efficiency. Paradoxically, even the introduction of the electronic health record, a powerful tool for documentation that can provide decision support as well as a platform for collaboration, communication, and continuity of care, has been critiqued for diverting the focus of the practitioner from the patient in front of them, to the demands of completing documentation on screen.[128] Thus, the relational dimension of caring for a patient, responding to suffering with presence and acknowledgment, is at risk of subordination to the bureaucratic requirements of chart completion, which also serve institutional needs for medico-legal documentation and billing capture. This shift appears parallel to a devaluation of care and attunement to the lifeworld of the patient in medical education and postgraduate residency training and, ultimately, in practice.[129] Medical students are socialized to conform to the demands of efficiency by either eliding a patient's experience of illness or synopsizing the "social history" into a soundbite that is often perfunctory and viewed as tangential to hospital-based management.[130] Caregiving is relegated to allied health professionals, including social workers and case managers, and set apart from the focus of biomedical care.[131] This pervasive lack of attunement to the social context of the patient and their network of caregivers also poses a serious risk to the effectiveness of therapeutic intervention when the social drivers of poor health remain unaddressed.[132] In particular, when health-risk behaviors reflect constrained personal agency in the setting of social structural barriers to health and help-seeking, conventional medical care delivery may be too narrow a scope of intervention to interrupt a cycle of social drivers of poor mental health. Likewise, for individuals living with chronic mental health conditions, such as cognitive decline, dementia, or schizophrenia, engagement of their caregiving network—family members or social services—as allies and supporting their efforts can facilitate uptake of and adherence to the medical therapeutics that can be offered. We write this not just as a critique, but as an exhortation and plea to the mental health professional community to elevate the centrality of care in mental healthcare delivery and to understand care as both an individual and social process. Social care also can be taught and evaluated with respect to quality and affects.

Further, the exercise of eliciting the identified patient's view and preferences through an explanatory model or semi-structured interview guide like the Cultural Formulation Interview in a global mental health encounter should not necessarily be viewed as an exercise in persuasion, although this is not necessarily a bad outcome if its elicitation surfaces concerns that can be resolved for the identified patient and they are empowered by a more informed understanding of therapeutic choices. These approaches to patient-centered interviewing, rather, should be understood as a means of demonstrating respect, conferring dignity, and centering the patient's perspective and voice in the clinical encounter. This kind of attunement is also invaluable in affirming the presence of the clinician and centering the patient's needs; it places the highest priority on resocializing and humanizing the clinical encounter.

Summing up

Tensions between local and globalizing approaches to nosology, risk, lived experience, and therapeutic management persist but have led to constructive debate and pragmatic action informing global mental health. Importantly, this debate has moved beyond the polarities of either an overly reductive and universalized understanding of mental illness or a solely academic stance postulating extreme cultural relativism that questions the existence of mental illness. These debates have instead been productive, integrative, and importantly, have engaged local perspectives and lived experience as an essential dimension for meeting pragmatic imperatives to respond to the suffering wrought by mental illness and its attendant stigma. Empirical data continue to accrue and inform best practices for community and other local engagement in bidirectional capacity-building and collaborative development of advancing the knowledge base and effectiveness and reach of delivery and other implementation.

In our brief introduction of a selection of clinically relevant social theories, we encourage students of global mental health to consider theory as an important lens to make sense of successes, failures, and setbacks in real-world situations, and to do so to refine their own engagement with the field of global mental health. To be useful as such, we suggest that a dialectic between pragmatic action and critical application of theory can help advance the quality and scope of response to mental health needs. This kind of dynamic interplay, moreover, can generate productive lines of inquiry toward optimization and scale-up of interventions across diverse contexts. And finally, we close this chapter by urging learners, educators, and practitioners to prioritize *care* as their operating approach for integrating theory and methods toward improving mental health and well-being, healthcare systems, and the economic and social circumstances of the communities they seek to benefit through their work in global mental health.

References

1.   Raviola G, Becker AE, Farmer P. A global scope for global health—Including mental health. *The Lancet*. 2011;378(9803):1613–5.
2.   Bukhman G, Mocumbi AO, Atun R, Becker AE, Bhutta Z, Binagwaho A, Clinton C, Coates MM, Dain K, Ezzati M, Gottlieb G. The Lancet NCDI Poverty Commission: Bridging a gap in universal health coverage for the poorest billion. *The Lancet*. 2020;396(10256):991–1044.
3.   Becker AE, Kleinman A. The history of cultural psychiatry in the last half-century. *Psychiatry: Past, Present, and Prospect*. 2014;74, 74–95.
4.   Desjarlais R, Eisenberg L, Good B, Kleinman A. *World mental health: problems and priorities in low-income countries*. Oxford: Oxford University Press; 1995. 382 p.
5.   Becker AE, Kleinman A. Mental health and the global agenda. *The New England Journal of Medicine*. 2013;369(1):66–73.
6.   Kleinman A. Global mental health: a failure of humanity. *The Lancet*. 2009;374(9690):603–4.
7.   Prince M, Patel V, Saxena S, Maj M, Maselko J, Phillips MR, Rahman A. No health without mental health. *The Lancet*. 2007;370(9590):859–77.
8.   Patel V, Collins PY, Copeland J, Kakuma R, Katontoka S, Lamichhane J, Naik S, Skeen S. The movement for global mental health. *The British Journal of Psychiatry*. 2011;198(2):88–90.
9.   Patel V, Saxena S, Lund C, Thornicroft G, Baingana F, Bolton P, Chisholm D, Collins PY, Cooper JL, Eaton J, Herrman H. The Lancet Commission on global mental health and sustainable development. *The Lancet*. 2018;392(10157):1553–98.
10. Farmer P. *Pathologies of power*. Berkeley, CA: University of California Press; 2004. 402 p.
11. Kasper J, Greene JA, Farmer PE, Jones DS. All health is global health, all medicine is social medicine: integrating the social sciences into the preclinical curriculum. *Academic Medicine*. 2016;91(5):628–32.
12. Holmes SM, Hansen H, Jenks A, Stonington SD, Morse M, Greene JA, Wailoo KA, Marmot MG, Farmer PE. Misdiagnosis, mistreatment, and harm-when medical care ignores social forces. *The New England Journal of Medicine*. 2020;382(12):1083–6.
13. Garcia MA, Homan PA, García C, Brown TH. The color of COVID-19: structural racism and the disproportionate impact of the pandemic on older Black and Latinx adults. *The Journals of Gerontology: Series B*. 2021;76(3):e75–80.
14. World Health Organization. *International classification of diseases*, 11th Revision. Geneva, Switzerland: World Health Organization; 2019.
15. American Psychiatric Association. *Diagnostic and Statistical manual of mental disorders fifth edition: DSM-5*. Washington, DC: American Psychiatric Association; 2013. 947 p.
16. Summerfield D. How scientifically valid is the knowledge base of global mental health? *British Medical Journal*. 2008;336(7651):992–4.
17. GBD 2019 Mental Disorders Collaborators. Global, regional, and national burden of 12 mental disorders in 204 countries and territories, 1990–2019: a systematic analysis for the Global Burden of Disease Study 2019. *The Lancet Psychiatry*. 2022;9(2):137–50.
18. Patel V, Sumathipala A. International representation in psychiatric literature: survey of six leading journals. *The British Journal of Psychiatry*. 2001;178(5):406–9.
19. Patel V, Kim YR. Contribution of low-and middle-income countries to research published in leading general psychiatry journals, 2002–2004. *The British Journal of Psychiatry*. 2007;190(1):77–8.

20. Baxter AJ, Patton G, Scott KM, Degenhardt L, Whiteford HA. Global epidemiology of mental disorders: what are we missing? *PLoS ONE*. 2013;8(6):e65514.

21. Erskine HE, Baxter AJ, Patton G, Moffitt TE, Patel V, Whiteford HA, Scott JG. The global coverage of prevalence data for mental disorders in children and adolescents. *Epidemiology and Psychiatric Sciences*. 2017;26(4):395–402.

22. Thomas JJ, Lee S, Becker AE. Updates in the epidemiology of eating disorders in Asia and the Pacific. *Current Opinion in Psychiatry*. 2016;29(6):354–62.

23. Farmer P, Kim JY, Kleinman A, Basilico M, editors. *Reimagining global health*. Berkeley, CA: University of California Press; 2013. 478 p.

24. Kleinman A. Four social theories for global health. *The Lancet*. 2010;375(9725):1518–19.

25. Kleinman A. Intellectual Toolkit I and II. In: *General Education 1093 syllabus*. Cambridge, MA: Harvard University; 2019.

26. Berger P, Luckmann T. *The social construction of reality: a treatise in the sociology of knowledge*. Garden City: Anchor; 1967. 219 p.

27. Mukherjee JS, Mugunga JC, Shah A, Leta A, Birru E, Oswald C, Jerome G, Almazor CP, Satti H, Yates R, Atun R. A practical approach to universal health coverage. *The Lancet Global Health*. 2019;7(4):e410–11.

28. Suri A, Weigel J, Messac L, Basilico MT, Basilico M, Hanna B, Keshavjee S, Kleinman A. Values and global health. In: Farmer P, Kim JY, Kleinman A, Basilico M, editors. *Reimagining global health*. Berkeley: University of California Press; 2013. pp. 245–86.

29. Jansen MP, Bijlmakers L, Baltussen R, Rouwette EA, Broekhuizen H. A sustainable approach to universal health coverage. *The Lancet Global Health*. 2019;7(8):e1013.

30. Mukherjee J, Shah A, Mugunga JC, Farmer P. A sustainable approach to universal health coverage–Authors' reply. *The Lancet Global Health*. 2019;7(8):e1014.

31. Persad GC, Emanuel EJ. The case for resource sensitivity: why it is ethical to provide cheaper, less effective treatments in global health. *Hastings Center Report*. 2017;47(5):17–24.

32. Kleinman A. *The illness narratives: suffering, healing, and the human condition*. New York: Basic Books; 1988. 284 p.

33. Kleinman A. *Writing at the margin: discourse between anthropology and medicine*. Berkeley, CA: University of California Press; 1995. 314 p.

34. Kleinman A. *What really matters: living a moral life amidst uncertainty and danger*. Oxford: Oxford University Press; 2007. 260 p.

35. Wolf-Meyer MJ. *Unraveling: remaking personhood in a neurodiverse age*. Minneapolis, MN: University of Minnesota Press; 2020. 316 p.

36. Galtung J. Violence, peace, and peace research. *Journal of Peace Research*. 1969;6(3):167–91.

37. Farmer P. On suffering and structural violence: a view from below. *Daedalus*. 1996;125(1):261–83.

38. Farmer PE, Nizeye B, Stulac S, Keshavjee S. Structural violence and clinical medicine. *PLoS Medicine*. 2006;3(10):e449.

39. Farmer P. *Infections and inequalities*. Berkeley, CA: University of California Press; 2001. 375 p.

40. Richardson ET, Morrow CD, Ho T, Fürst N, Cohelia R, Tram KH, Farmer PE, Wood R. Forced removals embodied as tuberculosis. *Social Science & Medicine*. 2016;161:13–18.

41. Kleinman A, Das V, Lock M, Lock MM, editors. *Social suffering*. Berkeley, CA: University of California Press; 1997. 404 p.

42. Merton RK. The unanticipated consequences of purposive social action. *American Sociological Review*. 1936;1(6):894–904.

43. Summerfield D. Afterword: against "global mental health". *Transcultural Psychiatry*. 2012;49(3–4):519–30.

44. Summerfield D. "Global mental health" is an oxymoron and medical imperialism. *British Medical Journal*. 2013;346:3509.

45. Richardson ET. On the coloniality of global public health. *Medicine Anthropology Theory*. 2019;6(4):101–118.

46.   Richardson ET. *Epidemic illusions: on the coloniality of global public health*. Cambridge, MA: MIT Press; 2020. 193 p.

47.   Pfeiffer J, Nichter M. What can critical medical anthropology contribute to global health? A health systems perspective. *Medical Anthropology Quarterly*. 2008;22(4):410–15.

48.   Nicholls D, Becker A. Food for thought: bringing eating disorders out of the shadows. *The British Journal of Psychiatry*. 2020;216(2):67–8.

49.   Anand S, Hanson K. Disability-adjusted life years: a critical review. *Journal of Health Economics*. 1997;16(6):685–702.

50.   Becker A, Motgi A, Weigel J, Raviola G, Keshavjee S, Kleinman A. The unique challenges of mental health and MDRTB: critical perspectives on metrics of disease. In: Farmer P, Kim JY, Kleinman A, Basiico M, editors. *Reimagining global health*. Berkeley, CA: University of California Press; 2013. pp. 212–44.

51.   World Health Organization. *WHO methods and data sources for global burden of disease estimates 2000–2015*. Geneva, Switzerland: Department of Information, Evidence and Research WHO; 2017.

52.   Murray CJ, Lopez AD. Measuring global health: motivation and evolution of the global burden of disease study. *The Lancet*. 2017;390(10100):1460–4.

53.   Keshavjee S. *Blind spot*. Berkeley, CA: University of California Press; 2014. 240 p.

54.   Kirmayer LJ, Pedersen D. Toward a new architecture for global mental health. *Transcultural Psychiatry*. 2014;51(6):759–76.

55.   Sartorius N. Diagnosis and classification: cross cultural and international perspectives. *Mental Health and Society*. 1978;5(1–2):79–85.

56.   Leighton DC, Harding JS, Macklin DB, Hughes CC, Leighton AH. Psychiatric findings of the Stirling County study. *American Journal of Psychiatry*. 1963;119(11):1021–6.

57.   Jablensky A, Sartorius N, Ernberg G, Anker M, Korten A, Cooper JE, Day R, Bertelsen A. Schizophrenia: manifestations, incidence and course in different cultures: a World Health Organization ten-country study. *Psychological Medicine Monograph Supplement*. 1992;20:1–97.

58.   Thornicroft G, Sartorius N. The course and outcome of depression in different cultures: 10-year follow-up of the WHO collaborative study on the assessment of depressive disorders. *Psychological Medicine*. 1993;23(4):1023–32.

59.   Kleinman A. *Rethinking psychiatry*. New York: The Free Press; 1988. 237 p.

60.   Kleinman A. Neurasthenia and depression: a study of somatization and culture in China. *Culture, Medicine and Psychiatry*. 1982;6(2):117–90.

61.   Lee S, Kleinman A. Are somatoform disorders changing with time? The case of neurasthenia in China. *Psychosomatic Medicine*. 2007;69(9):846–9.

62.   Guarnaccia PJ, Canino G, Rubio-Stipec M, Bravo M. The prevalence of ataques de nervios in the Puerto Rico Disaster Study: the role of culture in psychiatric epidemiology. *Journal of Nervous and Mental Disease*. 1993;181(3):157–65.

63.   Guarnaccia PJ, Rogler LH. Research on culture-bound syndromes: new directions. *American Journal of Psychiatry*. 1999;156(9):1322–7.

64.   Lewis-Fernández R, Guarnaccia PJ, Martínez IE, Salmán E, Schmidt A, Liebowitz M. Comparative phenomenology of ataques de nervios, panic attacks, and panic disorder. *Culture, Medicine and Psychiatry*. 2002;26(2):199–223.

65.   Lewis-Fernández R, Kirmayer LJ. Cultural concepts of distress and psychiatric disorders: understanding symptom experience and expression in context. *Transcultural Psychiatry*. 2019;56(4):786–803.

66.   Nichter M. Idioms of distress: alternatives in the expression of psychosocial distress: a case study from South India. *Culture, Medicine and Psychiatry*. 1981;5(4):379–408.

67.   Kirmayer LJ, Young A. Culture and somatization: clinical, epidemiological, and ethnographic perspectives. *Psychosomatic Medicine*. 1998;60(4):420–30.

68.   Yang LH, Kleinman A, Link BG, Phelan JC, Lee S, Good B. Culture and stigma: adding moral experience to stigma theory. *Social Science & Medicine*. 2007;64(7):1524–35.

69. Granzow K. Against settler colonial iatrogenesis: Inuit resistance to treatment in Indian hospitals in Canada. *Anthropology & Medicine*. 2021;28(2):156–71.

70. Kleinman A. *Patients and healers in the context of culture*. Berkeley, CA: University of California Press; 1980. 427 p.

71. Kirmayer LJ. Cultural competence and evidence-based practice in mental health: epistemic communities and the politics of pluralism. *Social Science & Medicine*. 2012;75(2):249–56.

72. Bracken P, Giller J, Summerfield D. Primum non nocere: the case for a critical approach to global mental health. *Epidemiology and Psychiatric Sciences*. 2016;25(6):506–10.

73. Cosgrove L, Mills C, Karter JM, Mehta A, Kalathil J. A critical review of the Lancet Commission on global mental health and sustainable development: time for a paradigm change. *Critical Public Health*. 2020;30(5):624–31.

74. Summerfield D. A short conversation with Arthur Kleinman about his support for the global mental health movement. *Disability and the Global South*. 2014;1(2):406–11.

75. Hedt-Gauthier BL, Jeufack HM, Neufeld NH, Alem A, Sauer S, Odhiambo J, Boum Y, Shuchman M, Volmink J. Stuck in the middle: a systematic review of authorship in collaborative health research in Africa, 2014–2016. *BMJ Global Health*. 2019;4(5):e001853.

76. Hedt-Gauthier B, Airhihenbuwa CO, Bawah AA, Cherian T, Connelly MT, Hibberd PL, Ivers LC, Jerome JG, Kateera F, Manabe YC, Maru D. Academic promotion policies and equity in global health collaborations. *The Lancet*. 2018;392(10158):1607–9.

77. Osborn TL, Wasil AR, Weisz JR, Kleinman A, Ndetei DM. Where is the global in global mental health? A call for inclusive multicultural collaboration. *General Psychiatry*. 2020;33(6):1–3.

78. Kulikoff XR, Morris J, Nguyen G, Smith A, Templin T. Health metrics priorities: a perspective from young researchers. *The Lancet*. 2016;388(10058):2353–4.

79. Patel V. Rethinking mental health care: bridging the credibility gap. *Intervention*. 2014;12(1):15–20.

80. Stein MA, Mahomed F, Patel V, Sunkel C, editors. *Mental health, legal capacity, and human rights*. Cambridge: Cambridge University Press; 2021. 412 p.

81. Brave Heart MYH, DeBruyn LM. The American Indian holocaust: healing historical unresolved grief. *American Indian and Alaska Native Mental Health Research*. 1998;8(2):56–78.

82. Gone JP. Redressing first nations historical trauma: theorizing mechanisms for indigenous culture as mental health treatment. *Transcultural Psychiatry*. 2013;50(5):683–706.

83. Baingana F, Al'Absi M, Becker AE, Pringle B. Global research challenges and opportunities for mental health and substance-use disorders. *Nature*. 2015;527(7578):S172–7.

84. Cueto M. A return to the magic bullet? In: Biehl J, Petryna A, editors. *When people come first*. Princeton, NJ: Princeton University Press; 2013. pp. 30–53.

85. Adams V. Evidence-based global public health: subjects, profits, erasures. In: Biehl J, Petryna A, editors. *When people come first: critical studies in global health*. Princeton, NJ: Princeton University Press; 2013. pp. 54–90.

86. Biehl J, Petryna A, editors. *When people come first: critical studies in global health*. Princeton, NJ: Princeton University Press; 2013. 446 p.

87. Osborn TL, Kleinman A, Weisz JR. Complementing standard Western measures of depression with locally co-developed instruments: a cross-cultural study on the experience of depression among the Luo in Kenya. *Transcultural Psychiatry*. 2021;58(4):499–515.

88. Gone JP, Kirmayer LJ. Advancing Indigenous mental health research: ethical, conceptual and methodological challenges. *Transcultural Psychiatry*. 2020;57(2):235–49.

89. Hansen H. *Addicted to Christ: remaking men in Puerto Rican Pentecostal drug ministries*. Berkeley, CA: University of California Press; 2018. 210 p.

90. Jenkins JH. *Extraordinary conditions: culture and experience in mental illness*. Berkeley, CA: University of California Press; 2015. 343 p.

91. Luhrmann TM, Marrow J, editors. *Our most troubling madness: case studies in schizophrenia across cultures*. Berkeley, CA: University of California Press; 2016. 286 p.

92. Brodwin P. *Everyday ethics: voices from the front line of community psychiatry*. Berkeley, CA: University of California Press; 2013. 233 p.

93.   Sue K. *Getting wrecked: women, incarceration, and the American opioid crisis.* California Series in Public Anthropology. Berkeley, CA: University of California Press; 2019. 241 p.

94.   Smedley BD. Stith AY, Nelson AR, editors. Institute of Medicine Committee on Understanding and Eliminating Ethnic and Racial Disparities in Healthcare, Board of Health Sciences Policy. *Unequal Treatment: Confronting Racial and Ethnic Disparities in Healthcare.* Washington, DC: National Academies Press; 2003.

95.   APA Work Group on Psychiatric Evaluation. The American Psychiatric Association practice guidelines for the psychiatric evaluation of adults: guideline V. Assessment of cultural factors. *Focus.* 2020;18(1):71–4.

96.   Kirmayer LJ. Rethinking cultural competence. *Transcultural Psychiatry.* 2012;49(2):149–64.

97.   McGregor B, Belton A, Henry TL, Wrenn G, Holden KB. Improving behavioral health equity through cultural competence training of health care providers. *Ethnicity & Disease.* 2019;29(Suppl 2):359.

98.   Moreno FA, Chhatwal J. Diversity and inclusion in psychiatry: the pursuit of health equity. *Focus.* 2020;18(1):2–7.

99.   Betancourt JR. Cultural competence—Marginal or mainstream movement? *The New England Journal of Medicine.* 2004;351(10):953–5.

100. Kleinman A, Benson P. Anthropology in the clinic: the problem of cultural competency and how to fix it. *PLoS Medicine.* 2006;3(10):e294.

101. Katz AM, Alegría M. The clinical encounter as local moral world: shifts of assumptions and transformation in relational context. *Social Science & Medicine.* 2009;68(7):1238–46.

102. Banaji MR, Greenwald AG. *Blindspot: hidden biases of good people.* New York: Bantam; 2013. 254 p.

103. Luhrmann TM. *Of two minds: an anthropologist looks at American psychiatry.* New York: Vintage; 2001. 337 p.

104. Curtis E, Jones R, Tipene-Leach D, Walker C, Loring B, Paine SJ, Reid P. Why cultural safety rather than cultural competency is required to achieve health equity: a literature review and recommended definition. *International Journal for Equity in Health.* 2019;18(1):1–7.

105. Tervalon M, Murray-Garcia J. Cultural humility versus cultural competence: a critical distinction in defining physician training outcomes in multicultural education. *Journal of Health Care for the Poor and Underserved.* 1998;9(2):117–25.

106. Abe J. Beyond cultural competence, toward social transformation: liberation psychologies and the practice of cultural humility. *Journal of Social Work Education.* 2020;56(4):696–707.

107. Lewis-Fernández R, Aggarwal NK, Hinton L, Hinton DE, Kirmayer LJ, editors. *DSM-5® handbook on the cultural formulation interview.* Washington, DC: American Psychiatric Pub; 2015. 364 p.

108. American Psychiatric Association. *Cultural Formulation Interview (CFI).* Washington, DC: American Psychiatric Association; 2013. [Internet]. https://www.psychiatry.org/getmedia /4b37a60b-dcbd-402c-9ee2-3af7f5c9dc70/APA-DSM5TR-CulturalFormulationIntervie wInformant.pdf. Accessed August 11, 2022.

109. American Psychiatric Association. *Supplementary modules to the core Cultural Formulation Interview (CFI).* Washington, DC: American Psychiatric Association; 2013. [Internet]. https://www.psychiatry.org/getmedia/aca8f5a2-9b1b-456c-a3b7-f7f852edcf7c/APA -DSM5TR-CulturalFormulationInterviewSupplementaryModules.pdf. Accessed August 11, 2022.

110. Smid GE, Groen S, de la Rie SM, Kooper S, Boelen PA. Toward cultural assessment of grief and grief-related psychopathology. *Psychiatric Services.* 2018;69(10):1050–2.

111. American Psychiatric Association. *DSM-IV: diagnostic and statistical manual of mental disorders,* 4th ed. Washington, DC: APA; 1994. 886 p.

112. Weiss MG, Aggarwal NK, Gómez-Carrillo A, Kohrt B, Kirmayer LJ, Bhui KS, Like R, Kopelowicz A, Lu F, Farías PJ, Becker AE, Hinton L, Lewis-Fernández R. Culture and social structure in comprehensive case formulation. *The Journal of Nervous and Mental Disease.* 2021;209(7):465–6.

113. Jarvis GE, Kirmayer LJ, Gómez-Carrillo A, Aggarwal NK, Lewis-Fernández R. Update on the cultural formulation interview. *Focus*. 2020;18(1):40–6.

114. Brett AS, Goodman CW. First impressions—Should we include race or ethnicity at the beginning of clinical case presentations? *The New England Journal of Medicine*. 2021;385(27):2497–9.

115. Lewis-Fernández R, Aggarwal NK, Kirmayer LJ. The cultural formulation interview: progress to date and future directions. *Transcultural Psychiatry*. 2020;57(4):487–96.

116. Metzl JM, Hansen H. Structural competency: theorizing a new medical engagement with stigma and inequality. *Social Science & Medicine*. 2014;103:126–33.

117. Kirmayer LJ, Kronick R, Rousseau C. Advocacy as key to structural competency in psychiatry. *JAMA Psychiatry*. 2018;75(2):119–20.

118. Gajaria A, Izenberg JM, Nguyen V, Rimal P, Acharya B, Hansen H. Moving the global mental health debate forward: how a structural competency framework can apply to global mental health training. *Academic Psychiatry*. 2019;43(6):617–20.

119. American Medical Association and Association of American Medical Colleges. *Advancing health equity: guide on language, narrative and concepts*; 2021. Available from: ama-assn.org/equity-guide.

120. Farmer P, Gutierrez G. *In the company of the poor: conversations with Dr. Paul Farmer and Fr. Gustavo Gutiérrez* (Griffin M, Block JW, editors). Maryknoll, NY: Orbis Books; 2013. 206 p.

121. Keshavjee S, Gelmanova IY, Pasechnikov AD, Mishustin SP, Andreev YG, Yedilbayev A, Furin JJ, Mukherjee JS, Rich ML, Nardell EA, Farmer PE. Treating multidrug-resistant tuberculosis in Tomsk, Russia: developing programs that address the linkage between poverty and disease. *Annals of the New York Academy of Sciences*. 2008;1136(1):1–1.

122. Farmer P, Léandre F, Mukherjee JS, Claude MS, Nevil P, Smith-Fawzi MC, Koenig SP, Castro A, Becerra MC, Sachs J, Attaran A. Community-based approaches to HIV treatment in resource-poor settings. *The Lancet*. 2001;358(9279):404–9.

123. Behforouz HL, Farmer PE, Mukherjee JS. From directly observed therapy to accompagnateurs: enhancing AIDS treatment outcomes in Haiti and in Boston. *Clinical Infectious Diseases*. 2004;38(Supplement 5):S429–36.

124. Shin S, Furin J, Bayona J, Mate K, Kim JY, Farmer P. Community-based treatment of multidrug-resistant tuberculosis in Lima, Peru: 7 years of experience. *Social Science & Medicine*. 2004;59(7):1529–39.

125. Eustache E, Gerbasi ME, Severe J, Fils-Aimé JR, Smith Fawzi MC, Raviola GJ, Darghouth S, Boyd K, Thérosmé T, Legha R, Pierre EL. Formative research on a teacher accompaniment model to promote youth mental health in Haiti: relevance to mental health task-sharing in low-resource school settings. *International Journal of Social Psychiatry*. 2017a;63(4):314–24.

126. Kleinman A. Catastrophe and caregiving: the failure of medicine as an art. *The Lancet*. 2008;371(9606):22–3.

127. Kleinman A. Caregiving as moral experience. *The Lancet*. 2012;380(9853):1550–1.

128. National Academies of Sciences, Engineering, and Medicine. *Taking action against clinician burnout: a systems approach to professional well-being*. Washington, DC: The National Academies Press; 2019. 312 p.

129. Kleinman A. *The soul of care: the moral education of a husband and a doctor*. Penguin Books; 2020. 262 p.

130. Good BJ. *Medicine, rationality and experience: an anthropological perspective*. Cambridge: Cambridge University Press; 1993. 262 p.

131. Kleinman A, Van Der Geest S. 'Care' in health care: remaking the moral world of medicine. *Medische Antropologie*. 2009;21(1):159.

132. Braslow JT, Messac L. Medicalization and demedicalization: a gravely disabled homeless man with psychiatric illness. *The New England Journal of Medicine*. 2018;379(20):1885–8.

Chapter 3

Promoting Global Mental Health Equity in Training Programs

Establishing Ethical and Reciprocal Partnerships

James L. Griffith, Michael Morse, Samah Jabr, Sherein Abdeen, and Sauharda Rai

Summary points

- Health equity and social justice are pillars upon which the global mental health (GMH) movement rests. The GMH movement seeks accessibility and quality of mental health services for low-resource populations throughout the world.
- Training in ethics is core to GMH training because asymmetries in resources and power—inherent to North-South institutional, investigator, and training collaborations—can lead to unintended adverse consequences that potentially undermine the GMH mission; foundational training in GMH ethics can support anticipation and mitigation of these adverse impacts on collaboration.
- GMH training programs should both exemplify and teach how to create partnerships that are mutually respectful, reciprocal, and beneficial to each partner.
- In this chapter, the authors describe and advocate practices, values, and ideas that facilitate how a GMH program can: 1) foster interpersonal interactions that local partners and collaborators experience as mutual, respectful, reciprocal, and trustworthy (ethics of alterity); and 2) adhere to ethical principles when objectively examined (procedural ethics).
- Mentoring trainees in pragmatic, field-tested ethical reasoning is beneficial to prevent trainees' moral distress from progressing into demoralization and cynicism when aspirations must be compromised due to limited resources or opportunities to effect change.

The 2007 *Lancet* series of global mental health articles became a clarion call for well-resourced governments, institutions, and organizations to act urgently to reduce mental health inequities among the world's populations, both between and within countries.[1] This series built on previous work over the prior decade to support the global mental health (GMH) movement, which presented economists, policymakers, and corporate leaders internationally with evidence that mental health inequities were resulting in enormous social suffering within vulnerable populations and taking an economic toll upon countries. In 2016, the World Bank and the World Health Organization's (WHO) "Out of the Shadows" meeting recognized mental health not only as a global health priority but also as a global development priority.[2] The *Lancet* 2018 Commission on Global Mental Health and Sustainable Development consolidated this message in its call for strategies to address prevention and quality gaps alongside treatment gaps in order to reduce the global burden of mental disorders.[3]

The GMH movement caught the imagination of young people beginning careers in the mental health and health services professions. Akin to the spirit of the Peace Corps in the 1960s, the idealism, compassion, and altruism of many of these trainees and early career mental health professionals in the Global North have motivated choices to work in the world's regions of greatest need where their work might have its greatest impact. Whereas much of the clinical and research

DOI: 10.4324/9781315160597-5

training foundational to mental health educational training in the Global North is relevant to low-resource settings, preparation for effective engagement with global mental health requires additional content expertise and skills beyond those generally covered by conventional training programs for mental health professionals. For psychiatrists, for example, preparation for effective engagement with global mental health requires additional skill sets beyond those provided by most US psychiatry residencies.[4]

Among these areas, educators, implementers, and practitioners encounter ethical challenges in global mental health collaboration and delivery—relating to resource gradients and local values among other issues—that idealism, compassion, and altruism alone cannot solve. These challenges have elevated ethics as a priority content area in GMH training.

Ethical challenges from asymmetries in power and resources

Providing a strong foundation in ethical reasoning for GMH learners is critical to their developing an awareness and approach to mitigate asymmetries in power and resources that are inherent to North-South institutional, investigator, and training collaborations. These asymmetries can undermine even well-planned and well-intended research or clinical collaborations. These impacts can be exacerbated by failures in communication or awareness; such lapses, moreover, lead to failures of mutual engagement and successful partnership in global mental health research and training.

Persisting resource gradients are often legacies of the brutal, extractive, and exploitative practices associated with colonialism. Across the continents of Asia, Africa, and Central and South America, the European colonial powers committed programs of genocide[5,6] and extracted wealth and raw materials while inflicting impoverishment, violence, and conditioned deference upon indigenous peoples.[7,8] Moreover, cycles of vengeance and revenge put in play by colonial regimes have persisted to the present. Present-day cycles of political violence—like that between the Hutus and Tutsis in Africa's Great Lakes Region, for example—had their origins in ethnic resentments engendered by colonial powers such as Belgium and Germany.[9,10]

Such forms of overt colonial violence have sown distrust that continues to resonate across generations, as well as enduring resource inequities between old colonial powers and their former colonies. The residue of colonial histories continues to undermine GMH collaboration and is a topic warranting proactive engagement with GMH trainees to avoid unintended missteps that risk interpretation as newfangled versions of colonialism or inadvertently replicate colonial power dynamics. Trainees from high-resource settings must be sensitized to these fraught histories and their sequelae. Before the planning or implementation of GMH programs, careful attention must be paid to building institutional and interpersonal relationships founded on trust and mutual respect. Proactive policies are necessary to mitigate unintended adverse consequences of research and services delivery programs.[11] Examples of such consequences include:

- Causing a "brain drain" of talented, well-trained health professionals from low-income to high-income countries.[12]
- Failing to organize efforts around local priorities (thereby giving rise to a form of academic colonialism).[13]
- Offering programs with short-term benefits but no design for long-term sustainability (which paradoxically can even worsen the long-term well-being of a population).[14]
- Designing research studies that prioritize scientific rigor over heeding local voices, needs, and concerns. This has been problematic, for example, for some clinical trials of new medications when a placebo arm has been included for the sake of scientific rigor.[15–17]

A starting point is to facilitate a culture of respect and trust with local partners. GMH learners should understand that resource and power gradients persist across well-funded research and educational institutions in the Global North—that deploy trainees, support investigators, and propose service delivery programming—and institutions in the Global South. Local partners need to feel safe from ghosts of a colonial past. To create the requisite culture of safety and mutual respect, GMH professionals and programs should develop their partnerships with several objectives in mind. Firstly, they must prioritize relationship building from the very outset of the project and uphold an ongoing commitment to sustain it. Secondly, they should carefully and intentionally structure interactions in a way to protect against inadvertent harms by drawing from approaches described later in this chapter.

In this chapter, we propose that ethics-relevant content in GMH training should encompass three key domains: 1) ethics of alterity that can guide the construction of trusting relationships; 2) procedural ethics that protect against inadvertent harm by prioritizing ethical principles of beneficence, autonomy, and justice in—while also integrating cultural validity into—the design and implementation of research studies and training; and 3) pragmatics for managing programs when a paucity of resources, cultural barriers, dysfunctional bureaucracies, political corruption, or healthcare inequities compel trade-offs between divergent aims that are each felt, by one or both parties, to be grounded in different ethical imperatives.

Ethics of alterity

Alterity refers to one's stance toward the other in self-other relations. The ethics of alterity, as articulated by philosopher Emanuel Levinas,[18] can help guide the creation of equitable and reciprocal partnerships when there are asymmetries in the relationship between partners.[19(pp.245–251)] "Asymmetry" is a different concept from "unequal." Relationships between GMH professionals from well-resourced institutions and local partners may not only be unequal in the division of power and resources, but also differ with respect to social and cultural processes that constitute perceptions, identities, and worldviews. The barriers to collaboration that stem from such differences cannot necessarily be resolved by a more equitable distribution of resources.

Emanuel Levinas, a survivor of a World War II Nazi work camp, devoted his life's work to understanding the descent of Germany into fascism and violence. He located the source of social violence in the human capacity to reduce another person to a concept or a category. He argued that the heart of violence is disrupting another person's continuity as a person by forcing the other into an unwanted role or identity: "Violence does not consist so much in injuring and annihilating persons as in interrupting their continuity, making them play roles in which they no longer recognize themselves."[18(p.21)]

Levinas argued that another human being is revealed as a person only through dialogue that permits uniqueness of the other to appear. A stance toward another person of respect, interest, and concern is prerequisite for such dialogue to occur.[18–20] Perhaps more than any other philosopher, Levinas gives guidance on how people can meet and collaborate across asymmetrical relationships. His teaching implies that relationships supporting collaboration, dialogue, and mutual expressions of respect should be established prior to either the design or the implementation of a global mental health project.

Similarly, existentialist philosopher Martin Buber studied how human beings face a moral choice between relating to another human being as a person ("I-Thou" relations) or as an object in the material world ("I-it" relations).[21] Levinas and Buber both described the ethical differences between regard for another person as a subject who, much like oneself, acts upon his or her world (subject-subject relatedness) or as an object (i.e., an abstract unit or category), who is acted upon (subject-object relatedness).

The philosophical studies of Levinas and Buber complement demonstrations from social psychology and social neuroscience research that human beings have a dual system for social cognition that enables other individuals to be perceived either as a person (subject) or as a category (object).[19,22] Subject-subject relations entail awareness of the other person's unique subjectivity, in terms of desires, concerns, intentions, and decisions. Subject-subject relations are built through egalitarian interactions, face-to-face dialogue, and collaborative sharing of power. Subject-subject relationships are about "doing with," rather than "doing to" others.[23]

Drawing a distinction between subject-subject and subject-object relations can serve as a practical tool for teaching application of ethical reasoning to power dynamics that may unfold in global mental health implementation. An over-reliance upon subject-object relatedness creates a setting at risk for adverse unintended consequences, for example, by substituting assumptions based on incomplete or inaccurate knowledge of a community's needs, priorities, or goals. Among approaches that can help to avoid this misstep in global mental health research or project design, community-based participatory research (CBPR) is an approach that embeds close attention to local perspectives in planning a research or services delivery agenda. CBPR creates a structure in which researchers, prior to initiating a study, spend time building trust, understanding, and psychological safety.[24-26]

Procedural ethics: Designing partnerships that are equitable and reciprocal

Procedural ethics denotes the processes involved in applying for and gaining institutional ethical approval for a research study.[27] Procedural ethics were developed to provide objective, rule-based criteria that would protect human subjects in research studies. The Nuremberg Code and the Belmont Report (issued by the National Commission for the Protection of Human Subjects of Biomedical Behavioral Research) identified autonomy, beneficence, and justice as fundamental ethical principles for protecting human subjects in research studies.[28] Universities in high-income countries typically mandate that investigators undergo training in research ethics. Institutional review boards (IRBs; also called "ethical review boards") provide oversight that ensures that research studies abide by these general ethical principles.[27] IRB oversight helps ensure a favorable risk/benefit ratio in research within any study population[24]—and thus provides an essential level of programmatic protection for potential study participants who reside in low-resource settings or who experience other vulnerabilities related to the social context.

Regardless of these universal principles for the ethical conduct of research, implementation of procedural ethics across diverse social contexts raises challenges when local social norms and cultural preferences impact how patient autonomy is valued or constructed across these settings.[13,27] For example, local preferences and conceptualization of individual agency in making health-related decisions—such as social norms for delegating decisions to family members, deferring to other collective decision-making processes, or prioritizing family or collective interests over individual ones—may alter the local salience of language in standardized subject participation consent documents.

Steps can also be taken to strengthen the local cultural validity of the ethical dimensions of proposed global mental health programs. These steps are the processes followed for ensuring the local cultural validity of psychiatric assessment.[13,29] These include utilizing existing local IRB oversight and processes where the study population is located, alongside those of the collaborating institution's IRB, and meeting the stipulations of both. In cases where there is no established or formalized ethical review, a new IRB can be locally constituted by including in-country clinicians, researchers, or community leaders as cultural consultants.[29] Creative methods for ensuring both cultural validity and methodological rigor are illustrated in studies by Siridhardhana and colleagues[13] and Chiumento and colleagues.[27]

Procedural ethics in health research protects human study participants. Although IRB procedures incorporate special provisions to enhance protection of study participants and populations with characteristics that may make them more socially vulnerable—such as youth, pregnant women, and those with economic hardship or low literacy—the conventional processes may still benefit from augmentation through the engagement of local stakeholders and knowledge that ensures both the protection of study participants within vulnerable study populations and alignment within the local context.

Pragmatics of managing ethical trade-offs

It is perhaps axiomatic that the closer to settings of extreme suffering, the greater the frequency and poignancy of forced choices among competing aims, each of which might be defensible by different ethical principles. This kind of dilemma can be daunting for a trainee.

While many mental health clinicians who practice in well-resourced settings might not routinely encounter patients living in extreme poverty, those who pursue a career in global mental health must anticipate working within settings where economic constraints may require contending with gut-wrenching decisions about allocating limited resources in addressing hardship. When GMH trainees encounter an obstacle in the field—perhaps relating to inadequate funding, dysfunctional bureaucracies, corruption, or other resource limitations—that requires them to recalibrate their aspirational expectations for delivering mental health care, the inevitable feeling of disappointment can snowball into a full-blown demoralization or cynicism, a path that, ultimately and unfortunately, can potentially end with abandonment of effort.[30] Examples of such dilemmas include 1) the choice to prioritize one dimension of a program's goals over another—even when the local need for each seems equally compelling—and 2) investing the best of one's labor to effect changes that may only have little chance for moving the needle on the social determinants of poor mental health. Such dilemmas can create a risk that learners will view ethics as classroom thought experiments that are out of place in the world of real politics. GMH training programs can provide trainees with practical wisdom gleaned from experienced researchers for navigating ethical dilemmas in the field.[29,31] Ample access to mentors should be provided who can lend guidance and serve as models for addressing moral dilemmas where high aspirations are challenged by limited resources. "On-the-job" training in ethical reasoning can be conducted as a trainee assumes roles and responsibilities of increasing complexity in research projects or services delivery programs. Seasoned GMH researchers and service providers have personal experiences and case illustrations that can be shared.

Trainees should be taught how procedural ethics and ethics of alterity protect not only local partners but also GMH professionals and trainees from well-resourced institutions. Few events can produce more profound disillusionment and self-condemnation than does the realization that one's project, which intended to do good, inadvertently left harm in its wake due to a failure to carefully observe the principles of procedural ethics. Ethics of alterity help ensure a bond between GMH partners that can simultaneously promote local priorities, adapt to setbacks, and celebrate small successes that broader population metrics may fail to register. As Levinas observed, it is only through coming to know another person through care, concern, and a respectful dialogue that one comes to know oneself as a person.[18,19(pp.245–251)] These kinds of relationships that form between GMH partners become intrinsically gratifying and are an important means of keeping disillusionment at bay.

Teaching with case studies and vignettes that examine the ethics of alterity, procedural ethics, and pragmatic ethical reasoning

Teaching with case studies, as a pedagogical method, has certain strengths for bringing ethical principles and ethical reasoning out of the classroom into real life where needs are tangible and urgent. Case studies and vignettes illuminate how ethical reasoning is deployed when researchers' sanguine aspirations collide with hard political and economic realities. They can, moreover, illustrate the smooth integration of ethics of alterity and procedural ethics. In addition, they can show how pragmatic ethical reasoning can be responsive to local situations while remaining within the purview of institutional or educational program mandates.[29] Such training is, of course, useful for all clinical trainees but is particularly essential for GMH trainees from high-income countries when working in regions where lived experience differs from theirs and especially where there are persisting power asymmetries and resource deficits that are legacies of colonialism.

Case studies or vignettes especially have value for teaching practices that anticipate, detect, and repair unintended adverse consequences. Readings on the social theory of unanticipated consequences of purposive social action can provide a useful theoretical framework to reflect on how plans unfolded, as well (see Chapter 2, this volume).[32,33] Case studies can teach about commonly occurring pitfalls that heighten risks for adverse unintended consequences of well-intended GMH programs. They also can illustrate salutary practices that diminish risks for unintended adverse consequences.

Pitfalls that heighten risks for adverse unintended consequences

Some pitfalls that can occur in global mental health engagements include the following:

(1) GMH professionals with inadequate cultural competencies fail to engage—or worse, even alienate—local populations.

It is often the case that graduates from psychiatry residencies and medical schools in high-income countries lack the skill sets needed for research or clinical work in low- or middle-income countries (LMICs). These critical but underdeveloped skills include family-centered treatment methods, the ability to recognize conditions that uniquely present with local idioms of distress, experience in training and supervising non-health professional mental health workers, and an understanding of how to integrate the tenets of human rights advocacy into clinical care.[4,29] Considering the importance of these skills, it is unfortunate that the current US Accreditation Council for Graduate Medical Education (ACGME) psychiatry residency requirements do not provide sufficient knowledge and skills for GMH,[4] and for this reason, a GMH training program may need to augment prior training—even at the most rigorous of high-income institutions—with additional skills training or self-directed learning modules that will address this knowledge gap and equip GMH researchers and service providers with skills they need for low- or middle-income contexts.

Vignette 1

When the 1999 war in Kosovo ended, 82% of the population were internally or externally displaced, over half knew someone who had been killed, and 25% of the population showed symptoms of PTSD[34] In response, an estimated 400 non-governmental organizations (NGOs) and other humanitarian missions converged on Kosovo to implement social services, primary care, and mental health services programs. However, this outpouring of international aid was met with ambivalence by Kosovar mental health professionals who spoke derisively of the "NGO caravan" and the "NGO mafia."[35] The Kosovars objected to a lack of regard for Kosovar values and cultural identity in clinical programs provided by the NGOs. For example, a University of Pristina psychiatry faculty member explained that: "In Kosovo a person is a family member, not an individual."[35] He described how strong families and family clans had enabled survival for Kosovars through 500 years of Ottoman occupation. However, some Kosovars perceived that most NGOs, modeled after American health services, disregarded the local importance of family units and traditional family roles in setting up care for symptomatic individuals. An exception was an American-Kosovar institutional partnership that successfully created a family-centered program of trauma recovery that mobilized family strengths in the therapeutic process, rather than the American community mental health model of diagnosing and treating individual patients one at a time.[36,37]

(2) GMH programs launched to fulfill funder-driven—or donor, institutional, or personal—agendas can alienate local communities when there is poor fit with local priorities.[38]

Non-governmental organization (NGO) programming is commonly funded by high-income countries or by wealthy philanthropists whose humanitarian agendas, however well-meaning, may not actually fit local needs. For example, NGO agendas may focus on short-term goals in responding to humanitarian emergencies, an approach that reflects crisis-driven fundraising from donors. Conversely, local requests for assistance may, instead, reflect priorities that relate to long-term challenges or to other chronic needs associated with a humanitarian crisis, such as poorly functioning public utilities and waste management, inadequately equipped schools, or lack of access to health care (see Chapter 10, this volume). Indeed, one such common agenda mismatch for psychiatric consultants is the assumption that mental health services should focus upon PTSD treatment and other mental disorders, when local priorities may instead center on daily life stressors and consequent routine suffering from demoralization and grief.[39-41]

Likewise, government agencies typically fund projects that are most productive from a national foreign policy perspective, although those state-wide projects potentially can deviate from local priorities of concern within smaller, domestic communities.[42] A related problem can occur when students or investigators from high-income-country research universities arrive preoccupied with career advancement and a personal research agenda that overshadows awareness or attunement to relationships, values, or culture of the local population with which they are engaging.

Therefore, effective GMH programs and collaborations require a clinician or researcher to utilize self-reflexive awareness of personal motivations and, when necessary, re-direct focus of concern to members of the local population.[43,44] Trainees and practitioners should be aware of how personal interests (e.g., their striving for high marks, promotion, tenure, etc.) may distract from, or even undermine, the chief agenda of serving local mental health needs. Vignettes 2-A and 2-B illustrate how these conflicts of interest can play out in different humanitarian responses to disasters.

Vignette 2-A

At the peak of the 2016 refugee crisis in Greece, thousands of Syrian and Afghan refugees were pouring onto the Lesvos beaches from rubber rafts, many with hypothermia. Well-intended volunteer clinicians had traveled to Lesvos planning to provide trauma therapy for the refugees as they arrived. Traumatized refugees, however, showed little interest in engaging with this offering of psychological aid. Rather, they sought food, dry clothing, and bus passes to keep moving as quickly as possible to the north into countries of the European Union, regardless of psychological stress symptoms that afflicted many.[45]

Vignette 2-B

A research program administrator in a low-income country in Asia reflected upon numerous US graduate students who traveled to his country to complete university graduate program research in global mental health: "Trainees often come to the field with raw theoretical trainings and very little or no practical experiences. They have limited time to understand the culture and setting but come with unmatched zeal and the stress of a 'need to perform.' There are instances where the trainees get too 'soaked up' in this need to perform, driven also by pressure and competition within their peer group and program. In their zeal, they end up violating respectful relationships that underpin our programs and ruin our partnerships."[a]

(3) Local partners can feel silenced by fears of losing desperately needed NGO funding, and by consequence may choose not to protest or push back against negative impacts of a particular NGO program for fear of offending researchers/service providers.

Grant funders can attach prescriptive requirements upon recipients that reflect the funder's political or moral values or demands of their funding cycle but are felt to be violations by recipient partners. Lacking a sense of agency, local partners may only report what they perceive the GMH professionals wish to hear.[4,29] Vignette 3 illustrates how local mental health professionals can be placed in such a dilemma.

Vignette 3

A US-based funder of a social service grant in West Bank Palestine stipulated that services must be provided by treatment teams that paired Palestinian clinicians with Israeli clinicians. The funder's intention was to facilitate reconciliation between Palestinians and Israelis who would staff the program. However, the Palestinian clinicians felt these forced partnerships to be egregious violations of personal integrity when not based upon existing relationships grounded in mutual trust. Nevertheless, their dependence upon NGO funding led them to stay silent lest a protest put funding at risk. The ultimate consequence of the funder's initiative was a heightening of tensions between the Palestinian and Israeli individuals, rather than reconciliation.[b]

(4) Well-resourced humanitarian programs can bypass or compete with local professionals in humanitarian disaster or post-conflict crisis responses, thereby weakening the long-term capacity of mental health services.

NGOs and grant-funded mental health services programs sometimes establish direct mental health services, which are often staffed by volunteer mental health professionals from high-income regions with a limited commitment for duration of time. However, these newly available services can inadvertently "poach" patients and thereby render local clinical operations financially

---

a Special thanks to co-author Sauharda Rai for contributing this vignette.
b Special thanks to co-author Michael Morse for contributing this vignette.

unstable. Such circumstances of well-meaning (but not well-thought-out) GMH aid can, ironically, ultimately undermine relief efforts. Vignettes 4-A and 4-B illustrate such adverse unintended effects of NGO intervention in Kosovo and Nepal.

Vignette 4-A

In the aftermath of the 1999 war in Kosovo, numerous NGOs set up social services, primary care, and mental health programs that provided direct services. However, the Kosovar public health programs then struggled to function due to staff depletion as workers left for higher-paying jobs with the NGOs. An administrator commented: "Before the war, we could afford to pay a driver 10 Deutschmarks a day to bring patients to the clinic. But now the NGOs can pay drivers 100 Deutschmarks a day, so we now have no driver." Within two to three years, the NGOs and their mental health services had all departed (Ferid Agani, personal communication with co-author James L. Griffith, 2002).

Vignette 4-B

The 2016 Nepal earthquake precipitated a humanitarian crisis with an influx of international NGOs with health and mental health services. A Nepali mental health professional reflected: "These organizations with ample financial resources sucked up the existing local mental health professionals in established organizations that were already working in those areas. Counselors and mental health staffs switched to work in the new organizations where a senior counselor might be paid five times the 25,000 Nepalese rupees salary that his old organization could afford. This destabilized the existing mental health services delivery system and the network of service providers in Nepal, so much so that this issue had to be raised in in emergency meetings."[c]

Salutary practices that attenuate risks for adverse unintended consequences

When collaborations between high-resourced and low-resourced partners are asymmetric in regard to power and resources, salutary practices can be employed to structure the evolving relationship between partners so that untoward consequences of GMH programs can be quickly identified and corrected. The following are some examples:

(1) Mitigate asymmetries in power by structuring interactions that foster subject-subject relations.[23]

Meet person-to-person, not as group member-to-group member.[23] Spend time together apart from agenda-driven meetings, such as by sharing meals or informal social gatherings outside of the workplace. Visit in family homes when the invitation is extended. Accept and offer hospitality.

(2) Learn the history of the local people and place.[23]

Learn the history of the population—including its history of migration, political movements, economic status, social welfare, and important historical events. Learn how the physical environment

---

c Special thanks to co-author Sauharda Rai for contributing this vignette.

and its resources and adversities may have shaped the identity of the population. Ensure that such approaches to learning incorporate diverse and inclusive perspectives of history, especially from those of underrepresented and underserved populations in the region.

(3) Ensure transparency regarding mutual expectations.

When possible, a memorandum of understanding (or a similar document) that states mutual expectations should be collaboratively developed and agreed upon between GMH professionals and local collaborators and/or other appropriate stakeholders. This document should articulate overall aims and the necessary steps to achieve them, criteria for determining success or failure, anticipated benefits and risks for stakeholders, and a collaborative process for making mid-course corrections or resolving disagreements. Such a document may be most important for building trust when there has been a local history of experiencing discrimination, exploitation, or betrayal in prior encounters with actors and institutions in the Global North.

(4) Embed dialogical practices within jointly constructed action plans.

Dialogical practices refer to the intentional structuring of interactions so that each collaborator feels sufficiently empowered to express their perspective, to expect that their perspective will be listened to with respect, and to participate in joint design of goal-directed activities.[22,46,47] Dialogical practices foster respectful speaking, listening, reflecting, and balanced discourse among collaborators. Whereas procedural ethics, such as the IRB process, provide ethical oversight by protecting the individual rights of participants, dialogical practices focus upon the responsivity of collaborators to one another's experiences as they interact. An example of a dialogical practice is the "smorgasboard approach" in project planning, in which the range of locally possible programming options is offered as options to local partners for selection according to their local priorities and in alignment with cultural preferences. Ensuring joint participation in project design and implementation, as well as related writing projects and presentations, constitutes another example of a dialogical practice.[22,36]

(5) Design GMH collaborations to facilitate the professional development of local collaborators.

Opportunities for professional development are, on balance, more accessible to mental health professionals in high-income countries than to their counterparts in low- and middle-income countries. All GMH collaborations, therefore, should embed local capacity-building goals in their design. Strengthening professional competencies and leadership skills of local partners is an important long-term strategy that can attenuate asymmetries in power over time. Local partners gain voice and agency as competencies are developed. Such capacity-building should go beyond ensuring that local collaborators have robust opportunities for first, senior, and other co-authorship and other attribution; beyond this first step, local partners should be provided with training in research methods, offered mentorship for writing for publications, given opportunities to present at international conferences, and invited to join committees of professional organizations. These are just a few examples of how programs can incorporate the career enrichment of local partners into their agenda. The Kosovar Family Professional Educational Collaborative (KFPEC) project, discussed in point (8) below, was designed specifically to accomplish these aims.[36]

(6) Ensure adequate selection and robust preparation and supervision of trainees who will be working in a setting differently resourced from their own.

Trainees should not just acquire knowledge and skills in general principles of cultural psychiatry but also cultivate a nuanced understanding of local social etiquette and important customs. That is, in addition to training in important general principles, a solid grounding in each community's local language, cultural norms, and social context is also central to productive, respectful engagement with partners in GMH training or collaboration. Such preparation—in addition to conventional training in the ethical conduct of research—should be a prerequisite for trainees embarking on work and collaboration within a new community. GMH training programs should therefore augment routine training toward further providing for relevant competencies essential to collaborations within populations 1) that are underserved, socially vulnerable, or characterized as having resource constraints; and 2) where social norms, cultural traditions, and language are different from the trainee's own.

At a minimum, programs should develop a formal set of expectations to be met before a trainee is deployed or granted approval for travel to conduct a project in a low-resource population. GMH programs should ensure that field-based opportunities for their trainees are thoughtfully planned, mentored, and resourced to avoid burdening local hosts and partners with the education of these newcomers. Moreover, each research project should be adequately reviewed, critiqued, and supervised by program faculty in addition to undergoing both institutional and local ethical reviews. A robust plan for supervision and mentorship—whether field-based or virtual—is essential to ensuring an ethical approach to institutional and other forms of collaborative training, as well as to meeting program obligations relating to programmatic goals for training and safety.

(7) Criteria for assessing a trainee's performance should be established before initiation of the project and, importantly, this performance rubric should include the trainee's ethical engagement as a category of assessment.

Means and expectations for accountability to mentors and supervisors at the host site should be clearly delineated. Trainees should anticipate how their presence in the host country can potentially impose a burden on the time and resources of local healthcare professionals and clinical systems. This awareness can lead to more careful planning so that 1) burdens are identified, mitigated, and offset, and 2) academic and other benefits of the project are assured for the host healthcare professionals, trainees, and clinical systems as well as for the trainee. Fulfilling these expectations suggests that travel to conduct projects in another country generally will occur only following foundational global mental health training.

(8) Start from priorities that matter most for a local population yet can be isomorphic with more global concerns.

GMH research and mental health services projects typically stem from identified needs that generalize to many low-resource populations, such as poor access to mental health services for common mental illnesses that are associated with a high burden of suffering and disability. However, it is important to recognize that local partners often have their own concerns particular to their communities that, for them, take precedence over the broader GMH problem(s) that researchers might be trying to attenuate in the Global South. First recognizing and then endeavoring to address these local concerns can yield solutions that also address larger societal problems in unanticipated ways. A case study vignette from the Kosovar Family Professional Educational

Collaborative (KFPEC) mission in Kosovo illustrates how a project can be re-directed from its initial scope to better fit local priorities.[36]

Vignette 8: When local priorities conflict with an NGO's stated mission

The Kosovar Family Professional Educational Collaborative (KFPEC) began with a proposal by US-based family therapists to provide trauma therapy for the highly traumatized population after the 1999 war and conflict resolution to reduce ethnic tensions between Kosovar Albanians and Serbians. In response, however, the local community of Kosovar mental health professionals requested instead that the American consultants help address the absence of a clinical system to care for chronically psychotic patients being repatriated from Serbian and Macedonian psychiatric hospitals. A rejection of their proposal had not been anticipated by the American team. This response generated internal debate about whether they could meet this need, since most members had little community psychiatry experience and few skills for treating patients with chronic psychoses. However, the Americans responded to the Kosovars' lead by recruiting additional community psychiatry expertise and by intensive study on evidence-based care of chronically psychotic patients. A successful project concluded five years later with family-centered programs for individuals living with chronic mental illness operating at seven new community mental health centers. Success of the project produced additional valuable byproducts—development of regional community mental health centers, a new cadre of psychiatrists trained in family-centered skills, creation of a new professional role for nurses as leaders of multi-family psychoeducation groups, and investment of Kosovar Ministry of Health financial resources in community-based care, rather than in a new psychiatric hospital as had been originally proposed.[36,48]

What are best practices for equitable and reciprocal partnerships? Learning from exemplar programs

In addition to case studies, exemplar GMH training programs can be identified that model equitable and reciprocal relationships between well-resourced and local institutional partners. Such exemplary programs and studies illustrate how GMH professionals from well-resourced research universities and NGOs from high-income regions can engage with local collaborators to provide evidence-based interventions that positively impact an underserved population, while sustaining attunement with their local identity, values, preferences, and priorities. The following are some examples:

(1) Incorporating community-based participatory research (CBPR) as a research methodology.

CBPR is an approach in which investigators engage a community throughout the planning and implementation of a study and community stakeholders can provide input into the study design and collaborate in interpretation of findings.[25] In addition to its benefits for successful study design and study participant engagement, CBPR is uniquely effective in the protection it provides vulnerable populations, both from the perspective of procedural ethics and the ethics of alterity. We recommend that GMH programs include training in CBPR and, when feasible, consider it an essential component for integration with other conventional empirical research methodologies. Ellis and colleagues[24] describe their use of a community participatory approach characterized by ethical and methodological rigor in their study involving Somali adolescents in a refugee community. Research participants were invited to become active members in the research process to diminish inequities between investigators and study participants and jointly articulate and agree upon ethical practices at every phase of the research process. For example, local leaders were convened as a community advisory board that advised overall project objectives, which were to increase access, to reduce stigma, and to improve quality of treatment available for Somali adolescents. The community advisory board provided advice for recruitment strategies, consent forms, and assessment procedures. Due to a wartime history of betrayals when personal information had been used against citizens, many Somalis feared providing personal information or trusting unfamiliar individuals. The community advisory board assuaged community members' concerns about trusting the researchers. Their involvement facilitated informed consent and assurance that participants would be treated with respect.

(2) Utilizing research ethics review creatively to address needs and vulnerabilities of unique populations.

Given their particular mental health needs, refugee populations are frequently studied by global mental health researchers. Yet, at the same time, they are uniquely vulnerable to violations of ethical research practices due to insufficient oversight by ethics review committees. This procedural ethics "blind spot" can sometimes be attributed to a lack of local regulatory ethical frameworks for stateless citizens or, in the case of an existing IRB, a lack of relevant experience with vetting studies involving this particularly vulnerable demographic with nuanced needs and concerns. Refugee populations are rendered still more at risk of inadvertent harm from GMH programs due to both 1) the potential inexperience of researchers in parsing ethical issues inherent in low-resource traumatized populations, and 2) the frequent lack of refugees' awareness of the risks of exploitation by researchers, which poses a barrier to their informed consent. It should also be noted that internally displaced refugees can be at greatest risk for insufficient IRB protections since they are not afforded international legal protections provided for refugees displaced from home countries.

Siriwardhana and colleagues (2013) describe the need for researchers to anticipate ethical risks through preparation that includes study of community perceptions of meanings of autonomy, beneficence, non-maleficence, and justice alongside an acknowledgment of how those local definitions might differ from conventions in the researchers' own culture.[13] Of course, it is also paramount that researchers are equipped with a foundational understanding of ethical conduct and ethical norms for GMH, and that they are in conversation with ethical review committees within their home institution and within the local community/study population (if applicable).[13] Working with the Tamil communities of Sri Lanka, they discuss unique ethical risks involved in working with a highly traditional, strongly religious, closed-to-outsiders population. They utilized both information volunteered by locals and active formal study on the part of the researchers to assess how the local population might perceive (and react to being study participants in) a GMH research project.[13] They identified risks specific to the local Tamil population, such as retraumatization by questions touching on sensitive topics or inadvertent breaches of privacy or confidentiality within the close-knit community. Research practices were tailored to fit the cultural expectations and preferences of this population. The investigators' commitment to an ethics of alterity was evident in a variety of measures used to balance power and open dialogue between investigators and participants. For example, Siriwardhana and colleagues identified the need for their team to match the gender of the interviewer and respondent to conform with local social norms as well as for investigators to speak with participants in individual interviews rather than interface in a larger focus group setting, due to concerns about confidentiality with others present. Other measures were designed to protect the researchers' prioritization of subject-subject relations from countervailing pressures to produce deliverables, meet deadlines, or advance career goals, and to provide a voice for participants. A post-research audit of ethical practices was added to further ensure ethical rigor.

(3) Ensuring reciprocity between all parties in a GMH training program by selecting curricular training objectives with the perspectives of all stakeholders in mind (e.g., GMH program faculty, local clinicians, and trainees).

The University of California, San Francisco (UCSF) Department of Psychiatry Health, Equity, Action, and Leadership (HEAL) Fellowship in GMH utilizes a systematic process for curriculum development that incorporates feedback from GMH program faculty, collaborating clinicians from selected underserved populations, and trainees.[49,50] With this particular approach, the UCSF fellowship partnered with clinical sites in a Navajo Nation reservation and in rural Nepal. This process for curriculum development is exemplary in the intentional mutuality it affords among partners, so that all parties' concerns and aspirations are heard as learning objectives for the fellowship are set. Learning objectives are chosen according to the priorities of trainees and clinical sites in both low- and high-income settings. This approach is intended to create a context for unencumbered dialogue across levels of hierarchy and power; likewise, this bidirectionality is intended to ensure more equitable relations between GMH trainees from well-resourced settings and their local partners based in low-resourced settings.

(4) Creating psychiatric residency training for low-resource populations through university-to-university partnerships.

The Toronto Addis Ababa Psychiatry Project (TAAPP) has provided a model program through which the University of Toronto Department of Psychiatry and Addis Ababa University collaborated to create domestic psychiatry residency training in their home country of Ethiopia.[51,52] TAAPP was initiated in 2003 by an agreement between the institutions and outlined an action plan for the University of Toronto to send teaching teams to meet with Addis Ababa psychiatry trainees for one-month consultations three times per year. As the training program gained traction, primary teaching responsibilities were progressively delegated to Ethiopian faculty. The program addressed pre-existing challenges in residency recruitment, curriculum development, faculty development, and continuing medical education at Addis Ababa. In addition to having Canadian faculty visit the Addis Ababa campus, the TAAPP also provided for Ethiopian partners to conduct observerships within the Canadian educational system in Toronto. By 2022, the program had helped increase the number of Ethiopian psychiatrists from 11 to 113. TAAPP-trained Ethiopian psychiatrists have continued to staff the country's regional psychiatry treatment units and to expand Ethiopia's medical educational capacity to three psychiatry residencies (in Ethiopia) that train future cohorts of psychiatrists to serve their country's mental health needs.

(5) Using clinical or educational collaborations to mentor the professional development of partners from low-resource populations by embedding dialogical practices that address asymmetries in power and resources in the mentoring process.

Griffith and colleagues (2005) describe the Kosovar Family Professional Educational Collaborative (KFPEC) as an inter-institutional project, undertaken by members of the American Family Therapy Academy and the University of Pristina Department of Psychiatry, to respond to the mental health crisis that followed the 1999 war in Kosovo.[36,48] The KFPEC embedded dialogical practices within a community mental health services program at each level of project administration and training. A primary aim was the professional development of Kosovar psychiatry trainees who had been banned from the Kosovar educational and healthcare systems during a decade of Serbian apartheid from 1990 to 1999.[36,48] Examples of these dialogical practices included:

- Twinning: Each administrative, clinical, teaching, and writing activity was conducted jointly by paired Kosovar and US colleagues.
- Topics and learning objectives for training workshops were determined by the Kosovan partners based on their assessments of needs of the local population, while US-based partners developed curricula and training methods to respond to these set priorities.
- Symposia and workshops at international conferences were jointly presented by American and Kosovar collaborators.
- Publications in professional journals provided opportunities for senior authorship and co-authorship by researchers from both countries.[36,48]
- Foundation grant funding for the KFPEC project was jointly administered but with majority Kosovar control.

Over a five-year period, the KFPEC successfully developed family-centered mental health services for the chronically mentally ill at seven new regional mental health centers in Kosovo. Local (Kosovar) psychiatry residents mentored through the KFPEC program stepped into leadership positions within this new community mental health system upon completion of residency training. When US involvement concluded in 2005, Kosovo's Ministry of Health had taken responsibility for funding these mental health services that were incorporated into the Republic's public mental health system as a mandated standard of care for patients with chronic psychotic illness. Over the ensuing decade, the program grew four-fold to service more than 1000 families in the region, demonstrating the program's sustainability (Ferid Agani, personal communication with the co-author, James L. Griffith, 2012).

The need for a dual ethical awareness that is also pragmatic

Training in ethics is a core component of equitable GMH training programs. The ethics needed for global mental health is grounded in establishing trusting relationships with local partners and communities as the initial step prior to creation of a research or services delivery agenda. Maintaining reciprocal trust also requires an ongoing commitment throughout the life of a project. This ethics of alterity augments a conventional research ethical review, which is focused on vetting that a finished research protocol is designed and implemented in compliance with a set of procedural ethical principles. In the field of global mental health, ethical engagement extends beyond these elementary principles. Importantly, in global mental health, the ethics of alterity equally applies to non-research collaborations as it does to research-based ones. And, further, this ethical imperative requires a continuous process and can never be considered a finished product. Planning and conducting a research proposal, analyzing results, and disseminating findings should not just be a joint engagement with local partners, but also must be continually evaluated and adjusted with respect to impacts on and feedback from local partners and local populations. This commitment to ongoing dialogue is essential to help protect the project and its partners from insidious effects of power and resource asymmetries between collaborators that, if left unaddressed, can manifest in unintended adverse consequences. Above all else, a GMH training program should be designed to promote health and social equity through its didactic and supervised field-based learning as well as how it attends to equity in partnerships and models ethical engagement with collaborators and stakeholders. To achieve this end, program instructors must provide trainees with conceptual frameworks, interpersonal skills training, and mentoring necessary for this mission of "doing with."

GMH training programs can be strong allies in joining with LMIC institutional partners and collaborators to redress the marginalization, stigmatization, and social injustices that afflict individuals living with mental illness in their regions—where the burden of social suffering from unmet mental health needs may be particularly high. We must continue to build political will among high-income stakeholders to support training a GMH workforce with policies that address health disparities within low-resource populations, but there is still a long way to go. Thus, teaching the pragmatics of ethical reasoning in the context of limited resources and resultant inevitable trade-offs between competing ethical aims provides trainees with skills needed to sustain purpose, commitment, and morale despite the numerous and deeply rooted challenges of social and political dysfunctions and injustices.

References

1. Prince M, Patel V, Shekhar S, Maj M, Maselko J, Phillips MR, Rahman A. No health without mental health. *The Lancet*. 2007;370:859–77.
2. The World Bank. Out of the shadows: making mental health a global priority April 13–14, 2016 [cited 2020 November 15]. Available from: https://www.worldbank.org/en/events/2016/03/09/out-of-the-shadows-making-mental-health-a-global-priority?cid=EXT_WBEmailShare_EXT
3. Patel V, Saxena S, Lund C, Thornicroft G, Bainganai F, Bolton P, et al. The Lancet commission on global mental health and sustainable development. *The Lancet*. 2018;392:1553–98.
4. Griffith JL, Kohrt BA, Dyer A, Polatin P, Morse M, Jabr S, et al. Training psychiatrists for global mental health: cultural psychiatry, collaborative inquiry, and ethics of alterity. *Academic Psychiatry*. 2016;40:701–6.
5. Hochschild A. *King Leopold's ghost*. New York: Houghton Mifflin; 1998. 360 p.
6. Conrad S. *German colonialism: a short history*. Cambridge: Cambridge University Press; 2012. 233 p.
7. Fanon F. *The wretched of the earth*. New York: Grove Press; 1963. 251 p.
8. Freire P. *Pedagogy of the oppressed*. New York: Continuum; 2000. 123 p.
9. Tuck E, Yang KW. Decolonization is not a metaphor. *Decolonization, Indigeneity, Education, & Society*. 2012;1(1):1–40.
10. Mamdani M. *When victims become killers: colonialism, nativism, and the genocide in Rwanda*. Oxford: James Currey Ltd; 2001. 384 p.
11. Weine SM, Kohrt BA, Collins PY, Cooper J, Lewis-Fernandez R, Okpaku S, Wainberg ML. Justice for George Floyd and a reckoning for global mental health. *Global Mental Health*. 2020;e22:1–5.
12. Arnold PC. Why the ex-colonial medical brain drain? *Journal of the Royal Society of Medicine*. 2011;104:351–4.
13. Siriwardhana C, Adikan A, Jayaweera K, Sumathipala A. Ethical challenges in mental health research among internally displaced people: ethical theory and research implementation. *BMC Medical Ethics*. 2013;14(1):1–8.
14. Eaton J De Silva M, Rojas G, Patel V. Scaling up mental health services. In: Patel V, Minas H, Cohen A, Prince MJ, editors. *Global mental health principles and practice*. New York: Oxford University Press; 2014. pp. 297–334.
15. Berk M. The place of placebo? The ethics of placebo-controlled trials in bipolar disorder. *Acta Neuropsychiatrica*. 2007;19:74–5.
16. Rothman KJ, Michels KB. The continued unethical use of placebo controls. *New England Journal of Medicine*. 1994;331:394–8.
17. Weijer C. Placebo-controlled trials in schizophrenia: are they ethical? Are they necessary? *Schizophrenia Research*. 1999;35:211–18.
18. Levinas E. *Totality and infinity: an essay on exteriority*. Pittsburgh, PA: Duquesne University Press; 1969. 307 p.
19. Griffith JL. *Religion that heals, religion that harms*. New York: Guilford Press; 2010. 274 p.

20. Kirmayer L. Empathy and alterity in psychiatry. In: Kirmayer LJ, Lemelson R, Cummings CA, editors. *Re-visioning psychiatry*. New York: Cambridge University Press; 2015. pp. 141–67.

21. Buber M. *I and thou*, 2nd ed. New York: Macmillan; 1958. 266 p.

22. Kohrt B, Griffith J. Global mental health and community cultural psychiatry: envisioning the ecological therapeutic alliance. In: Kirmayer L, Lemelson R, Cummings CA, editors. *Revisioning psychiatry: cultural phenomenology, cultural neuroscience, and global mental health*. Cambridge: Cambridge University Press; 2015. pp. 575–612.

23. Griffith JL. Engaging remote and underserved populations. *Focus*. 2020;18:47–8.

24. Ellis BH, Kia-Keating M, Uusuf SA, Lincoln A, Nur A. Ethical research in refugee communities and the use of community participatory methods. *Transcultural Psychiatry*. 2007;44(3):459–81.

25. Roberts L. *Community-based participatory research for improved mental healthcare: a manual for clinicians and researchers*. New York: Springer; 2013. 168 p.

26. Roberts L, Adelsheim S, Reicherter D, Joshi SV, editors. *Partnerships for mental health: narratives of community and academic collaboration*. New York: Springer; 2015. 202 p.

27. Chiumento A, Khan MN, Rahman A, Frith L. Managing ethical challenges to mental health research in post-conflict settings. *Developing World Bioethics*. 2016;16:15–28.

28. Fischer BA. A summary of important documents in the field of research ethics. *Schizophrenia Bulletin*. 2006;32(1):69–80.

29. Song S. An ethical approach to lifelong learning: implications for global psychiatry. *Academic Psychiatry*. 2011;35:391–6.

30. Dean W, Talbot SG, Caplan A. Clarifying the language of clinician distress. *JAMA*. 2020; 323(10):923–4.

31. Sriram CL, King JC, Mertus JA, Martin-Ortega O, Hermann J, editors. *Surviving field research: working in violent and difficult situations*. New York: Routledge; 2009. 241 p.

32. Kleinman A. Four theories for global health. *The Lancet*. 2010;375:1518–19.

33. Merton RK. The unanticipated consequences of purposive social action. *American Sociological Review*. 1936;1(6):894–904.

34. Cardoza B, Vergara A, Agani F, Gotway CA. Mental health, social functioning, and attitudes of Kosovar Albanians following the war in Kosovo. *JAMA*. 2000;284:569–77.

35. Griffith JL. Developing community mental health services in post-war Kosovo: what lessons learned? Presented at the 2006 Annual Meeting of the Society for Study of Psychiatry and Culture, in Washington, DC, October 11–15, 2006.

36. Griffith JL, Agani F, Weine S, Ukshini S, Pulleyblank-Coffey E, Ulaj J, et al. A family-based mental health program of recovery from state terror in Kosova. *Behavioral Sciences & the Law*. 2005;23(4):547–58.

37. Griffith JL, Keane J. Where is the family in global mental health? *Families, Systems, and Health*. 2018;36(2):144–7.

38. Keshavjee S. *Blind spot: how neoliberalism infiltrated global health*. Oakland, CA: University of California Press; 2014. 240 p.

39. Fernando GA, Miller KE, Berger DE. Growing pains: the impact of disaster-related and daily stressors on the psychological and psychosocial functioning of youth in Sri Lanka. *Child Development*. 2010;81(4):1192–210.

40. Rasmussen A, Nguyen I, Wilkinson J, Vundia S, Raghavan S, Miller KE, Keller AS. Rates and impact of trauma and current stressors among Darfari refugees in Eastern Chad. *American Journal of Orthopsychiatry*. 2010;80(2):227–36.

41. Miller KE, Omidian P, Rasmussen A, Yaqubi A, Daudzai H, Nasiri M, et al. Daily stressors, war experiences, and mental health in Afghanistan. *Transcultural Psychiatry* 2008;45(4):611–38.

42. de Almeida JMC, Minas H, Cayetano C. Generating political commitment for mental health system development. In: Patel VMH, Cohen A, Prince MJ, editors. *Global mental health principles and practice*. New York: Oxford University Press; 2014. pp. 450–68.

43. Menezes A Jr., Moreira-Almeida A. Religion, spirituality, and psychosis. *Current Psychiatry Reports*. 2010;12(3):174–9.

44. Kirmayer LJ, Swartz L. Culture and global mental health. In: Patel V, Minas H, Cohen A, Prince MJ, editors. *Global mental health principles and practice*. New York: Oxford University Press; 2014. pp. 41–62.

45. Perras NN, Dendeluri S, Kocher E, Dyer AR, Krueger C, Mihajlovic K, King A, May C. The dilemma of Syrian refugees' migration to the West. (Poster). Annual Meeting of the American Psychiatric Association, Atlanta, Georgia, May 15, 2016.

46. Habermas J. *The theory of communicative action, volume two: lifeworld and system: a critique of functionalist reason*. Boston, MA: Beacon Press; 1987. 403 p.

47. Shotter J. *Getting it: withness-thinking and the dialogical in practice*. New York: Hampton Press; 2011. 232 p.

48. Weine SM, Ukshini S, Griffith J, Agani F, Pulleyblank Coffey E, Ulaj J, et al. A family approach to severe mental illness in post war Kosova. *Psychiatry*. 2006;68(1):17–28.

49. UCSF Dept of Psychiatry. UCSF psychiatry HEAL fellowship in global mental health. 2018. https://psych.ucsf.edu/ucsf-psychiatry-heal-fellowship-global-mental-health. Accessed August 27, 2022.

50. Gajaria A, Izenberg JM, Nguyen V, Rimal P, Acharya B, Hansen H. Moving the global mental health debate forward: how a structural competency framework can apply global mental health training. *Academic Psychiatry*. 2019;43(6):617–20.

51. Alem A, Pain C, Araya M, Hodges B. Co-creating a psychiatric resident program with Ethiopians, for Ethiopians, in Ethiopia: the Toronto Addis Ababa Psychiatry Project (TAAPP). *Academic Psychiatry*. 2010;34:424–32.

52. Andermann L. The development of psychiatric education in Ethiopia: 15 years of TAAP. 2020 Annual Meeting of the Society for Study of Culture and Psychiatry; October 10, 2020.

Strategies for Training in Global Mental Health

Chapter 4

Developing a Global Mental Health Training Curriculum

Bibhav Acharya, Colin Buzza, Jennifer Guo, Madhur Basnet, Erick Hung, and Craig Van Dyke

Summary points

- Developing a curriculum using theory or a structured framework is more likely to meet the needs of the learners and the training sites, harmonize multiple aspects of the educational experience, and create generalizable lessons for the field.
- Using a case example in global mental health (GMH), we illustrate Kern's six-step process for curriculum development: problem identification, targeted needs assessment, goals and learning objectives, educational strategies, implementation, and evaluation.
- GMH training has special considerations that may not be covered by traditional frameworks, particularly relating to stigma, challenges in obtaining institutional support, addressing structural and institutional marginalization of vulnerable populations, and the financial and human resources needed for a successful program.

Introduction

Academic institutions in high-income countries (HICs) have developed training opportunities in GMH, largely driven by increasing learner interest.[1] Such programs in HICs and low- and middle-income countries (LMICs) range from *ad hoc* clinical rotations and field experiences to formal training programs that may take place across a resource gradient (i.e., learners from relatively higher-resourced academic institutions in both HICs and LMICs working in relatively low-resource settings). There are multiple challenges in developing a successful GMH educational program. Such programs may rely on expert opinion rather than a theory-driven, structured process of curriculum development.[2] This often leads to mismatch between the needs of the learners, the needs of the host sites, and the curricular materials. Furthermore, academic institutions may not have adequate resources for all aspects of a GMH training program, such as faculty members with content expertise in clinical sciences, social sciences, educational theory, and ethics in low-resource, cross-cultural settings. Finally, there may be lack of funding for learners if they cannot generate revenue from clinical care when the host sites are in LMICs, and whose training costs may not be defrayed by the academic department's general funds. There is a lack of guidance to address these multiple challenges and to develop, fund, and effectively implement a GMH curriculum.

In this chapter, we address the challenges of developing and implementing a GMH curriculum with generalizable lessons based on experiences from a university-based program that trains fellows in HICs and LMICs. We provide in-depth guidance utilizing Kern's six-step approach to curriculum development[3] based on a case study of creating and implementing a post-residency fellowship in GMH based at a major research university, for learners from HICs and LMICs. The fellowship includes educational experiences in the classroom, online, and on-site in LMICs

DOI: 10.4324/9781315160597-7

(initially Nepal, and after two years, Mexico as well) and in an under-resourced region in a HIC (Navajo Nation in the United States).[2] We describe common pitfalls and strategies in conducting the key steps of curriculum development: problem identification, targeted needs assessment, goals and learning objectives, educational strategies, implementation, and evaluation and feedback. For each step, we draw on examples from our experience and provide practical suggestions to address potential challenges. We discuss the challenges and advantages of creating a general, structured curriculum for all learners rather than an individualized program for each learner. We describe the development of assessment tools for GMH training, including the role and limitations of traditional assessment models and competency-based evaluations. We share strategies to garner financial and human resources to support GMH training programs. Additionally, we discuss specific issues in GMH training that may not be covered by traditional frameworks such as Kern's. While the context and circumstances will vary among the readers, the general approach and our lessons can inform similar efforts in academic institutions in HICs and LMICs.

BOX 4.1 CASE EXAMPLE OF DEVELOPING THE CURRICULUM FOR THE UNIVERSITY OF CALIFORNIA, SAN FRANCISCO (UCSF) PSYCHIATRY HEAL FELLOWSHIP IN GLOBAL MENTAL HEALTH

Context: Before the GMH fellowship was built, the HEAL (Health, Equity, Action, and Leadership) Initiative, based at UCSF, was already providing global health training opportunities for physicians in family medicine, internal medicine, and pediatrics. In 2015, HEAL's partner sites in seven LMICs demonstrated an interest in hosting psychiatrists, given the large mental illness burden in their patient population and the paucity of mental health services. Their interest came at a time when the UCSF Department of Psychiatry and Behavioral Sciences was expanding its research and training capacity in GMH. This provided an opportunity for a partnership between HEAL and the UCSF Department of Psychiatry to develop a fellowship in GMH.

Curriculum development working group: The fellowship director made an open call to the Department of Psychiatry to build a working group for curriculum development. Four psychiatry residents, a fellow in public-sector psychiatry, and another faculty member formed the team that worked together for 18 months to develop the curriculum.

Curriculum development: The curriculum development team utilized Kern's six-step process in curriculum development,[3] given its extensive use in medical education and the fellowship director's expertise and prior experience with the model.[4] We conducted a literature search for problem identification and a general needs assessment to understand common challenges in GMH training and practice. Based on the results, we conducted a targeted needs assessment by conducting 19 key informant interviews with trainees and professionals from the United States and abroad. The key informants included clinicians (generalist physicians, medical directors, and psychiatrists) practicing in low-resource settings, GMH educators, and psychiatry residents who self-identified as potential applicants for the GMH fellowship. The goal of the interviews was to describe: (1) the current capacities of the low-resource sites and their mental health needs that a psychiatry fellow could potentially fulfill; and (2) the competencies that a psychiatry fellow would require to meet those needs but would not typically have already acquired by the end of a four-year general adult psychiatry residency. The interviews were analyzed to identify these competency domains; a total of 20 competency domains, with specific goals and learning objectives, were identified. These findings provided the basis for developing the curricular content. The domains included: Structural Determinants of Mental Health, Cultural Aspects of Mental Health, Understanding the Health System and Resources in Mental Health, Engagement in the Health System, General Provision of Care, Emergency Psychiatry and Inpatient Care, Adult Community Psychiatry, Child and Adolescent Psychiatry, Geriatric Psychiatry, HIV Psychiatry, Psychotherapy, Substance Use, Training and Education, Clinical Supervision, Interprofessionalism and Leadership, Advocacy, Health Equity and Ethics, Self-Reflection and Self-Care, Quality Improvement, and Research in Global Mental Health.

Alignment with an existing, general global health curriculum: Because this fellowship was built on an existing global health program, the curriculum development team conducted an alignment process that would be skipped for a program that is being built completely from scratch. In our case, the team categorized all learning objectives into ones that were broadly applicable to global health training and ones that were specific to GMH. The team aligned with HEAL to ensure that the first category of objectives was already covered by the existing general global health curriculum, allowing the Psychiatry Department to focus on the objectives that were specific to GMH. In accordance with the ethical guidelines in global health training,[5] we incorporated the principle of reciprocal training: sites that received rotating fellows from UCSF would nominate local, full-time employees as "site fellows" to receive training and support from the fellowship. Because the site fellows are full-time employees, their curricular engagement was limited to mentorship support, so much of our case is based on curriculum development for the fellows who rotated between sites as full-time fellows (and thus required a comprehensive curriculum).

Faculty recruitment and development of curricular materials: The fellowship director identified UCSF Department of Psychiatry and Behavioral Sciences faculty members who had content expertise in at least one of the 20 domains determined in the previous step. This resulted in involvement of faculty members who may not have had expertise in GMH but did have specific expertise in relevant domains (e.g., clinical supervision of generalists to deliver mental health care). Faculty members refined the learning objectives and reviewed the literature in GMH and their respective domain. With close collaboration and feedback from the fellowship director, faculty members developed original educational modules to meet the learning objectives. For objectives that were primarily knowledge-based (e.g., learning the indications and adverse effects of psychotropic medications in the World Health Organization [WHO] Essential Medications list),[6] the faculty developed narrated lectures that could be electronically deployed in the fellowship training sites via an online platform for progressive knowledge acquisition. For objectives that required experiential learning (e.g., understanding parenting practices and expectations of normal child development), guided projects were developed. For objectives that required in-person work (e.g., learning to supervise psychotherapeutic techniques), workshops were developed and deployed during the initial in-person training at UCSF before the fellows departed to their sites in Nepal, Mexico, and Navajo Nation. On-site mentors and UCSF faculty visiting the sites conducted direct support for and evaluation of trainees. Fellows provided feedback on the curriculum via structured online responses and during biweekly calls with the faculty. Feedback was collected and discussed among faculty and the curriculum was adjusted accordingly. For example, after a few years of the fellowship, fellows gave feedback that longitudinal 1:1 contact with faculty was more helpful than the original model of having the faculty member spend one week on-site with the fellow(s). Based on this feedback, the fellowship began pairing each fellow with a faculty member for weekly 1:1 calls during the entire fellowship.

Fellow rotations and financial resources: All fellows (US-trained psychiatrists, called "rotating fellows," and the site fellows from Nepal, Mexico, and Navajo Nation) spend the first two weeks in San Francisco for an initial training. The rotating fellows then spend 5.5 months at each site. When in the United States, their clinical care activities generate revenue, which is combined with departmental support and philanthropic donations to cover operating expenses including travel costs, faculty effort, educational funds, and fellows' salaries and benefits, particularly when they are in LMICs and are not generating revenue. The site fellows are full-time employees at low-resource sites and they spend the majority of their time working locally, with visits to UCSF and to other sites as noted above.

The importance of using theory or a framework to develop a curriculum

A common approach in curriculum development is to collect opinions of faculty experts within the academic institution and develop a set of learner experiences based on available resources.[7] This approach does not utilize a conceptual framework for curricular development but it can be appealing when faculty members do not have protected time to develop an educational program and there is pressure to rapidly initiate a program. However, this approach has numerous disadvantages.[7] First, this lacks a conceptual framework that provides a basis and coherent approach to addressing the challenges in curricular development. Second, the absence of a framework limits the generalizability and validity of the curriculum development process. Third, without a framework, there is no conceptual basis for creating different experiences for learners across the training spectrum (i.e., undergraduates, medical or nursing students, residents and fellows, and professionals).[7]

In this section, we illustrate pitfalls in not utilizing a framework for curriculum development. All frameworks begin by identifying the problem. Without a clearly stated problem, recognized not just internally but also in the wider literature, the program may lack a compelling purpose. A poorly defined problem leads to a poorly defined mission, which leads to disparate understandings of what successful outcomes should be among learners, educators, and institutions. Similarly, a poorly defined problem can lead to poorly defined metrics. Because such metrics may be used to make decisions about continued funding and other support, skipping this important step can threaten the longevity of the program.

Failure to engage learners in developing the curriculum risks a mismatch between what the faculty believe is important and what the learners identify as their needs. Continued failure to recognize learners' needs may result in poor learner participation, which is essential for sustained success of the program.

If learning objectives for specific educational interventions (e.g., a lecture) are not well defined, the program will be unable to fill the gap that it intends to address. Faculty may resort to delivering canned presentations about their previous work that may not be applicable to the learners. In addition, listing specific learning objectives allows the program to match the type of objectives (e.g., knowledge, skills, or attitudes) to the type of educational strategy (lecture, experiential learning, or reflective exercises), and provide specific metrics to measure success.

For these reasons, we argue that the advantages of relying exclusively on expert opinion do not justify the significant pitfalls in building an effective and durable educational program. Kern's six-step approach to developing a curriculum in medical education is widely used, has a strong evidence base, and has available guidelines.[3] Another commonly used framework is Bandura's social learning theory,[8] which focuses on skills acquisition via observation, retention, learner demonstration, and motivation. Frameworks such as social learning theory and the five-stage model for adult learners,[9] and various other health professional educational programs[10,11] commonly utilize aspects of cognitive and behavioral frameworks. While these frameworks provide important guidance for learner engagement, Kern's is the only framework we are aware of that encompasses the complete process of developing, implementing, and testing a medical curriculum. Therefore, we demonstrate GMH curricular development using Kern's six-step process (Box 4.2), based on our experience with the UCSF Psychiatry HEAL Fellowship in GMH. It is important to note that although we present the steps in a linear manner, the implementation is iterative (e.g., after developing the learning objectives, it may be necessary to return to the literature to develop a deeper understanding of a particular issue).

BOX 4.2 KERN'S SIX-STEP PROCESS OF CURRICULUM DEVELOPMENT[3]

Step 1: Problem Identification and General Needs Assessment
Step 2: Targeted Needs Assessment
Step 3: Goals and Objectives
Step 4: Educational Strategies
Step 5: Implementation
Step 6: Evaluation and Feedback

Kern's six-step process of curriculum development

Step 1: Problem identification and general needs assessment

A critical first step in curriculum development is to define the educational gap that the curriculum is attempting to address. The worldwide burden of mental illness and the large treatment gap among people with mental illness are well-documented challenges in the field.[12] However, an educational program should define a problem that is feasible to address with the available resources such as available time, prior training of the specific learners, and the educational infrastructure. A month-long experience for undergraduate students needs to address a much more limited GMH problem than the problem addressed by a two-year fellowship for psychiatrists.

A useful strategy for this step is to conduct a literature review to understand the scope of problems in the focus area. A general needs assessment begins with a review of landmark publications that define the major problems in the field. Becker and Kleinman[12] provide an overview of the problems in treatment, research, and access to equitable care in GMH. The WHO Comprehensive Mental Health Action Plan[13] provides priority areas that need to be addressed. It includes specific goals set by the World Health Assembly, the meeting of worldwide health ministers to implement and scale up mental health services by 2020. The WHO World Mental Health Report published in June 2022 highlights successes and challenges.[14] The National Institutes of Mental Health (NIMH), the primary source of support for GMH research from the United States federal government, has published Grand Challenges in GMH,[15] which provides priority areas for GMH research. Similarly, the *Lancet* series in GMH in 2007[16] and 2011,[17] and the publication from the *Lancet* Commission on Global Mental Health and Sustainable Development in 2018 outline major challenges, strategies, and successes.

After completing this step, which includes familiarization with the most up-to-date literature and state of science (via accessing recent papers and professional networks such as scientific conferences), educators should develop an updated list of challenges that their educational programs can feasibly address. The general problem targeted by our case study (see Box 4.1) was the need to enhance the capacity of general healthcare delivery systems in providing mental health treatment in clinical settings where psychiatrists are extremely rare or absent. Other programs may focus on treating specific illnesses, addressing public perceptions of mental health, reducing stigma, promoting well-being, or improving mental health in school systems.

Step 2: Targeted needs assessment

After defining the general problem(s), educators need to identify the specific needs relevant to all individuals and institutions involved in the educational program. This begins by identifying the relevant stakeholders. It is essential to include not just the learners (e.g., medical students) but also others who will be affected by the program (e.g., the LMIC-based supervisors). Furthermore, to ensure the educational mission is appropriately aligned with priorities of low-resource sites, it is also critical to understand the needs of the sites and, if relevant, the patient populations. Key stakeholders to engage include: learners who can provide their aspirations and goals, leaders at the sites who can describe overall capacity and needs, clinicians and other professionals who will be interfacing with the learners to meet the site's needs, and potential mentors at the sites who can discuss limitations and capacities to oversee, support, and evaluate the learners. The process of identifying and engaging key stakeholders requires keen attention to the historical and cultural contexts (see Chapters 1 and 2) and ethical collaboration (Chapter 3).

Learner perspectives can be gathered from potential applicants to the program and from learners who have completed a similar program elsewhere. Learners may be identified based on having graduated from or being enrolled in a particular program. Potential applicants can offer knowledge about the skills they would like to acquire and the reasoning behind their aspirations. Graduates of comparable programs can provide their insights into the value, learning objectives, core components, educational benefits, strengths, weaknesses, and aspects of their program experience that they would change.

In interacting with the host sites, it is critical to be very explicit about the educational program's resources and what they can and cannot deliver. Given the inherent imbalance in power and resources between academic institutions and the host sites, it may be challenging to engage in a truly transparent communication where both sides can freely discuss their needs and capacities. The sites may be concerned that their response to the needs assessment conversations may lead to loss of opportunities to collaborate with academic institutions. These fears may cause the sites to hesitate sharing their limitations in mentoring the learners and stating their true needs (e.g., training and supporting the local generalist clinicians to deliver mental health care). Sites may offer needs that they perceive are important to the institutions (e.g., direct patient care by learners) to ensure a partnership. Adding GMH programs with sites that already have existing global health partnerships with other departments in the academic institution may be a strategy that facilitates equitable relationships. Because collaborations can drain the already limited resources of host sites, the academic institutions may want to proactively invest resources to defray such costs.[18] As an example, the long-standing program Academic Model for the Prevention and Treatment of HIV (AMPATH) requires a fee from HIC-based universities to cover the costs associated with managing the partnership.[19] The ethical considerations in navigating the complicated power dynamics in global health partnerships are further explored in Chapter 3.

In addition to assessing the stakeholders' needs (i.e., asking "what are the priorities for content to learn and competencies to acquire?"), it is equally important to conduct a capacity evaluation (i.e., asking "what resources and capabilities are already available?"). As noted earlier, the stakeholders include not just the learners but others who will be directly affected by the curriculum. As Figure 4.1 shows schematically, the difference between the stakeholders' current and ideal situations is what we are terming the "identified need." To determine the identified need for learners it will be important to ask: what is their current knowledge, skills, and experience, and where would they like to be at the completion of the educational program? Understanding the stakeholders' needs allows the program leadership to define the educational gap that it must address. In the case study, the site leadership's needs (e.g., they wanted a psychiatrist to help build a healthcare delivery system that leverages existing resources) were matched with those of the learners (e.g., recent graduates of US psychiatry residency programs want to learn to build mental healthcare delivery systems that strengthen the local capacity).

There are several strategies to conduct needs assessments and capacity evaluations. Depending on the scope of the program, quantitative methods (e.g., survey instruments) can be used in conjunction with qualitative methods. The latter are more time-intensive but are more effective in defining the problems that are specific to the program. Focus groups are appropriate to gather general perspectives from a group with a shared identity (e.g., psychology graduate students who self-identify as having an interest in GMH). Key informant interviews can generate in-depth details about learner perspectives and can be semi-structured to ensure a balance of obtaining specific information relevant to programmatic planning while also allowing open-ended exploration of additional learner interests.

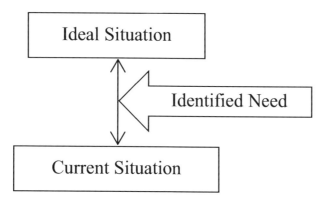

Figure 4.1 Understanding the current and ideal situations for the stakeholders helps identify the specific needs that the educational program needs to address.

Source: Figure used with permission from Bibhav Acharya.

At this stage, educators may want to compare how the findings from this step of targeted needs assessment aligns with their findings from Kern's first step. By returning to the literature, educators may also investigate if other programs have reported their experiences with the same problems. By the end of this step, educators should have identified a clear set of needs for the sites and their learners. Being able to meet these needs will provide the answer to a key question in strategic planning, namely: what does success look like for the individuals directly affected by the curriculum (i.e., learners, their supervisors in host sites and academic institutions, and any other stakeholders that are relevant to the educational context)?

Step 3: Development of competencies, goals, and objectives

The results from the previous two steps of Kern's six-step process provide guidance for developing the overall goals, objectives, and competencies for the program, which comprise the third step. This approach facilitates a cohesive and strategic process in curriculum development. In medical education, goals are often overarching aims (e.g., to improve clinical psychologists' understanding of structural competency in GMH) and objectives are specific, measurable, achievable, realistic, and time-limited (e.g., by the completion of the training module, community health workers will be able to use a case-detection tool to accurately identify at least 90% of patients with alcohol use disorder).[3,20,21] Competencies are abilities and attributes that the learner will acquire by engaging in the educational program.[22] Competencies are usually categorized by knowledge (e.g., knowing the appropriate indications and safe dosages of psychotropic medications in the WHO essential medication list), skills (e.g., demonstrable ability to identify factors that increase the risk for mental illness in children in a classroom setting), and attitudes (e.g., enhanced self-efficacy among emergency responders to de-escalate behavioral emergencies).

Completing the previous step of a targeted needs assessment will provide a list of competencies that the learners lack at the beginning of the educational program (Figure 4.1, "current situation") and will acquire at the end (Figure 4.1, "ideal situation"). For example, interviews with clinicians at host sites may reveal clinical task-sharing to non-professionals as a critical training need that leads to the identification of training and supervision of non-professionals as key competencies. GMH competencies will often go beyond clinical domains and incorporate health systems, leadership, advocacy, social sciences, education and training, cross-cultural navigation, and incorporation with the general global health competencies. Our case study (Box 4.1) identified learning objectives that were incorporated into 20 domains.[2] This list included specialized clinical skills given the lack of sub-specialists such as geriatric, addictions, and child and adolescent psychiatrists in low-resource settings. The domains included several non-clinical skills such as competencies in training, supervision, interprofessionalism, and systems-strengthening (see Box 4.1 for full list).

Though this step is based on results from the specific, targeted needs assessment among the program's stakeholders, the results can be refined and iterated by consulting the literature, where competencies for global health and GMH have been described in various forms. The Consortium of Universities for Global Health (CUGH) developed competencies for students in global health, with four levels that track the advancing learner[23] while a workshop under the United States National Academy of Medicine (formerly, Institute of Medicine) Neuroscience Forum published GMH competencies for non-specialists in Sub-Saharan Africa to screen, diagnose, and treat mental illnesses.[24] Researchers and educators have outlined a vision for psychiatrists, psychologists, nurses, and generalist clinicians focused on GMH,[25] and described examples of successful partnerships.[26,27] Finally, the Accreditation Council for Graduate Medical Education (ACGME) described guidelines for integrating GMH competencies into graduate medical training in the United States.[28]

Well-defined goals, learning objectives, and competencies provide indicators to assess the learners and the educational program. After completing this step, educators can begin designing the strategies to meet the goals.

Step 4: Educational strategies

Before implementation, educators should describe the content and process of the educational interventions. Once the learning objectives have been adequately defined and identified as cognitive (knowledge), psychomotor (skills), or affective (attitudes), the appropriate teaching methods can be determined. Incorporation of learning theories, specifically tailored for adult learners,[9] will provide an appropriate match for the objectives. Cognitive objectives may be met by didactics and assigned readings (e.g., a lecture for medical students on drug-drug interactions between common psychotropic medications and antiretrovirals used in low-resource settings). However, such methods are often not appropriate to meet affective (i.e., attitudinal) objectives, which may be better achieved by exercises in self-reflection (e.g., addressing feelings of helplessness among residents who routinely work with victims of intimate partner violence). Similarly, psychomotor objectives may require demonstration, role-play, and observed patient interactions (e.g., delivering intramuscular haloperidol decanoate or conducting motivational interviewing).

The content of the educational intervention should align with the objectives identified in the previous step of identifying competencies, goals, and objectives. By convention, it is common to identify a specific topic (e.g., suicide risk assessment and management) and recruit a faculty member with content expertise to develop and deploy the material to learners. The risk with this approach is that the content may not specifically meet the learning objectives identified, for example, given specific challenges for mental health assessment and care delivery in low-resource settings. For example, the needs assessment process may have identified a specific challenge that there is no safe place to admit patients with high risk of suicide in LMICs. A standard suicide assessment lecture will likely fail to include possible options for addressing this situation, so the program leadership needs to review the educational content to ensure the material will allow learners to achieve the stated objectives in the settings in which they are likely to practice. This "peer-reviewed" process of providing feedback on educational content is not common, and can often take faculty members by surprise. The UCSF Fellowship clarified this process when faculty members were invited to build and implement educational interventions. Although this required additional investments in time, it assisted faculty members who are not GMH experts, but have content or practice expertise (e.g., suicide assessment and management), to tailor their coursework for a GMH-focused audience.

Educational content for GMH can also be modeled after existing resources, such as the WHO's Mental Health Gap Action Programme (mhGAP), which includes clinical protocols for low-resource settings[29] and psychotherapy tools that have been validated in LMICs such as interpersonal psychotherapy,[30] cognitive behavioral therapy,[31] problem solving/management therapy,[32] and psychological first aid.[33]

Finally, GMH training relies on robust social-ecological learning, which emphasizes the overall environment of the training site. The importance of developing appropriate educational content (e.g., lectures) is mirrored by the importance of ensuring that the environment fosters learning (e.g., that it includes other learners and mentors who have experience and interest in teaching), provides positive role-modeling (e.g., including that unethical practices are avoided or promptly addressed), and helps build a community of practice (e.g., provides opportunities to work alongside learners in other disciplines, which is particularly important in GMH to avoid stigmatization and isolation of mental health from other disciplines).

Step 5: Implementation

After determining the content and process of the educational intervention, the next step relates to planning the mechanics, logistics, and resources for implementation of the curriculum. Field-based experience in low-resource settings is invaluable to trainees. Programmatic collaboration with sites in global health settings is also compelling because of the opportunity to provide service and educational opportunities in LMIC settings with high clinical need, although such training experiences also require thoughtful planning to navigate complexities in logistics, medical liability, resource availability, and equity. In addition, as noted earlier and in Chapters 1–3 in this volume, there is a need to minimize the risk of burdening already low-resourced collaborators in LMICs. For these reasons, many programs may opt to develop a local or domestic GMH experience in low-resource settings in HICs. These programs address the needs of marginalized populations, namely immigrants, refugees, indigenous people, the urban poor, and those in rural, underserved regions. These experiences address health disparities while equipping learners with certain GMH competencies. Another strategy is to incorporate a combination of domestic and international experiences, as exemplified by the UCSF Fellowship. This arrangement assists with financial resources, since the clinical revenue from the work conducted domestically may defray part of the costs of the international experiences. Regardless of the site location, a long-term, reciprocal training partnership is an important factor for experiences that are not only ethically sound but also helpful in leveraging limited resources.[34,35] Long-term relationships between partner sites and academic institutions allow shared learning, leading to continuous improvement of the educational experience of learners in LMICs and HICs and fostering bidirectional learning. Reciprocal training can be achieved when the partner site not only hosts the visiting learners but also nominates its own staff for training and mentorship from the academic institutions. The UCSF Fellowship sends rotating fellows to Navajo Nation, Nepal, and Mexico, while the partners in these three sites nominate their own staff members to join the fellowship, attend in-person training at UCSF, receive mentorship from UCSF faculty, and enroll in a master's program sponsored by the fellowship. The fellowship also arranges for the site fellows to travel to another low-resource site to facilitate cross-site/peer learning (e.g., a fellow from Mexico spent a week in rural Nepal, learning about the mental health program there, and sharing her experiences from Mexico).

Specific challenges arise in the mechanics and logistics of delivering educational content for GMH training. First, on-site mentorship may be limited because specialty expertise may not be available or local specialists may be fully occupied and overwhelmed by clinical demands, and thus may have little additional bandwidth for supervision, mentorship, and other teaching of learners. Second, travel time and cost to visit the site may limit academic faculty from the trainee's home institution from sustaining frequent and/or lengthy visits for on-site mentorship and training. Because of this, most global health programs have in-person training/education before the learner leaves the home institution for the site followed by ongoing training, either delivered remotely (e.g., video conferencing) or via on-site educators. For these models, it becomes important to determine the type of training that will be delivered in-person versus remotely. The UCSF Fellowship delivers skills-building and attitude-focused training in-person. This includes a module on learning to teach and supervise motivational interviewing skills for generalist clinicians, and a session on advocating for mental health service support from health systems leadership. In addition, each faculty member has developed a narrated presentation on their specific domain expertise and these were added to a shared, online drive for the fellows to review on their own. Every two weeks, video conferencing among fellows from all sites and UCSF faculty allows longitudinal learning, support for emerging issues, and discussions on the narrated lectures. The logistics for this set-up require: reliable teleconferencing infrastructure with back-up systems (e.g., phone calls if video conferencing fails), a regular time for the calls that takes the different time zones into consideration, assurance from sites that fellows will be free during the calls, and an approach that allows structured learning (e.g., discussing cases of acute agitation after watching a lecture on that topic) and unstructured or open discussions (e.g., fellows sharing anything they think is important, including challenges in self-care, ethics, social injustice, isolation in GMH work, limitations of the local healthcare systems, or success stories). In addition, each fellow is paired with a faculty member to meet once a week throughout the fellowship to obtain close mentorship and support. Depending on the fellow's background and interests, these 1:1 meetings allow advanced work such as conducting mental health research, or acquiring leadership skills by obtaining coaching on challenging situations at work.

The importance of interdisciplinary learning in GMH coupled with the relative dearth of faculty with expertise in GMH pose a challenge to build a team of educators for a GMH program. The process of identifying content experts (e.g., faculty with clinical expertise in collaborative care models or faculty with research expertise in cross-cultural mental health research, despite not having GMH experience) and the "peer review" described earlier in "Educational strategies" can bridge this gap. This allows domain experts to create content based on their experience in high-resource settings, which can be further adapted to local delivery settings by GMH experts. To ensure that the content addresses gaps in GMH competencies, GMH experts must conduct the peer review, and this process should be completed before learners access the educational materials (e.g., lectures).

Step 6: Evaluation and feedback

A robust educational program evaluates the learners, educators, sites, and the entire curriculum. Each evaluation category presents its own challenges and can provide important data to improve the educational experience. The strategies for evaluating faculty, the sites, and the overall program are not substantially different from domestic educational programs. In this section, we focus on learner evaluation.

Traditional evaluation methods for learners include assessing performance on specific learning objectives as a measure of competency. These can be based on the review of the learner's achievement of specific learning objectives identified in the earlier steps. However, there are specific limitations of this strategy, particularly in GMH training. Certain competencies may never be "achieved" in the conventional sense of the word. As is described in detail in Chapter 2 of this volume, a well-known criticism of "cultural competency" is that it is not a set of skills or facts to be mastered via didactics.[36,37] Effective and sensitive cross-cultural engagement requires a stance that facilitates constant revision of cultural understanding with humility and ongoing guidance.[38] As such, competency in engagement across cultural difference should be regarded as a process rather than mastery of content; instead, the goal is to develop an attitude of life-long humility.[39] In addition, some competencies, including ones related to skill in practicing cultural humility, are challenging to assess using tests or brief assessments and require longitudinal, progressive changes in multiple domains from multiple viewpoints (often called "360 evaluations").[39–41]

A challenge in learner evaluation is that faculty members based in academic institutions may not have much opportunity to engage in direct observation of learners and must largely rely on the evaluations of overburdened site-based supervisors, worsening an already unequal collaboration. In addition, site-based supervisors may be concerned about criticizing the learners or the program because negative evaluations may not only adversely affect the learner's professional career, but also negatively impact the institutional collaboration. Furthermore, the definitions of "excellent," "average," and "poor" performance that are often used in evaluations may not be well calibrated between the academic institution and the host site. A longitudinal partnership that maintains an appropriate balance between the burden and value of evaluation, along with providing supervisors with *feedback about feedback*, is important to address these concerns. Finally, many GMH competencies can be achieved by working in teams while learner evaluations are often individualized. This has been addressed in some settings by "360 evaluations" where the learner is evaluated by every person with whom they work. The obvious downside of this strategy in GMH is the substantial increase in the burden of these tasks among members at the sites who are pushed to their limit in meeting the clinical demand for their services. In such cases, institutions should provide resources to support the extra time and effort needed for such evaluation.

The process of iterative curriculum development depends on strategic data collection, such as prioritizing data that will be used to make changes (vs. routine data collection because that has been the norm). Ultimately, educators will want to minimize the burden of evaluation, while ensuring that feedback is not a goal but a part of a process to address challenges and iteratively improve the educational program.

Special considerations

Although Kern's framework is relevant to GMH training, it does not cover all pertinent GMH training needs. The foremost need is that GMH training necessitates a firm grounding in values of health equity.[42] A training program may meet the learners' needs (e.g., exposure to healthcare delivery challenges in LMICs), but unless grounded in values of equity, it will not bring concrete benefit to the sites. This result would be unacceptable. Educators in the academic institutions might not be fully aware of this issue in scenarios where staff at the host sites prioritize the academic collaborations and maintaining goodwill. However, without valuing equity, the program may be burdening and exploiting the host site while unilaterally benefiting learners from high-resource institutions.

Another important aspect of GMH training is the stigma of mental health that is prevalent globally. Mental health problems, and by association, clinicians who focus on them, have long been stigmatized.[43,44] Although gains are being made, learners may have difficulties in navigating stigma from patients, families, providers, and institutions, as drivers of stigma may be different in settings with minimal access to safe and effective mental health services.[14] They may also need to be prepared to assert the importance of mental illness and its treatment with their colleagues. Although the presence of stigma may discourage learners, it provides an opportunity to address an important bottleneck to high-quality care. With close support from mentors, learners may advocate for their patients and develop interventions to address stigma, thus improving their own experience at the sites while also contributing to reducing stigma.

Although interest in and attention to GMH has been increasing, it is not yet a common discipline within academic institutions.[45] GMH educators may encounter disinterest from institutional leadership when developing a GMH educational program. As educational programs usually do not generate revenue but require financial investment, educators will need to demonstrate the value of GMH programs in alternative ways. Educators may illustrate interest in GMH via conducting learner surveys and supporting student advocacy for GMH programs. Furthermore, it can be helpful to highlight the presence of GMH programs in competing institutions, resulting in loss of promising trainees and faculty members. In addition, the business plan for the program should make every attempt to reduce the financial cost to the academic department. This may be achieved by: (1) combining domestic clinical work that can generate revenue; (2) incorporating the GMH program with an existing, global health training program that facilitates pooling of resources (e.g., program staff to assist with logistics) to scale up the program without the substantial investment needed for a standalone GMH program; and (3) leveraging research infrastructure to create opportunities for GMH learners. The UCSF Fellowship has utilized all three strategies, minimizing program expenses and improving sustainability.

Finally, an important challenge for learners is that they will need to adapt their knowledge and skills learned in HICs (e.g., diagnostic frameworks based on the *Diagnostic and Statistical Manual*,[46] highly trained mental health professionals, and a robust healthcare system). Consequently, learners will need specific strategies to understand and incorporate local knowledge (e.g., local understanding of emotional and behavioral challenges, utilization of traditional healers and community health workers, and a less robust healthcare system). As described in detail in Chapter 2, GMH learners will need support from social scientists, including cultural anthropologists, to navigate the pluralistic nature of mental illness and treatment. Ultimately, learners are now at a critical point in history, where the long-standing debate on cultural differences has given way to invigorated commitment to understand these differences and to leverage this new knowledge, not as an excuse for inaction, but to guide improved care for all people living with mental illness.

Conclusion

Educational programming focused on global mental health must deliver a curriculum effective for training while navigating numerous resource challenges. We strongly advocate for an approach that utilizes a theory or a framework to develop an educational program. Our experience using Kern's six-step approach has assisted in identifying a well-defined problem, setting clear targets for success, and implementing a set of educational strategies that are designed to meet those goals. The role of the learners' environment is critical to the success of the program. Leveraging existing resources, both within global health in general and mental health disciplines in particular, can assist with containing overall costs of the program. As the demand for GMH training continues to grow worldwide, we hope that our experience can assist educators and learners to build robust programs to develop a new generation of scholars and practitioners in GMH.

References

1. Tsai AC, Fricchione GL, Walensky RP, Ng C, Bangsberg DR, Kerry VB. Global health training in US graduate psychiatric education. *Academic Psychiatry*. 2014;38(4):426–32.
2. Buzza C, Fiskin A, Campbell J, Guo J, Izenberg J, Kamholz B, et al. Competencies for global mental health: developing training objectives for a post-graduate fellowship for psychiatrists. *Annals of Global Health*. 2018;84(4):717–26.
3. Kern DE, Thomas PA, Hughes MT. *Curriculum development for medical education: a six-step approach*. Baltimore, MD: Johns Hopkins University Press; 2009. 240 p.
4. Acharya B, Tenpa J, Basnet M, Hirachan S, Rimal P, Choudhury N, et al. Developing a scalable training model in global mental health: pilot study of a video-assisted training Program for Generalist Clinicians in Rural Nepal. *Global Mental Health*. 2017;4:e8.
5. Crump JA, Sugarman J. The working group on ethics guidelines for global health training: ethics and best practice guidelines for training experiences in global health. *American Journal of Tropical Medicine and Hygiene*. 2010;83(6):1178–82.
6. World Health Organization. WHO model lists of essential medicines [Internet]. WHO. [cited 2017 September 23]. Available from: http://www.who.int/medicines/publications/essentialmedicines/en/
7. Bordage G. Conceptual frameworks to illuminate and magnify. *Medical Education*. 2009;43(4):312–19.
8. Bandura A. *Social learning theory*. Englewood Cliffs, NJ: Prentice Hall; 1977. 247 p.

9. Dreyfus SE. The five-stage model of adult skill acquisition. *Bulletin of Science, Technology & Society*. 2004;24(3):177–81.

10. Davis DA, Thomson MA, Oxman AD, Haynes RB. Changing physician performance: a systematic review of the effect of continuing medical education strategies. *JAMA*. 1995;274(9):700–5.

11. Davis D, O'Brien MA, Freemantle N, Wolf FM, Mazmanian P, Taylor-Vaisey A. Impact of formal continuing medical education: do conferences, workshops, rounds, and other traditional continuing education activities change physician behavior or health care outcomes? *JAMA*. 1999;282(9):867–74.

12. Becker AE, Kleinman A. Mental health and the global agenda. *The New England Journal of Medicine*. 2013;369(1):66–73.

13. World Health Organization. Mental health action plan 2013-2020 [Internet]; 2013. [cited 2016 April 1]. Available from: http://apps.who.int/iris/bitstream/10665/89966/1/9789241506021_eng.pdf?ua=1

14. World Health Organization. World mental health report: transforming mental health for all [Internet]. Geneva: World Health Organization; 2022. [cited 2022 August 15]. Available from: https://apps.who.int/iris/handle/10665/356119

15. Collins PY, Patel V, Joestl SS, March D, Insel TR, Daar AS, et al. Grand challenges in global mental health. *Nature*. 2011;475(7354):27–30.

16. Horton R. Launching a new movement for mental health. *The Lancet*. 2007;370(9590):806.

17. Patel V, Boyce N, Collins PY, Saxena S, Horton R. A renewed agenda for global mental health. *The Lancet*. 2011;378(9801):1441–2.

18. Binagwaho A, Allotey P, Sangano E, Ekström AM, Martin K. A call to action to reform academic global health partnerships. *BMJ*. 2021;375:n2658.

19. Sors TG, O'Brien RC, Scanlon ML, Bermel LY, Chikowe I, Gardner A, et al. Reciprocal innovation: a new approach to equitable and mutually beneficial global health partnerships. *Global Public Health*. 2022; 25:1–13.

20. Davis AK, Parran TV, Graham AV. Educational strategies for clinicians. *Primary Care*. 1993;20(1):241–50.

21. Frenk J, Chen L, Bhutta ZA, Cohen J, Crisp N, Evans T, et al. Health professionals for a new century: transforming education to strengthen health systems in an interdependent world. *The Lancet*. 2010;376(9756):1923–58.

22. Epstein RM, Hundert EM. Defining and assessing professional competence. *JAMA*. 2002;287(2):226–35.

23. Jogerst K, Callender B, Adams V, Evert J, Fields E, Hall T, et al. Identifying interprofessional global health competencies for 21st-century health professionals. *Annals of Global Health*. 2015;81(2):239–47.

24. Collins PY, Musisi S, Frehywot S, Patel V. The core competencies for mental, neurological, and substance use disorder care in sub-Saharan Africa. *Global Health Action*. 2015;8(1):26682.

25. Fricchione GL, Borba CPC, Alem A, Shibre T, Carney JR, Henderson DC. Capacity building in global mental health: professional training. *Harvard Review of Psychiatry*. 2012;20(1):47–57.

26. Griffith JL, Kohrt B, Dyer A, Polatin P, Morse M, Jabr S, et al. Training psychiatrists for global mental health: cultural psychiatry, collaborative inquiry, and ethics of alterity. *Academic Psychiatry*. 2016;40(4):701–6.

27. Alem A, Pain C, Araya M, Hodges BD. Co-creating a psychiatric resident program with Ethiopians, for Ethiopians, in Ethiopia: the Toronto Addis Ababa Psychiatry Project (TAAPP). *Academic Psychiatry*. 2010;34(6):424–32.

28. Craig Van Dyke MD, Tong L, Mack K. Global mental health training for United States psychiatric residents. *Academic Psychiatry*. 2011;35(6):354.

29. World Health Organization. *Mental health gap action programme. mhGAP intervention guide for mental, neurological and substance use disorders in non-specialized health settings: version 2.0*. Geneva: World Health Organization; 2016.

30. World Health Organization. Group Interpersonal Therapy (IPT) for depression [Internet]. WHO. [cited 2018 March 22]. Available from: http://www.who.int/mental_health/mhgap/interpersonal_therapy/en/

31. World Health Organization. Thinking Healthy [Internet]. WHO. [cited 2018 March 22]. Available from: http://www.who.int/mental_health/maternal-child/thinking_healthy/en/

32. World Health Organization. Problem management plus (PM+) [Internet]. WHO. [cited 2018 March 22]. Available from: http://www.who.int/mental_health/emergencies/problem_management_plus/en/

33. World Health Organization. Psychological first aid: guide for field workers [Internet]. WHO. [cited 2018 March 22]. Available from: http://www.who.int/mental_health/publications/guide_field_workers/en/

34. Citrin D, Mehanni S, Acharya B, Wong L, Nirola I, Sherchan R, et al. Power, potential, and pitfalls in global health academic partnerships: review and reflections on an approach in Nepal. *Global Health Action.* 2017;10(1):1367161.

35. Acharya B, Maru D, Schwarz R, Citrin D, Tenpa J, Hirachan S, et al. Partnerships in mental healthcare service delivery in low-resource settings: developing an innovative network in rural Nepal. *Globalization and Health.* 2017;13:2.

36. Tervalon M, Murray-García J. Cultural humility versus cultural competence: a critical distinction in defining physician training outcomes in multicultural education. *Journal of Health Care for the Poor and Underserved.* 1998;9(2):117–25.

37. Melby MK, Loh LC, Evert J, Prater C, Lin H, Khan OA. Beyond medical "missions" to impact-driven short-term experiences in global health (STEGHs): ethical principles to optimize community benefit and learner experience. *Academic Medicine: Journal of the Association of American Medical Colleges.* 2016;91(5):633–8.

38. Acharya B, Hirachan S. Including international medical graduates in global mental health training. *Academic Psychiatry.* 2015;40(4):667–671.

39. Hook JN, Davis DE, Owen J, Worthington Jr. EL, Utsey SO. Cultural humility: measuring openness to culturally diverse clients. *Journal of Counseling Psychology.* 2013;60(3):353–66.

40. Khoury NM, Suser JL, Germain LJ, Myers K, Brown AEC, Lu FG. A study of a cultural competence and humility intervention for third-year medical students. *Academic Psychiatry.* 2022;46(4):451–4.

41. Foronda C, Prather S, Baptiste DL, Luctkar-Flude M. Cultural humility toolkit. *Nurse Educator.* 2022;47(5):267–71.

42. Kohrt BA, Marienfeld CB, Panter-Brick C, Tsai AC, Wainberg ML. Global mental health: five areas for value-driven training innovation. *Academic Psychiatry.* 2016;40(4):650–8.

43. Kleinman A, Hall-Clifford R. Stigma: a social, cultural and moral process. *Journal of Epidemiology and Community Health.* 2009;63(6):418–9.

44. Keusch GT, Wilentz J, Kleinman A. Stigma and global health: developing a research agenda. *The Lancet.* 2006;367(9509):525–7.

45. American Psychiatric Association - Global Mental Health [Internet]. [cited 2022 August 16]. Available from: https://www.psychiatry.org/psychiatrists/international/global-mental-health

46. American Psychiatric Association. *DSM-5 task force: diagnostic and statistical manual of mental disorders: DSM-5.* Arlington, VA: American Psychiatric Association; 2017.

Chapter 5

Mentorship in Global Mental Health

Brandon A. Kohrt, David Citrin, Bikash Gauchan, Dristy Gurung, Manaswi Sangraula, Byamah B. Mutamba, Bonnie N. Kaiser, Abdelrhman Elnasseh, Markos Tesfaye, Eshetu Girma, Nilanga Abeysinghe, Pragya Rimal, and Joop T. V. M. de Jong

Summary points

- Mentor–mentee relationships in global mental health should be grounded in the mission to promote equity in access to and use of high-quality mental health services.
- Mentors should model and promote key competencies of humility and reflexivity, development and maintenance of strong collaborations, and participatory research skills to identify locally salient clinical and community needs.
- To assure equitable global mental health careers for women, transgender, and non-binary persons, mentors should establish mandatory gender sensitivity training for researchers, develop leadership packages for women and other marginalized groups, and promote equitable decision-making power among supervisors of different genders.

Introduction

Throughout Homer's *Odyssey*, the protagonist Telemachus is trying to learn about his father, Odysseus, who left Ithaca when he was an infant. When Telemachus becomes a young adult, the goddess Athena appears to him in the form of Mentor, an old man whom Odysseus had asked to look after his son. Athena—as Mentor—tells Telemachus to leave Ithaca and go abroad to learn about his father. Following Mentor's advice, Telemachus sails away from home and begins his own journey seeking knowledge and eventually finding his father. The character of Mentor is the eponym by which we now refer to the process of more experienced figures giving advice and direction to others as they develop their professional identities.[1] In global health, Mentor is even more apropos in their encouragement to set out exploring the world to pursue experience and knowledge.

The purpose of this chapter is to present a vision of how mentoring can be conducted in the field of global mental health. We take a broad view of the diverse types of mentorship, including mentorship from senior to early career mental health researchers and practitioners in low- and middle-income country (LMIC) institutions, mentorship from senior to early career researchers from high-income country (HIC) institutions pursuing mental health research in LMICs, and bidirectional mentorship between global mental health scholars in LMIC and HIC institutions. We describe the implementation of common mentorship practices as they apply to global mental health, but we also highlight some areas in which mentorship should significantly deviate from how it is commonly practiced in academic medicine.

The chapter is structured in four sections. In Part I, we ground global mental health mentorship in the mission of global equity in health care rather than a dominant focus on professional development. In Part II, we set out key tasks for mentorship ranging from cultivation of humility and reflexivity to establishing global networks of colleagues. In Part III, we issue a call to

DOI: 10.4324/9781315160597-8

action for mentors to address gender disparities in the promotion of female global mental health researchers. We conclude in Part IV with the logistics related to mentor qualities, conducting meetings, institutional resource needs, and managing-up approaches for mentees. All of the authors have contributed to the main text of this chapter; in addition, individual authors and author pairs have provided case studies that are presented in boxes to illustrate specific aspects of global mental health mentorship.

By the conclusion of this chapter, new mentors will be able to select a mentorship framework and style, current mentors can reflect upon and revise their practices, and mentees will have a better understanding of expectations for support and supervision through the mentor–mentee relationship. Early career scholars and practitioners in global mental health will be able to seek out and structure the guidance needed to play a transformative role in reducing the inequity in access to and use of high-quality mental health care around the world.

Part I Mentorship toward global equity in mental health care

Mentorship is traditionally defined as the structured cultivation of professional development, ethical practice, and emotional well-being of early career practitioners in a field through the support of senior practitioners.[1-3] In the 1970s, interest in mentorship grew in the United States in the field of business, but it has seen tremendous growth in the past two decades in academic medicine.[1] As university-based global health programs have proliferated, and the number of health professional students engaging in global health has exponentially risen, mentorship has also gained widespread attention in global health training programs.[4]

Mentorship has been critiqued as a particularly American phenomenon grounded in a cultural emphasis on individual self-promotion.[3,5] At the extreme, it is seen as mutual exploitation by mentor and mentee to each promote their own careers, a critique which we agree with insofar as mentorship is typically conducted in US institutions. Mentorship research is dominated by US scholarship, and there are few publications on the practice from Europe and other regions of the world.[3] Success is most often quantified in terms of retention in a specific field, academic publications, grant funding, and promotion of a specific program, institute, or university.[1,3,6] There have even been randomized controlled trials of academic medicine mentoring, with the outcome being the number of peer-reviewed publications.[7] It is important to note that the currencies of publications and grant funding are what allow career progression, but their prioritization at the expense of neglecting mission-related work and ethics is potentially hazardous. These shortcomings in mentorship evaluation interact with other problems related to publishing, such as the tendency for HIC authors to dominate "privileged" authorship positions, at the expense of LMIC authors.[8-10] Although adhering to professional codes of ethics is often a topic of mentoring, few publications mention broader societal benefits of mentorship beyond individual career development.[3,6]

This is where we would like to deviate from a primary focus on individual professional success by proposing a mentorship framework grounded in practices that promote global equity in mental health care. This alternative approach to mentorship is based on indicators of success related to eradicating disparities in the burden of mental health care, providing equal opportunities for global mental health research, assuring equitable access to high-quality mental health care, and protecting and promoting the rights of persons with mental illness. This is especially important because of power differentials between and within institutions in HIC and LMIC countries and because of great risk for unintended consequences in the practice of global health and development.[11] Mentoring geared primarily to publications, grant funding, and promotion may increase the chance of unintended consequences, lead to HIC researchers' exploitation of LMIC collaborators, and violate the "First, do no harm" ethical stance.[12]

It is natural for mentorship in global mental health to be moored in a mission of equity. The common definition of global health proposed by Jeffrey Koplan and colleagues, and adapted by Vikram Patel and colleagues, defines global mental health as "an area for study, research and practice that places a priority on improving [mental] health and achieving equity in [mental] health for all people worldwide."[13,14(p.xi)] The current field of global mental health is predated by the World Health Organization (WHO) Collaborative Study on Strategies for Extending Mental Health Care in the 1970s–1980s[15] and the WHO World Health Report in 2001,[16] which was the first annual report focusing on mental health.[16] These reports emphasized addressing disparities in access to mental health care. The *Lancet* Global Mental Health Group extended this goal with a series of papers in 2007 and follow-ups in 2011 that combined advocacy for "No health without mental health" and a roadmap for scaling up services in LMICs.[17] This spawned the Movement for Global Mental Health (MGMH), whose mission is to reduce the gap between the burden of mental illness and the availability of effective mental health services throughout the world.[18] Research priorities have also reflected equity and access, with the US National Institute of Mental Health (NIMH), during the leadership of Pamela Collins, prioritizing implementation science research funding to reduce the global treatment gap between burden and availability of quality services.[19]

This focus on equity is also prominent in the minds of educators in the field of global mental health. In a 2015 priority setting exercise for a value-driven global mental health agenda, psychiatrists, other mental health professionals, and social scientists gave the highest ranking to the values of equity and equality.[20] A focus on equity helps to frame which research projects and service initiatives are designed and implemented, such as research with actionable recommendations for improving access to and quality of care. With an equity approach, research initiatives to change policy also play a much larger role than they are often given in academic medicine.[21] Our proposed mentorship framework provides a compass to guide professional development with this focus on equity as a central organizing principle and highlights areas of potential conflict between goals associated with individual academic advancement and those promoting the mission of global mental health.

Part II Key domains for global mental health mentorship

Humility and reflexivity

In the priority setting exercise mentioned above, humility and reflexivity were highlighted as key domains for development and should be modeled by mentors and promoted in mentees.[20] We advocate humility and reflexivity over concepts such as cultural competence. Cultural competence is problematic in two ways: first, it assumes a level of knowledge and skill that one has achieved (i.e., one is now competent in a specific cultural group), which is patronizing and unrealistic given the breadth and depth of cultural knowledge that few would ever acquire to be competent; second, it assumes a static and bounded view of culture versus a complex dynamic, multi-cultural world.[22–24] Chapter 2 in this volume discusses the limitations inherent to the cultural competence construct in greater detail.

Humility is an ideal stance from which to initiate dialogue and to address differences in culture and power. The French philosopher and Holocaust survivor Emmanuel Levinas characterizes all human relationships as the interaction of the self and "the Other," whereby the Other is separate and not fully knowable but at the same time not beyond engagement through dialogue.[25] For Levinas, there is an ethical duty to engage with "the Other." Therefore, humility and reflexivity are crucial, given that the field of global mental health is constantly about encountering, and being seen as, "the Other." This humility is just as important on the part of the mentor, who should model acceptance and awareness of their inability to fully know "the Other," whether "the Other" is a patient with mental illness, a different health system, a HIC or LMIC collaborator, or even a mentee.[26] Chapter 3 in this volume also discusses the relevance of Levinas to ethical engagement in global mental health settings.

In addition to humility, reflexivity is a vital attribute of mentors. Within the field of mental health, we have the benefit that most mentors and mentees will already have had training in the concepts of transference and countertransference. This lens is extremely helpful when considering how a global mental health researcher is perceived by a collaborator, research participant, or patient whose social identity or cultural experience is different, and how they respond to being placed in that frame. David Addiss, a global health infectious disease specialist and Buddhist chaplain, writes about the "savior complex" in global health.[27] This complex could easily emerge when unrealistic expectations are placed upon HIC trainees, and then HIC trainees seek to fulfill that identity as part of their role in global mental health. There is also an inflated sense of being a hero, whereas the service/contributions might not be received that way. Therefore, it is crucial that mentors promote their mentees' capacity for reflexivity and self-evaluation to help them tolerate ambiguity, recognize power differentials, and be aware of biases and assumptions.[20]

Global mental health skill sets

Once a mentorship relationship starts with the mission to promote equity in global mental health, and humility and reflexivity have been established as the framework for engagement, it is much more feasible to address other skill sets in a safe (e.g., free from gender-based violence), effective, and ethical manner. Some of the first skill sets to consider are clinical competencies and service provision. If no clinical infrastructure is available in a local setting where collaboration or training is planned to receive referrals and provide care, it may not be appropriate to conduct some forms of research. Mental health research scholarship in Ethiopia is exemplary among LMICs. This success, in part, comes from local initiatives to assure the development of clinical services to support needs aligned with and generated by research. Box 5.1 provides an example of establishing services and research literacy through mentorship that became a formal degree program.

BOX 5.1 FROM MENTORSHIP TO FORMAL DEGREE PROGRAMS TO ESTABLISH CLINICAL SKILL SETS IN RURAL ETHIOPIA

Markos Tesfaye, MD(Psych), PhD, Department of Psychiatry, St Paul's Hospital Millennium Medical College; Eshetu Girma, MPH, PhD, Addis Ababa University School of Public Health

In 2007, the Department of Psychiatry at Jimma University employed one of us (Tesfaye) as the first full-time Ethiopian psychiatrist in the southwestern region of the country. Months later, an Austrian humanitarian organization *Menschen fur Menschen* (People for People), completed the construction of a new 30-bed psychiatric facility with outpatient services within Jimma University Specialized Hospital, as a tertiary-care hospital that also included psychiatric services. For the three psychiatric nurses who ran the old psychiatric clinic for two decades, it was like "moving to a palace." It opened with colorful fanfare in 2008 with ceremonial guests from as far away as northern Europe.

However, the academic department, including the psychiatric facility, continued to be plagued by the shortage of human resources. There were 28 psychiatrists for the entire country, and all held full-time positions elsewhere, so they were unable to leave to work in Jimma. As a psychiatrist (Tesfaye) and public health PhD student (Girma) working in

Jimma at the time, we wanted to find a way to develop the human resources needed to deliver mental health services. Unfortunately, the calls announced to recruit graduates from the medical school who could become psychiatrists proved to be futile. Simultaneously, retaining experienced psychiatric nurses was difficult because they aspired to further training and better placements, which typically included urban centers such as Addis Ababa, Nairobi, or high-income countries.[28] A call posted on the World Psychiatric Association's website for expatriate psychiatrists resulted in few applicants, none of whom were suitable.

This led us to consider how to develop a professional cadre who would be willing to work in the field of mental health and in a setting like Jimma. Out of this situation, a two-year graduate training program in mental health for non-physicians (e.g., public health officers and nurses) was conceived. A concept note for the program was presented to the Federal Ministry of Health of Ethiopia. The outcomes of the meeting included affirmation of the need for such a program, setting core competencies, and defining the future roles and career paths of non-physician mental health specialists within the healthcare system. We knew that mentorship would be important to ensure that trainees completed the program and were then motivated to use their skills to deliver mental health services.

Institutional commitment was considered crucial, and mentorship would not be possible without trainees who could access the program. Jimma University expressed commitment to host the program. Thus, trainees could enroll in the program without paying tuition fees because the university covered their costs through its government funding. This was based on an expectation that the trainees would serve in government facilities for a few years. They would receive government salaries, which were lower and associated with a greater workload than that of health workers in the private sector. However, even with the free training, the number of psychiatry faculty to educate trainees remained inadequate to meet the local mental health needs. At Addis Ababa University, the dearth of faculty to develop a mental health workforce had been addressed through collaborations with HIC universities, which included mentoring trainees and early career faculty to become instructors.[29] A similar approach was considered a viable option to realize the mental health specialist training at Jimma University. Ultimately, Ludwig Maximillian University (LMU) in Germany—where one of us (Girma) was doing his PhD studies—and the neuropsychiatry group at Brigham and Women's Hospital in the United States, along with other universities, supported the development of the curriculum and made a commitment to support the training by teaching courses and providing mentorship for trainees' research projects. In addition, LMU offered financial support for purchasing educational materials and textbooks. The public health departments of the international partners in Europe and North America offered courses relevant to research and public mental health.

The program, a Master's of Science in Mental Health, is open to applicants from all over Ethiopia and was launched in January 2010. The teaching was arranged in such a way that Ethiopian psychiatrists focused on clinical training and supervision while visiting faculty from partner institutions abroad gave two-week in-person courses. The teaching methods aimed to facilitate the acquisition of knowledge and skills.[30] Faculty from partner institutions were involved in mentorship and supervision of trainees' research projects via email communications. Local faculty from the school of public health directly mentored students for research projects. One of us (Tesfaye) served as a role model and mentor for the other (Girma) while he was a PhD student. His PhD work was on stigma against people with mental illness. During and after the PhD work, we both then mentored the master's students' mental health research projects. In addition to research, Girma taught a course on social determinants of mental health to master's students. Because of the lessons learned during the PhD work and inspiration from Tesfaye, Girma is currently involved in a US NIMH-funded anti-stigma project in Sodo district, Southern Ethiopia.

After receiving their degree from the master's program, graduates are obliged to return to the institutions or regional health offices that offered their stipends during their training. As a result, almost all of the mental health specialists at the time of this writing work in public hospitals or public universities across Ethiopia, where they are engaged in clinical care, teaching, and research. Four of the graduates became faculty within the Department of Psychiatry at Jimma University, where they also mentor medical students to encourage them to go into psychiatry. The majority of the courses are now taught by Ethiopian faculty. The program and the host department (Psychiatry) are also serving as a resource for other departments at Jimma University and elsewhere through their involvement in mental health research and projects, including mentorship of PhD, postgraduate, and undergraduate students, and early career faculty in other medical and public health schools and humanities departments around the country. After initiating the training program, mental health research publications in local and international peer-reviewed journals have increased. In addition, graduates from the Jimma University program have enrolled in PhD programs. There is also increasing demand for the Jimma graduates to take on leadership positions and provide psychosocial services for NGO programs, including NGOs working in refugee camps.

In conclusion, mentorship and training of mental health professionals at different professional levels have been—and will continue to be—crucial for service expansion in Ethiopia. Partnerships with other institutions could help overcome the challenges of setting up training programs in resource-limited settings, while state funding for such programs can ensure sustainability.

Knowledge of research priorities established by leaders in the field is also helpful for mentees to identify the skill sets they will need to advance global mental health. In 2011, the Grand Challenges in Global Mental Health (GCGMH)[19] was published. The top priorities focused on implementation challenges to improving access to care. Contemporaneous with the establishment of the GCGMH, a priority setting activity was conducted for mental health and psychosocial support research in humanitarian settings.[31] This yielded key questions, including identifying stressors faced by populations in humanitarian settings; determining methods to assess mental health in humanitarian settings; documenting how affected populations describe mental health; selecting indicators for monitoring and evaluation; adapting interventions to different sociocultural settings; and determining the effectiveness of family- and school-based preventive interventions. Other skill sets identified through the value-driven approach to global mental health include participatory approaches, community-based research, and ethnographic and qualitative research methods. These skills are vital in complementing quantitative approaches, working with interpreters and cultural brokers, and evidence-based advocacy.[20,32]

Networks and collaborations

Because global mental health is a field that is as rich as the number of settings and projects that exist in its broad scope, it is not surprising that global mental health initiatives cover everything from suicidality in circumpolar populations to rare neuropsychiatric conditions affecting children in East Africa. Therefore, it is likely that the best group of mentors for any given project will be spread around the world. This points toward the need for mentoring from multiple individuals at different institutions and settings. As opposed to basic sciences, where it may be possible to have mentorship and activities contained within one wet lab, the players in a global mental health "lab" will be quite dispersed. A distributed network of mentors could comprise a team that, in aggregate, offers the expertise best suited to the project; this might include local on-site mentors immediately available wherever the project is; regional experts who are familiar with the language and culture of the population; methodological experts who can provide input on the study design, implementation, and analysis; experts on the diseases or health conditions of interest; experts in pedagogy (given the importance of learning how to teach others); and experts in various clinical settings (inpatient, outpatient, emergency, consultation, primary care-based), etc. This network of mentors can then be a launching point to develop strong collaborations.

Utilizing a distributed network of mentoring can ensure that mentees receive adequate support and supervision and also distributes the responsibilities for providing this mentorship. For example, in one of our projects in rural Nepal, a medical student connected with one local mentor and three remote mentors over the course of each week, which gave her adequate support but required no more than 15–60 minutes per remote mentor per week. There was an on-site facilitator who was able to mentor on local conditions and assure integration into the project and local health professional community. Then there was a content expert mentor who was a PhD student who had just completed fieldwork over two years in the area. There was also a qualitative research methods expert who had briefly been to the site and was available to focus on the data collection techniques and subsequent analysis. The weekly Skype calls with the senior mentor could then be used to troubleshoot any problems without having to cover all content and methods issues. It is important to note that co-mentoring also has a range of challenges, despite its benefits. Mentees may, for example, receive conflicting advice from different mentors, the expectations of mentors may differ, and mentees may feel overwhelmed trying to integrate the advice from multiple mentors when designing projects, writing papers, or making career plans. Team meetings among the mentorship team or joint meetings with the mentee can preempt this kind of problem.

Whereas the origins of mentoring are rooted in the vertical transmission of knowledge, advice, and socio-emotional support from a senior career professional to an earlier career professional or student, there is increasing appreciation of mentorship in horizontal relationships, such as through peer mentoring. Many LMICs are developing peer mentoring programs. See Box 5.2 on the Sri Lankan government's effort to promote peer mentorship in counseling.

BOX 5.2 DEVELOPMENT OF PEER MENTORING IN SRI LANKA

Nilanga Abeysinghe, M.Couns, PhD, School of Psychology, Faculty of Humanities and Sciences, Sri Lanka Institute of Information Technology, Sri Lanka

The mental health sector in Sri Lanka operates with a considerably low number of mental health professionals. There are approximately 100 psychiatrists and 50 psychologists in a country of more than 22 million people.[33] However, there are over 800 counselors attached to a few ministries, schools, and statuary bodies contributing to psychosocial and mental health care. Counselors working for the state sector in Sri Lanka are stationed at the divisional administrative office level within each district and at schools to ensure easy access to the community and students.

A range of state and non-state institutions offer formal and informal counseling training. Individuals who complete the equivalent of a one-year counseling diploma and a first degree are eligible to join the state sector as a counselor. However, the non-state sector recruits counselors with diploma-level qualifications with a high school education or less. Currently, there are many courses training counselors with curricula ranging from a few weeks to over 18 months. As the country does not have a mechanism to register counselors and regulate the counseling service, each training program and counseling association tends to have its own standards for training and evaluation.

Among the many efforts by the state and non-state sectors to enhance and maintain the quality of counseling services, one approach has been the introduction of a peer supervision model to a group of state-sector counselors attached to two ministries in 2015. This attempted to overcome the issues arising from the country's shortage of trained senior clinical supervisors. Peer supervision was seen as necessary because senior counselors were limited in number and had not received adequate training in mentorship.

The peer supervision training and support programs were carried out as part of a continuing professional development program conducted in collaboration between the government and the NGO sector. The peer mentorship in this model took the form of a cohort of peers providing support and constructive skill correction to one another. The hope is that this "cohort-peer" model will evolve into "near-peer" models in which individuals who have recently completed training and are only a few years ahead can provide additional support to one another. This initiative may help improve counseling quality, promote self-care, and retain counselors in the field. However, research is needed to evaluate the practices and outcomes of this new approach in Sri Lanka.

We are particularly interested in measuring how peer supervision can improve the competency of counselors in Sri Lanka. Therefore, we carried out a project adapting a clinical competency tool to assess counselors and then exploring the impact of mentoring on this outcome. This is done explicitly through a focus on clinical skills rather than clinical knowledge, which can be assessed through standardized testing in training programs. The clinical skills model I am using is based on a tool developed for mental health competency in task-sharing initiatives, the ENhancing Assessment of Common Therapeutic factors tool (ENACT), which trains peers as role-players and raters in observed structured clinical evaluations (OSCEs).[34] In LMICs, peer supervision using structured evaluations has been shown to be acceptable, feasible, and to improve quality. The use of structured tools is important to minimize social desirability bias when rating peers and to help peers focus on key areas for strengthening skills.[35] Based on the acceptability of the model, we are in the process of developing training modules in five categories: communication skills, emotional engagement, social relations, assessment, and planning and process. The successful training of these factors is expected to allow peer supervisors to provide objective and standardized feedback using a reliable tool (ENACT—Sri Lanka), allowing counselors to improve the quality standards of counseling practice.

In LMICs, peer mentoring may extend to mentorship among LMIC organizations. The collective group of organizations, Transcultural Psychosocial Organization, has been doing this for decades (see Box 5.3), and similar models are now in place for sister organizations in the extended Partners In Health (PIH) family of organizations (PIH is a non-profit organization that delivers health care to marginalized populations in 12 countries).

BOX 5.3 STRUCTURED DEVELOPMENT OF LOCAL CAPACITY AND AUTONOMY

Joop de Jong, MD, PhD, Professor of Cultural and International Psychiatry at the VU University Medical Center, Amsterdam, and at the Amsterdam Institute of Social Science Research (AISSR) of the University of Amsterdam, the Netherlands

Transcultural Psychosocial Organization (TPO) is a network of organizations in low- and middle-income countries affected by humanitarian disasters. Most of the programs have been running for more than two decades and were developed in settings where there was no primary care system (Cambodia), only one residential psychiatric facility (Mozambique, Uganda, Burundi, Ethiopia, Eritrea), NGOs mainly active in physical health or human rights (Nepal, Namibia), and a health department in exile (Tibetans in India).[36] I founded and co-developed TPO through mentoring and capacity-building approaches that led to 11 long-standing projects where TPO either supported a local NGO to add mental health and psychosocial support services (MHPSS) to a human rights or physical health perspective or supported a government department or ministry to develop MHPSS. Many of these have now become independent, self-sustaining organizations, securing 100% of their own funding.

When we set up TPO, I used a set of principles based on previous experiences that have been described elsewhere.[36] TPO used a learning model that developed along three strategies:

1. **Local leadership**: When invited to set up a project, we did an assessment, similar to what is now described in the international guidelines for mental health and psychosocial support in humanitarian settings,[37] then formulated a project proposal and looked for funding that included support for expatriate expertise in the domains of anthropology, psychology, and psychiatry, if this expertise was not locally available. Local and international professionals formed a core group of trainers that would cascade down, training trainers in the health, education, women's rights, and other relevant sectors. Guidance or mentoring took place locally during field trips, while jointly seeing families or individuals with problems. Psychosocial problems were preferentially addressed within community structures or groups, with services in the healthcare system generally reserved for serious neuropsychiatric disorders. The relation with TPO headquarters was based on trust: I intervened as little as possible because the local team was best equipped to adapt the program to local circumstances. Guidance was limited to two visits a year in the field and an annual visit of the local director(s) to Amsterdam. Communication happened in the medieval way of thick letters that might take an entire day to compose. Over the years, I refined TPO's blueprint, which in combination with perpetually evolving local proposals and plans served as the guideline. Apart from a strong element of decentralization in the center-periphery relation and the role of trust, there was nothing special regarding program development in TPO. Our book *Trauma, War and Violence* provides insight into how diverse our programs developed across a range of countries.[36]

2. **Cross-country discussions of challenges and lessons learned**: TPO's development took place during our biennial two-week meetings with 25–35 participants, one or two per country from our network. Before the meeting, we engaged in several systematic and interactional rounds to elicit questions, themes, concerns, and changing priorities. Headquarters developed a program that evoked so much enthusiasm that meetings often continued till late in the evenings. Each country would first present its achievement during the past two years, followed by questions and feedback. A

couple of major themes would be addressed per meeting, and we often invited experts for a couple of days to address certain topics. For example, these topics included: to what extent should we focus on psychosocial issues versus treating serious psychiatric disorders?; what preventive interventions would be suitable in different places, and would that include peace building?; can sport contribute to reconciliation between competing ethnic or religious groups?; how do we reintegrate former combatants, child soldiers, and survivors of sexual violence without being stigmatized by their environment?; how can countries set up sustainable and reliable fundraising, accountancy, and monitoring systems? One of the issues at each of these meetings was research, the third hallmark of the organization.

3. **Securing humanitarian funding for research and developing human resources for high-quality research**: Based on my previous experience in war zones and post-conflict areas, it seemed sensible to spend approximately 25% of our resources on research. The research aims were essential to inform the work; for instance, we wanted to know what the concerns of the population were, how cultural factors helped them to cope with the past and ongoing adversity, what kind of stressors they had been exposed to, and how a wide range of mediating and moderating variables resulted in psychopathology, disability, and quality of life. However, in that period, most scholars thought that research in humanitarian emergencies was impossible. Research proved to be one of the most contentious issues due to the multidisciplinary staff we hired in a time when mixed methods were less common than they are today. For example, the anthropologists proposed in-depth participatory observation because that would provide reliable insights, whereas they considered epidemiology a neo-positivistic anomaly that would only yield biased answers. Eventually, we all agreed on collecting local expressions and idioms of distress in addition to studying "universal" psychological problems or assessing societal cost-effectiveness.

There were hurdles to achieving our aim of developing local research capacity, such as eliciting a truly local research agenda via a bottom-up approach and retaining research capacity in the country offices. One of the consequences of successful mentoring and capacity-building can be that collaborators in low-resource settings move to high-resource organizations and countries; therefore, mentoring needs to be a continual process.

One of the common hurdles published in the field of global health addresses "medical brain drain," the migration of professionals from low-resource settings to high-resource settings, and potential solutions. Some of the reasons for migration include income, corruption, political instability, working conditions, and career opportunities. Some of the suggested solutions include policies to increase funding for health system strengthening for LMICs, policies to increase domestic earnings or to reward professionals for staying, and having more "exchange programs" with expectations of returning,[38-40] all of which could benefit from mentoring.

Dissemination, publication, and grants

If the above issues are foregrounded—a focus on equity, humility, prioritizing collaborations, and prioritizing local research questions—then the process of dissemination, publication, and obtaining grants is more likely to be consistent with the mission of global mental health. Moreover, if the above are addressed, then there will be an ethical duty of dissemination of research findings and other lessons to help move the field forward, by demonstrating the successes and challenges. Through this approach, publications are not simply for the purpose of academic promotion, but rather for the advancement of services and science.

A common issue in HIC-LMIC collaborations is the tendency for HIC authors to occupy more prestigious authorship positions (e.g., first and senior). Particular attention should therefore be paid to supporting LMIC authors, not only in terms of authorship position in the final product but also in supporting their growth as writers. Mentors can guide mentees on thinking about publication even before research or clinical programs begin. First, the ownership of and access to data should be clearly outlined. Trainees can draw up data use agreements that outline what data they will use, how they will use it, and list intended publications, with a specification of what publications are specifically tied to degree completion if applicable. In addition, these data use agreements can highlight how collaborators and partners have access to data and potential directions for other publications. This way, when it comes time to write, there is already an idea of who is involved, their expectations, and what different products will be pursued. Collaborators can all agree to the data use and publication plan before any research starts and iteratively update the plans as research is underway.

It is helpful to have multiple publications in mind as the study is designed, as this allows multiple mentees to take leadership roles in developing the manuscripts and multiple personnel—including early career investigators—to have opportunities for first authorship. If there is only one or very few possible publications that could be produced out of a collaborative project, then the design should be redrawn to assure multiple potential outputs and roles for various team members in different aspects of authorship. Elsewhere, we have provided guidance on the specific steps of collaborative writing among LMIC–HIC research teams in global mental health.[41]

The experience of writing grants and implementing grant-funded research is crucial for LMIC-based early career investigators to advance the field and to access sources of support to engage in global mental health. LMIC-based investigators will often have in-depth experience of the issues that need to be addressed to fill gaps in local and national mental health services. Some funding institutions, governments, and other organizations, such as the Wellcome Trust, Grand Challenges Canada, the UK Medical Research Council, and the US National Institutes of Health, have supported early career LMIC investigators and helped launch their independent research careers. Box 5.4 describes an example of the role of mentorship in a grant led by an early LMIC investigator; one of the key lessons from that experience was the need for mentorship in grant management, not only technical research skills. LMIC researchers and clinicians are less likely to have protected time to work on grant writing.

BOX 5.4 INTEGRATING MENTORSHIP IN LMIC EARLY CAREER INVESTIGATOR-LED GRANTS

Byamah B. Mutamba, MD(Psych), MPH, PhD, Butabika Hospital, Uganda, and YouBelong Uganda

Grand Challenges Canada (GCC) has provided grant mechanisms for LMIC early career investigators to independently conduct research and gain experience with pilot grants to work toward larger research initiatives in LMICs. The GCC Stars in Global Health program was part of a consortium dedicated to supporting Bold Ideas with Big Impact™ in global health and, most importantly, could fund innovators in LMICs. In 2012 at the time of the call for proposals for the GCC Stars program, the Ministry of

Health in Uganda was grappling with an emergence of a localized epidemic of a neuropsychiatric condition—the Nodding Syndrome, which is characterized by disabling seizures affecting children. As a Ugandan psychiatrist who had recently completed an MSc in Public Health in Developing Countries at the London School of Hygiene and Tropical Medicine, I was selected by the ministry to be part of a multidisciplinary team tasked with designing and implementing a health system intervention for the patients, families, and communities affected by Nodding Syndrome. The national response strategy for Nodding Syndrome outlined the need for care at the individual and population levels; however, no family mental health intervention had been described for the families caring for the affected children.

Based on this pressing public mental health need and my position with responsibilities to develop and pilot mental health interventions, this was an ideal opportunity to apply for a GCC Stars grant, which targeted "innovators" uniquely situated to transform LMIC health services. I had local mentorship from a senior psychiatrist in Uganda, Professor Seggane Musisi, in developing and then later implementing the research project. In 2013, I received the GCC grant. Following receipt of the funding, GCC was in regular communication by email with information about the grant signing and the start of project processes. A program officer was assigned by GCC to work with each of the innovators at the outset and through the life of the project using various methods, including update calls, project progress, and final project reports. Meetings and engagements with the program officer focused on the innovators' outcomes and milestones as outlined in the Results-Based Management and Accountability Framework (RMAF) of each project. The innovator's progress on their outcomes and their financial reports would determine the amount of funds that would be advanced to the innovator's organization for the next phase.

Engagement with the GCC program officer was predominantly by email when providing requested information or through progress and final project reports. Most of the time during the grant period, particularly during project implementation, the innovator did not have much engagement, physical or virtual, with the program officer. It may not have been possible for program officers to be more engaged with the innovators; however, a mechanism to regularly engage with the innovator, especially guidance about project management, could have been instituted, e.g., scheduled monthly/quarterly phone or video calls. It felt like innovators were left on their own for so long without support, until those times when a progress or final report was required. At the time of report submission, it may not have been possible to institute changes that could have affected the achievement of project milestones. The "local" mentor offered mostly technical oversight and was not very involved with project management. This raises important questions about how to provide adequate support for new investigators so that they can prepare proper documentation addressing both financial and scientific activity related to the grant, as well as how international funders supporting new investigators engage with, support, and provide incentives to local mentors. Training and support to improve mentorship could be a worthwhile investment in these types of endeavors.

Conversely, the "independence" of the innovator and the flexibility of the GCC budget allowed researchers to own the implementation process and innovate without many restrictions, considering that innovators understood their concepts better than the program officers. This was a good opportunity to "learn by doing," which I believe benefited me as an innovator. It is also worth noting that GCC qualified that the level of engagement would depend on the size of the project and other factors, with a focus on the innovator's project outcomes and milestones which are initially part of the grant application.

Local meetings, such as the GCC-Makerere University Seminar in Uganda in 2013 and proposal development "Bootcamp" Workshop for African Innovators in Kenya in 2016 combined with GCC international conferences, provided a "face-to-face" platform for innovators, program officers, and other experts to meet, share, and learn face to face. This presented unique opportunities for collaboration and further engagement.

A Grand Challenges Canada Stars in Global Health grant provided technical and financial support for an innovative mental health implementation research project in Uganda. This mainly involved an LIC–LIC mentor–mentee relationship involving the senior professor—Prof. Musisi—at Makerere University. In addition to providing me an opportunity to be mentored, the study grant also created an opportunity for me to mentor a postgraduate student in psychiatry who participated as a research assistant. Prof. Musisi and I supervised him and facilitated his work through the study grant to collect data and write up his master's thesis.

Through the GCC Stars program for early career researchers, I then had the opportunity to become an investigator on a much larger GCC grant being implemented across three countries. This helped me establish a platform for collaboration for mentorship from scholars around the world, and some of those mentorship relationships continue to date. In particular, the relationships formed through the larger GCC grant introduced me to one of my mentors when I was conducting my PhD.

The GCC grants for early investigators provided me with opportunities to benefit from LIC-LIC and HIC-LIC mentor–mentee relationships. Of note, all were based on informal networks within the global mental health field. Moving forward, I would recommend that similar grant programs include well-defined opportunities for early career investigators to receive formal mentorship and to receive training in becoming a mentor, detailing the requirements, principles, and methods for mentor–mentee relationships. These could apply to both LMIC-LMIC and HIC-LMIC arrangements allowing for initiating and sustaining "willing mentor and willing mentee" engagements.

Part III Achieving equity and reducing disparities in global mental health professional development for women

Seventy-five percent of the global health workforce is composed of women; however, very few women are represented in leadership and decision-making roles.[42] Despite advocacy within the global health field for greater equity in health for women, as committed to the Sustainable Development Goals (SDGs), equity in the health workforce has rarely been addressed.[43] Female leadership and mentorship are shown to have a "ripple effect" and have a huge impact in creating positive changes in health systems, which ultimately helps in achieving the development agenda set out in the SDGs.[44,45] Some examples of the impact of gender parity in global health leadership include a drop in neonatal deaths,[46] adolescent girls receiving higher education,[47] and women being more involved in income-generating activities.[48]

The potential for the beneficial impact of women working in global mental health is no different. Gender has been shown to be a critical determinant of mental health, as women are shown to have a higher prevalence of anxiety, depression, and mood disorders.[49] In Nepal, suicide was first documented as the leading cause of death among women of reproductive age in

2009.[50] Similarly, maternal depression and postpartum psychosis are some other mental disorders that women face globally. Women in decision-making positions have been shown to prioritize and make policy changes that address concerns most related to them.[51] However, despite these benefits, there are increased challenges for women to climb the career ladder in global health. Women's roles in decision-making in the health sector, especially in LMICs, have been minimal, with the exception of some settings such as Rwanda, Uganda, and Liberia. Despite this, there has been very little discussion to explore and address this issue, especially among health workforce communities in LMICs.

Within academic medicine programs in the United States, there has been a growing effort to support women's professional development through mentoring programs.[52-55] However, there has been limited attention to how mentoring can be used by and for women in LMIC institutions. Though there is great interest in global health and research among women in secondary school and at the college level,[56] only 19% of health researchers are women in South and West Asia. A series of focus groups and key informant interviews carried out in a study on the challenges faced by women while working in the global mental health sector in Nepal revealed issues that are common to women in many LMIC and HIC institutions. The major challenges identified are outlined below, and proposed solutions through mentoring are presented in Box 5.5.

Not being taken seriously

When dealing with policymakers, health managers, and other stakeholders in the global mental health field, early career and young women face the challenge of not being taken seriously. Some examples shared by participants highlighted the following issues: being treated as a student or someone passing time before getting married; not providing serious or technical answers during interviews conducted by women or trying to dumb down the answers; being asked about marital status and salary scale during introduction; and being ignored if there is a male colleague present and making eye contact with male colleagues while answering, even though the questions were asked by the women.

Safety and health issues

In global mental health, women must work in close coordination with government and community stakeholders at the field level, and much of their work depends upon the decision-making power held by those stakeholders. When dealing with such government stakeholders and other community gatekeepers, women face covert or overt forms of sexual harassment. It is difficult to call out the person for their behavior for a multitude of reasons. For example, they may be an important stakeholder in decision-making, and that might make it difficult for the project to be successful in the community. Similarly, mobilizing in rural communities in global mental health projects is tough due to the difficult topography in many LMICs where transportation, accommodation, and health services are limited or non-existent. Female researchers in Nepal voiced their concern about walking for long hours even during menstruation and camping at locations without access to proper latrines or staying in unsafe lodges. There was a perception that male staff did not anticipate and make accommodations to mitigate these challenges. Although male staff are often aware of security and harassment risks when conducting rural health research, focus group respondents perceived that this might typically be brought up during the hiring process in asking women whether they are capable of working in remote areas and communities, rather than finding mechanisms to improve the safety and health of women in these working conditions.

Gender differences in leadership and mentorship roles

When women are in leadership positions in organizations, respondents perceive that female staff have the opportunity to discuss issues in an environment where they may feel more comfortable, which may be more conducive to problem-solving. Further, they perceive that male supervisors and mentors may be unwilling to explore problems faced by female staff, and they may lack gender-sensitive communication skills, making them unapproachable for advice and support when faced with difficult situations. Focus group respondents reported that female supervisors can be more empathetic and may consider all the issues to inform decision-making and action. In institutions where there is only male leadership, female employees may turn to female colleagues or other female mentors to share their problems and relieve their stress.

Box 5.5 provides potential action steps to address these common barriers in male-dominated global mental health institutions.

BOX 5.5 POTENTIAL MENTORSHIP SOLUTIONS TO ADDRESS BARRIERS IN MALE-DOMINATED INSTITUTIONS IN GLOBAL MENTAL HEALTH

Dristy Gurung, MSc, Transcultural Psychosocial Organization (TPO) Nepal, Institute of Psychology, Psychiatry and Neuroscience, and King's College London; Manaswi Sangraula, PhD, MPH, Department of Psychology, The New School, New York City

We conducted focus groups and key informant interviews with Nepali male and female staff members to identify barriers and potential solutions in male-dominated global mental health institutions.[57] Both male and female groups were asked for potential solutions or mitigation strategies. The female focus group realized that women face a double burden in the workplace: though they themselves face the barriers, they are often also expected to create, push for, and implement individual and/or organizational-level solutions, rather than an expectation that male staff should seek solutions. While the female focus group promoted organizational solutions, the male group focused on changing social norms and perspectives; in other words, women sought to change institutional practices, whereas most male respondents said the barriers should be addressed outside the organization through changing societal norms. Specific institutional solutions are proposed below.

1. **Mandatory trainings on gender sensitivity and communication**: Though counselors, psychologists, and other mental health clinicians are given extensive training on communication skills through their education and practice, researchers, managers, and other employees of the same organization may not have ever received such training. This creates a discrepancy in employees' interpersonal skills. Moreover, a different set of communication skills is necessary to excel as a supervisor. While such skills are facile to some, requiring all employees to participate in a communications and gender training increases awareness of unproductive communication in the workplace and gives both men and women the tools to listen and to resolve conflict. Women also expressed that overt and subtle harassment issues often go unaddressed in the workplace. Trainings on how to avoid, recognize, and report harassment are necessary for both males and females while working in communities and the office. With the knowledge and tools to recognize gender-specific challenges through effective trainings, all genders will be better equipped to serve as successful mentors and supervisors.

2. **Leadership package for women**: Because of gendered expectations regarding household duties, some women—and especially working mothers—can only devote time to work during the usual nine-to-five hours and cannot easily work after hours. This leaves them little time to focus on the capacity-building and professional education necessary to be competitive candidates for leadership positions. To address this, women suggested creating a leadership package that would provide capacity-building during office hours, caring for caretakers workshops (training to enhance skills to relieve stress and decrease fatigue and burnout of those who are in caregiving positions in the workplace and/or at home), and professional development trainings. Such strategies have been successfully implemented in many companies where mid-level working women are given protected time away from work and are encouraged to attend leadership conferences and other workshops.[56]

3. **Promotion of equal decision-making power among female supervisors**: Gender-responsive leadership is necessary in all levels of an organization to reduce discrimination and increase leadership participation among women. This includes increasing visibility and leadership responsibilities for female leaders. A female participant shared, "when we take issues to the (female supervisor), it should be the case that she doesn't have to get approval from someone else ... we shouldn't always have to receive final approval from a male [in the organization]." The women firmly stated that their familial roles as mothers, lack of time flexibility—due to the patriarchal division of labor—and needing increased safety measures when working in communities should not affect hiring practices for community or leadership positions. A woman should first be hired based on her qualifications and then should be protected with policies and safety protocols for her to excel in her position. Furthermore, giving validity and importance to the stereotypically "softer" skills that a good leader should have, such as diplomacy, empathy, and negotiation, is a strategy to promote women that are already in leadership.[43] External stakeholders such as governments, donors, and universities need to evaluate the status and nature of gender-responsive leadership in the agencies that they partner with to promote leadership among female supervisors.

4. **Individual coping and mitigating strategies**: At the individual level, women often use tactics to fill the void when gender-responsive institutional policies are lacking. Such approaches include collectively raising issues with other female coworkers to male supervisors, informally educating male coworkers about unique issues faced by women, and designating talking points for male and female coworkers before meeting with government officials or community leaders who are likely to be all male. Women mentioned "freezing" when discussing important issues with male supervisors, due to the deep-seated hierarchy system in Nepal and in the workplace. They expressed often wishing they had spoken up or phrased something differently after the fact. Using email where responses can be given more thought, rather than an in-person discussion, is used to mitigate this challenge. Women also felt the need to "step-up" during meetings in the community to be taken seriously and provide other women in the room space to speak. Men suggested for women to "increase their self-confidence" as a mitigating strategy. After using many individual tactics to combat gender discrimination with varying levels of success, another female mentioned to "just ignore and don't engage." Participants mentioned that not paying attention to every gender-ignorant comment and injustice is also necessary for self-preservation, getting promoted by male-dominated leadership teams, and maintaining longevity in the workplace as well

as reducing burnout. Female mentors should be trained on how to counsel early career female staff on communication strategies to promote a safe and equitable working environment. However, this does not relieve male supervisors of their responsibility in being trained to support early career women. Leaders of all genders must be held accountable for educating themselves on the unique challenges that women face in the workplace and implementing strategies to mitigate these challenges.

5. **Providing external resources and capacity-building for informal support systems**: When organizations lack concrete policies and programs to address gaps in gender equality, women often form their own support systems within the workplace. They turn to close female colleagues and supervisors to provide second opinions. Women also shared that expressing their frustrations with colleagues lowered their stress levels by increasing solidarity and also providing a space for women to strategize together about how to address specific challenges. Many women expressed the relief that they feel when another female colleague accompanies them in the field. The women that they informally turn to for support become their mentors. Women expressed that this form of mentorship allowed for understanding and motivation at the individual level that formal male supervisors were not able to provide, due to the lack of understanding of gender issues. In the field of global mental health, it would be beneficial for resources to be shared by female mentorship programs in HIC institutions with LMIC institutions. Avenues for capacity-building to strengthen existing informal mentorship groups should be explored and implemented.

Part IV Characteristics and logistics of good mentoring relationships

Many of the logistics and qualities of good mentoring relationships have been written about extensively in academic medicine.[1,2,7,54] Here, we focus on the specifics for global mental health and logistics within LMIC settings. Box 5.6 provides a case study of the organization Possible's approach to developing effective communication systems for mentors and coaches.

BOX 5.6 DEVELOPING EFFECTIVE COMMUNICATION SYSTEMS AND MEETING PRACTICES FOR MENTORSHIP AND COACHING IN AN LMIC HEALTH INITIATIVE

David Citrin, MPH, PhD, Possible and University of Washington; Bikash Gauchan, MBBS, MD, Possible; Pragya Rimal, MA, Possible

Possible is a non-profit healthcare organization that works via a public–private partnership (PPP) with Nepal's Ministry of Health to strengthen healthcare delivery systems. The partnership is deeply sensitive to the contentious nature of PPPs in the arena of global healthcare delivery[58–60] and has created shared goals aimed at addressing public sector delivery gaps in rural areas and providing a platform for research and innovation. Through this approach, the Nepali government provides facilities, staff, supplies, and co-financing, and Possible assumes management authority and is held accountable for direct healthcare delivery within government infrastructure. Possible employs more than 280 staff, including networks of full-time Community Healthcare Workers (CHWs) who integrate care and patient health data at the community level via an integrated, home-to-facility electronic health record (EHR) system.[61,62]

Possible has developed and integrated mental health services within primary care delivery through a collaborative care model.[63,64] This model, described in detail in Chapter 6, consists of primary care providers (PCPs), psychosocial counselors, offsite consultant psychiatrists who are based at Nepali academic medical centers, a mental health research analyst, and a mental health advisor, who is a faculty member based at a US academic medical center. The site also hosts global mental health fellows, whose curriculum is described in Chapter 4. Utilizing EHR templates at the facility level, clinical mental health protocols are standardized and care is regularly monitored and evaluated to improve services. In addition, CHWs coordinate follow-up and referral care at the household level for patients enrolled via digital applications run on smartphones that can speak to the facility-based EHR. The collaborative mental health program is designed, implemented, evaluated, and modified collaboratively. Implementation research is carried out in the service of continuous programmatic improvement and to generate evidence that can shape national and global mental health policies.

A primary challenge within the collaborative care model, and in building adaptive healthcare delivery systems in LMICs more broadly, is creating appropriate structures of support and mentorship. This is especially challenging when, for example, collaborative models like Possible's are composed of offsite consultant psychiatrists and academic clinicians whose primary affiliation is with a Nepali academic institution, visiting fellows from the United States with limited on-site placement, and full-time on-site care providers in need of day-to-day management, feedback, and guidance. This mix of team members and tiers of care requires a diverse and adaptable set of mentorship strategies for the range of skill sets required for the entire collaborative care model; however, having multiple mentors can often lead to role confusion. In addition, when care delivery is the main priority, dedicating time toward mentorship activities may seem like a distraction or a chore.

In response to these challenges, we have developed a model for both direct line management and coaching geared toward fostering collaborative relationships so that managers and coaches can derive clarity of roles, and better leverage each other effectively to support organization-wide goals and individual team members alike. Below we discuss our practices that guide the relationship between mentees, managers, and coaches at Possible, and provide templates for holding structured one-on-one meetings.[a]

A structured approach for meetings with managers and coaches

To address the challenges outlined above, Possible has developed an approach to collaborative care that includes providing (i) direct managers for all full-time mental healthcare providers (i.e., PCPs and counselors), and for US- and/or Nepal-based academic faculty, to ensure all team members understand and can align their work with organizational priorities; and (ii) a coach who meets monthly with academic faculty in a structured way to ensure that their engagement with Possible is meeting the career needs of the faculty

---

a Meeting templates are created in Asana (www.asana.com), an online project management tool used by every team member across the organization. Here we present the structure of the Asana 1:1 page in Word format.

member. Having a manager and a coach for the range of skill sets required for the collaborative care model is key and helps to minimize role confusion. Similarly, holding structured one-on-one (1:1) meetings with regularly established frequency helps to facilitate efficiency, clear action steps, and longitudinal professional development and relieves the pressure from mentees who can feel as if requesting a meeting with their manager or coach is a burden or inappropriate. This is important for reducing gender disparities in career development because senior leaders and mentors are less likely to engage with female staff.[65] In some contexts and depending on the senior mentors' attitudes and engagement, mandating coaching meetings can provide a platform to ensure access to coaches for all team members, regardless of gender.

As Possible's experience shows, the structure of organization, hierarchy, and human resource composition will influence what labels and structures are used. Possible chose the term "coach" over "mentor" because they felt the term "coach" emphasizes an intense relationship to create excellence in healthcare delivery, particularly for patients and organizational priorities. Additionally, mentor connotes seniority, whereas a coach can be a peer or someone from a different field. Finally, the notion of a coach emphasizes the role of direct observation and feedback. It is vital that the manager and coach leverage each other effectively to bring value to the work of Possible and the academic clinician, rather than create conflict. Table 5.1 spells out these roles to address potential overlap in areas of responsibility.

Possible employs structured meeting templates used to help team members prepare for one-on-one meetings between managers and their "direct reports" and between academic faculty and coaches.

How to conduct meetings is an area people often do not think about as being evidence-based and needing training (hence most academics are terrible managers). Templates consist of tasks set in preparation for the meeting (e.g., outlining key updates and other agenda items for discussion) and are meant to be adapted over time (e.g., adding or removing sections, or changing agenda prompts in favor of other high-yield topics). Below are key guidelines for executing an excellent 1:1 session with a manager or mentor/coach.

Building an agenda that will lead to an excellent meeting is a task in and of itself.

During early iterations of these meetings, realistically the meeting DRI (directly responsible individual) can expect to spend up to 30 minutes building an agenda arranged according to the priority of items. Over time, this will become a more familiar and natural process, but facilitating efficient and effective 1:1s is a skill that is built with practice like any other.[66]

Provide a description for all key updates to facilitate discussion of these items, and/or allow them to be skipped.

Managers and mentors/coaches should commit to having read through the details provided ahead of time. This is particularly useful in the case of quick key updates that are more of an FYI than a conversation. This makes the flow of the meeting efficient and gives more time to the priority items in need of more in-depth discussion.

Table 5.1 Areas of responsibility between manager and faculty mentor/coach for academic faculty

Domain	Manager Role	Mentor/Coach Role
Identification of particular expertise/resource needs	Communicates gaps in resources, particularly during annual strategy sessions.	Mentors/coaches are assigned following identification.
Organizational onboarding	Onboarding and orientation to all systems are conducted by Possible's People Operations (HR) team and the manager.	Mentor/coach to help identify career goals/needs and explain the nuances of how faculty interface with direct delivery teams.
Organizational culture & management tools	Managers drive and continue to reinforce organizational culture, including lexicon, readings, task management, and partnership management.	Mentor/coach assists and reinforces organizational culture at all opportunities to stem ingrained bad/incommensurate habits created by the workflow practices of most academic institutions and healthcare organizations.
Weekly learning, Audits of Reports (AoRs) and goals, and performance reviews	Conducts weekly 1:1s, develops areas of responsibility, quarterly goals and targets, and conducts performance reviews.	Schedules monthly coaching meetings, documented in Kanban-style planning software such as Asana; assists in quarterly goal development as needed.
Program planning	Drives this process through close alignment on programmatic goals as spelled out by the manager and organizational strategy.	Mentor/coach assists in this role in consultation with and deference to team member's manager.
Writing manuscripts	Provides feedback and edits/comments and identifies mode/style of write-up relevant to programs and program teams. The manager will typically/generally be a co-author on manuscripts because of their intrinsic participation in whatever the academic clinician is writing about/studying.	Guides team members in this process, e.g., identifies appropriate journals, reviews and edits manuscripts, helps to identify co-authors; process occurs with input from the manager.
Time management/split	Responsible for identifying priorities and work triage; works closely to identify key times for faculty to spend on-site.	Mentor/coach assists in negotiating clinical time at the home institution and aims to overlap with team members during the on-site time.
Research support	Identifies strategic areas for research based on programmatic priorities and the relevance, acceptability, and feasibility of research in the communities where we work.	Ensures close collaboration with research team members, including driving research protocol development and IRB submission.
Academic promotion	Assists as needed.	Mentor/coach assists team member in creating and updating CV, and preparing promotion portfolio.
Grants writing and revenue	Assists as needed.	Mentor/coach assists team members in identifying funding and revenue sources, and in grantsmanship (e.g., grants program officer communications, clear and timely writing and submission).

Source: Content adapted with permission from Possible.

Order the agenda to ensure the true priorities are at the front.

Meetings, in general, tend to go over the time allotted, which leads to having to review the last few items quickly to squeeze them in. Meeting DRIs should plan for that and put the highest priority items up front to ensure time is well spent by meeting agenda priorities.

Review and finalize the agenda 24–48 hours ahead of time.

Both the meeting members (manager and direct report, or faculty and coach) will add to the agenda throughout the week, and a thorough review by the meeting DRI will allow agenda items to be fresh in their minds. Similarly, the process of organization, re-ordering, revising, and pruning of the agenda in the lead-up to the meeting is critical to ensuring the meeting is focused on top priorities and there is a clear sense of deliverables.

Conclusion

The concepts we have outlined for mentorship specific to global mental health can be extrapolated to a range of mentorship needs in global health and academic medicine initiatives more broadly. We have advocated for a mentorship framework that is not solely focused on individual self-promotion but is grounded in addressing the global gap in equity for access to and use of high quality mental health services. Engaging with this global mission can best be initiated from a position of humility and reflexivity that should be cultivated in the mentoring relationship. Moreover, transforming mental health services worldwide will only be achieved through equitable, transparent, and sustainable collaborations. Mentorship that is embedded in such collaborations should focus on how to build and maintain these relationships. Finally, despite the fact that more than two-thirds of the workforce delivering task-sharing interventions are women[67] and that women bear the greatest burden of mental illnesses such as depression and anxiety,[49] the global mental health leadership and research community continues to be dominated by men. Ultimately, to achieve the goals of global mental health, institutions will need to make gender equity a top priority in mentorship programs.

References

1. Berk RA, Berg J, Mortimer R, Walton-Moss B, Yeo TP. Measuring the effectiveness of faculty mentoring relationships. *Academic Medicine.* 2005;80(1):66–71.
2. Zerzan JT, Hess R, Schur E, Phillips RS, Rigotti N. Making the most of mentors: a guide for mentees. *Academic Medicine.* 2009;84(1):140–4.
3. Frei E, Stamm M, Buddeberg-Fischer B. Mentoring programs for medical students: a review of the PubMed literature 2000–2008. *BMC Medical Education.* 2010;10(1):32.
4. Cole DC, Johnson N, Mejia R, McCullough H, Turcotte-Tremblay A-M, Barnoya J, et al. Mentoring health researchers globally: diverse experiences, programmes, challenges and responses. *Global Public Health.* 2016;11(9):1093–108.
5. Merriam S. Mentors and protégés: a critical review of the literature. *Adult Education.* 1983;33(3):161–73.
6. Kashiwagi DT, Varkey P, Cook DA. Mentoring programs for physicians in academic medicine: a systematic review. *Academic Medicine.* 2013;88(7):1029–37.
7. Williams SN, Thakore BK, McGee R. Coaching to augment mentoring to achieve faculty diversity: a randomized controlled trial. *Academic Medicine.* 2016;91(8):1128–35.
8. Hedt-Gauthier BL, Jeufack HM, Neufeld NH, Alem A, Sauer S, Odhiambo J, et al. Stuck in the middle: a systematic review of authorship in collaborative health research in Africa, 2014–2016. *BMJ Global Health.* 2019;4(5):e001853.

9. Morton B, Vercueil A, Masekela R, Heinz E, Reimer L, Saleh S, et al. Consensus statement on measures to promote equitable authorship in the publication of research from international partnerships. *Anaesthesia.* 2022;77(3):264–76.

10. The Lancet Global Health. Closing the door on parachutes and parasites. *The Lancet Global Health.* 2018;6(6):e593.

11. Kleinman A. Four social theories for global health. *The Lancet.* 2010;375(9725):1518–9.

12. Griffith JL, Kohrt B, Dyer A, Polatin P, Morse M, Jabr S, et al. Training psychiatrists for global mental health: cultural psychiatry, collaborative inquiry, and ethics of alterity. *Academic Psychiatry.* 2016;40(4):701–6.

13. Koplan JP, Bond TC, Merson MH, Reddy KS, Rodriguez MH, Sewankambo NK, et al. Towards a common definition of global health. *The Lancet.* 2009;373(9679):1993–5.

14. Patel V, Minas H, Cohen A, Prince M. *Global mental health: principles and practice.* Oxford: Oxford University Press; 2014. 498 p.

15. Sartorius N, Harding TW. The WHO collaborative study on strategies for extending mental health care, I: the genesis of the study. *The American Journal of Psychiatry.* 1983;140(11):1470–3.

16. World Health Organization. *The world health report 2001: mental health: new understanding, new hope.* Geneva: World Health Organization; 2001. 122 p.

17. Lancet Global Mental Health, Chisholm D, Flisher AJ, Lund C, Patel V, Saxena S, et al. Scale up services for mental disorders: a call for action. *The Lancet.* 2007;370(9594):1241–52.

18. Patel V, Collins PY, Copeland J, Kakuma R, Katontoka S, Lamichhane J, et al. The movement for global mental health. *The British Journal of Psychiatry.* 2011;198:88–90.

19. Collins PY, Patel V, Joestl S, March D, Insel TR, Daar AS. Grand challenges in global mental health. *Nature.* 2011;475:27–30.

20. Kohrt BA, Marienfeld CB, Panter-Brick C, Tsai AC, Wainberg ML. Global mental health: five areas for value-driven training innovation. *Academic Psychiatry.* 2016;40(4):650–8.

21. Wallerstein N, Duran B. Community-based participatory research contributions to intervention research: the intersection of science and practice to improve health equity. *American Journal of Public Health.* 2010;100(S1):S40–6.

22. Kirmayer LJ. Beyond the new cross-cultural psychiatry: cultural biology, discursive psychology and the ironies of globalization. *Transcultural Psychiatry.* 2006;43(1):126–44.

23. Taylor JS. Confronting "culture" in medicine's "culture of no culture". *Academic Medicine.* 2003;78(6):555–9.

24. Willen SS, Kohler A. Cultural competence and its discontents: reflections on a mandatory course for psychiatry residents. In: Kohrt BA, Mendenhall E, editors. *Global mental health: anthropological perspectives: anthropology and global public health.* New York: Routledge; 2016. pp. 239–54.

25. Levinas E. *Totality and infinity: an essay on exteriority.* Pittsburgh, PA: Duquesne University Press; 1961. 238 p.

26. Kohrt BA, Griffith JL. Global mental health praxis: perspectives from cultural psychiatry on research and intervention. In: Kirmayer LJ, Lemelson R, Cummings CA, editors. *Re-visioning psychiatry: cultural phenomenology, critical neuroscience, and global mental health.* New York: Cambridge University Press; 2015. pp. 575–612.

27. Addiss DG. Spiritual themes and challenges in global health. *Journal of Medical Humanities.* 2018; 39, 337–348

28. Araya M, Mussie M, Jacobson L. Decentralized psychiatric nursing service in Ethiopia: a model for low income countries. *Ethiopian Medical Journal.* 2009;47(1):61–4.

29. Alem A, Pain C, Araya M, Hodges BD. Co-creating a psychiatric resident program with Ethiopians, for Ethiopians, in Ethiopia: the Toronto Addis Ababa Psychiatry Project (TAAPP). *Academic Psychiatry.* 2010;34(6):424–32.

30. Tesfaye M, Abera M, Gruber-Frank C, Frank R. The development of a model of training in child psychiatry for non-physician clinicians in Ethiopia. *Child and Adolescent Psychiatry and Mental Health.* 2014;8(1):6.

31. Tol WA, Patel V, Tomlinson M, Baingana F, Galappatti A, Panter-Brick C, et al. Research priorities for mental health and psychosocial support in humanitarian settings. *PLOS Medicine.* 2011;8(9):e1001096.

32. Kohrt BA, Mendenhall E, Brown PJ. How anthropological theory and methods can advance global mental health. *The Lancet Psychiatry*. 2016;3(5):396–8.

33. Ministry of Health. *Mental health directorate*. Sri Lanka: Sri Lanka Ministry of Health; 2017.

34. Kohrt BA, Jordans MJD, Rai S, Shrestha P, Luitel NP, Ramaiya MK, et al. Therapist competence in global mental health: development of the enhancing assessment of common therapeutic factors (ENACT) rating scale. *Behaviour Research and Therapy*. 2015;69:11–21.

35. Kohrt BA, Ramaiya MK, Rai S, Bhardwaj A, Jordans MJD. Development of a scoring system for non-specialist ratings of clinical competence in global mental health: a qualitative process evaluation of the enhancing assessment of common therapeutic factors (ENACT) scale. *Global Mental Health*. 2015;2:e23.

36. de Jong JTVM, editor. *Trauma, war, and violence: public mental health in socio-cultural context*. New York: Kluwer Academic/Plenum Publishers; 2002. 454 p.

37. IASC. *Guidelines on mental health and psychosocial support in emergency settings*. Geneva: Inter-Agency Standing Committee; 2007. 182 p.

38. Karan A, DeUgarte D, Barry M. Medical "brain drain" and health care worker shortages: how should international training programs respond? *AMA Journal of Ethics*. 2016;18(7):665–75.

39. Owusu Y, Medakkar P, Akinnawo EM, Stewart-Pyne A, Ashu EE. Emigration of skilled healthcare workers from developing countries: can team-based healthcare practice fill the gaps in maternal, newborn and child healthcare delivery? *International Journal of MCH and AIDS*. 2017;6(2):121–9.

40. Walton-Roberts M, Runnels V, Rajan SI, Sood A, Nair S, Thomas P, et al. Causes, consequences, and policy responses to the migration of health workers: key findings from India. *Human Resources for Health*. 2017;15(1):28.

41. Kohrt BA, Upadhaya N, Luitel NP, Maharjan SM, Kaiser BN, MacFarlane EK, et al. Authorship in global mental health research: recommendations for collaborative approaches to writing and publishing. *Annals of Global Health*. 2014;80(2):134 42.

42. Dhatt R, Thompson K, Lichtenstein D, Ronsin K, Wilkins K. The time is now – a call to action for gender equality in global health leadership. *Global Health Epidemiology and Genomics*. 2017;2:e3

43. Dhatt R, Theobald S, Buzuzi S, Ros B, Vong S, Muraya K, et al. The role of women's leadership and gender equity in leadership and health system strengthening. *Global Health, Epidemiology and Genomics*. 2017;2:e8.

44. Dora C, Haines A, Balbus J, Fletcher E, Adair-Rohani H, Alabaster G, et al. Indicators linking health and sustainability in the post-2015 development agenda. *The Lancet*. 2015;385(9965):380–91.

45. Downs J, Mathad J, Reif L, McNairy M, Celum C, Boutin-Foster C, et al. The ripple effect: why promoting female leadership in global health matters. *Public Health Action*. 2016;6(4):210–1.

46. Bhalotra S, Clots-Figueras I. Health and the political agency of women. *American Economic Journal: Economic Policy*. 2014;6(2):164–97.

47. Beaman L, Duflo E, Pande R, Topalova P. Female leadership raises aspirations and educational attainment for girls: a policy experiment in India. *Science*. 2012;335(6068):582–6.

48. Beath A, Christia F, Enikolopov R. Empowering Women through Development Aid: Evidence from a Field Experiment in Afghanistan. *American Political Science Review*. Cambridge University Press; 2013;107(3):540–57 https://doi.org/10.1017/S0003055413000270.

49. Seedat S, Scott K, Angermeyer MC, Berglund P, Bromet EJ, Brugha TS, et al. Cross-national associations between gender and mental disorders in the world health organization world mental health surveys. *Archives of General Psychiatry*. 2009;66(7):785–95.

50. Suvedi BK, Pradhan A, Barnett S, Puri M, Chitrakar SR, Poudel P, et al. *Nepal maternal mortality and morbidity study 2008/2009: summary of preliminary findings*. Kathmandu, Nepal: Family Health division, Department of Health Services, Ministry of Health, Government of Nepal; 2009.

51. Chattopadhyay R, Duflo E. Women as policy makers: evidence from a randomized policy experiment in India. *Econometrica*. 2004;72(5):1409–43.

52. Fleming GM, Simmons JH, Xu M, Gesell SB, Brown RF, Cutrer WB, et al. A facilitated peer mentoring program for junior faculty to promote professional development and peer networking. *Academic Medicine: Journal of the Association of American Medical Colleges*. 2015;90(6):819–26.

53. Bussey-Jones J, Bernstein L, Higgins S, Malebranche D, Paranjape A, Genao I, et al. Repaving the road to academic success: the IMeRGE approach to peer mentoring. *Academic Medicine.* 2006;81(7):674–9.

54. Mark S, Link H, Morahan PS, Pololi L, Reznik V, Tropez-Sims S. Innovative mentoring programs to promote gender equity in academic medicine. *Academic Medicine.* 2001;76(1):39–42.

55. DeCastro R, Griffith KA, Ubel PA, Stewart A, Jagsi R. Mentoring and the career satisfaction of male and female academic medical faculty. *Academic Medicine: Journal of the Association of American Medical Colleges.* 2014;89(2):301–11.

56. Downs JA, Reif LK, Hokororo A, Fitzgerald DW. Increasing women in leadership in global health. *Academic Medicine: Journal of the Association of American Medical Colleges.* 2014;89(8):1103–7.

57. Gurung D, Sangraula M, Subba P, Poudyal A, Mishra S, Kohrt BA. Gender inequality in the global mental health research workforce: a research authorship scoping review and qualitative study in Nepal. *BMJ Global Health.* 2021;6(12) http://dx.doi.org/10.1136/bmjgh-2021 -006146.

58. Biehl J, Petryna A. *When people come first: critical studies in global health.* Princeton, NJ: Princeton University Press; 2013. 446 p.

59. Pfeiffer J, Chapman R. Anthropological perspectives on structural adjustment and public health. *Annual Review of Anthropology.* 2010;39:149–65.

60. Roehrich JK, Lewis MA, George G. Are public–private partnerships a healthy option? A systematic literature review. *Social Science & Medicine.* 2014;113:110–9.

61. Harsha Bangura A, Ozonoff A, Citrin D, Thapa P, Nirola I, Maru S, et al. Practical issues in the measurement of child survival in health systems trials: experience developing a digital community-based mortality surveillance programme in rural Nepal. *BMJ Global Health.* 2017;2(2):e000203.

62. Raut A, Yarbrough C, Singh V, Gauchan B, Citrin D, Verma V, et al. Design and implementation of an affordable, public sector electronic medical record in rural Nepal. *Journal of Innovation in Health Informatics.* 2017;24(2):186–95.

63. Acharya B, Ekstrand M, Rimal P, Ali MK, Swar S, Srinivasan K, et al. Collaborative care for mental health in low-and middle-income countries: a WHO health systems framework assessment of three programs. *Psychiatric Services.* 2017:appi. ps.201700232.

64. Acharya B, Maru D, Schwarz R, Citrin D, Tenpa J, Hirachan S, et al. Partnerships in mental healthcare service delivery in low-resource settings: developing an innovative network in rural Nepal. *Globalization and Health.* 2017;13(1):2.

65. McKinsey & Company. Women in the workplace 2017. LeanIn.org; 2017.

66. Rogelberg SG. *The surprising science of meetings: how you can lead your team to peak performance.* New York: Oxford University Press; 2019. 180 p.

67. Singla DR, Kohrt BA, Murray LK, Anand A, Chorpita BF, Patel V. Psychological treatments for the world: lessons from low- and middle-income countries. *Annual Review of Clinical Psychology.* 2017;13(April):5.1–5.33.

Chapter 6

Implementation of Integrated Care Models

Lessons for Training and Practice in Low-Resource Settings

Christopher Kemp, Lydia Chwastiak, Inge Petersen, Arvin Bhana, Bradley H. Wagenaar, Jürgen Unützer, and Deepa Rao

Summary points

- Models for the integrated delivery of mental health care show great promise in both high- and low-resource settings and may help close the treatment gap given limited financial support and a global shortage of specialist care providers.
- We describe the Collaborative Care model and other leading integrated care models established and tested in low-resource settings.
- We discuss specific implementation-related challenges associated with task-sharing, supervision, and workforce availability, and put forward recommendations for the implementation of integrated care in low-resource settings.

Introduction

Mental disorders are the leading cause of years lived with disability globally.[1] Yet, in low- and middle-income countries (LMICs) and other low-resource settings, 75% of those in need of treatment for a mental disorder never receive care.[2,3] To overcome this staggering treatment gap, there is a critical need to identify, test, and scale effective mental health services.[4,5] The development of such services must take significant financial resources and workforce shortages into consideration; we cannot rely exclusively on specialists to deliver mental health interventions.[6] Few LMICs prioritize mental health or have the financial or political capital to develop mental health programs in parallel to other services.[7] Many are also confronted with the growing syndemics of chronic and infectious disease, especially among the most vulnerable and underserved members of society.[8] In such settings, a critical first step will be to leverage available resources and the infrastructure of existing community-based and clinical environments to deliver mental health services at scale. Evidence from high-income countries (HICs) suggests that integration of mental health into routine primary and specialist care services can be cost-effective and equitable, even for low-income patients or patients with co-morbid illness.[9] Integrated care is a promising strategy to increase access to effective mental health services globally. We define integrated care as the coordination or simultaneous delivery of mental health services with primary care or specialty medical care (e.g., diabetes care, antenatal care, or HIV care).

Implementation of integrated care is a challenge in both high- and low-resource settings. Integrated models must retain the *core* components and *active ingredients* of proven treatment modalities, while also addressing *complementary* elements of local health system organizations and cultural context. To ensure adoption and fidelity to evidence-based protocols, integrated models must incorporate effective systems for training, supervision, and mentorship of treatment providers. These concerns are especially relevant when models rely on providers who have limited previous training in treating mental illness. However, few have documented the challenges

DOI: 10.4324/9781315160597-9

associated with implementation of integrated mental health care in low-resource settings, or have drawn lessons from these challenges that are relevant to future training and education. In this chapter, we draw from and describe a range of leading integrated care models established and tested in low-resource settings, including rural regions in the United States and in LMICs. We discuss the challenges and opportunities of implementing integrated care in low-resource settings. Finally, we put forward recommendations for the implementation of facility-based, integrated models of mental health care. This chapter will be most relevant to academic leadership and trainees in HICs and LMICs interested in preparing for the transition from conventional and isolated care delivery models toward care integration.

Models of integrated care

Several models for integrated mental health care have been developed, tested, and scaled in high- and low-resource settings. These are not necessarily distinct; many have overlapping features and characteristics. We first introduce Collaborative Care, which is the model with the most robust global evidence base. We then describe other approaches to integrating the delivery of mental health care into primary or specialty care in low-resource settings.

Collaborative Care

Collaborative Care is a promising and well-studied model designed to support the integration of services for common mental disorders into primary or specialty care, incorporating systematic identification of patients, active measurement-based case management by competent staff, and specialist supervision or consultation.[10] Based on the principles of effective chronic illness care, Collaborative Care involves teams of professionals with complementary skills working together to care for patients.[11] Collaborative Care teams typically include four key roles: patients, primary care providers (PCPs; e.g., physicians or nurse practitioners), behavioral health providers (BHPs, also known as care managers; e.g., counselors, clinical social workers, psychologists, or psychiatric nurses), and psychiatric consultants (e.g., psychiatrists). Collaborative Care makes use of the strategy of *task-sharing*.[12] Healthcare tasks are shared among PCPs, BHPs, and psychiatric consultants to help patients improve their mental and physical health outcomes (Figure 6.1).

BHPs/care managers are central figures in Collaborative Care. They are located at primary care facilities and: (1) support patient self-care; (2) monitor patient outcomes on key indicators; (3) proactively follow up with those who are not improving; and (4) coordinate care between the patient and their care team. They deliver brief, evidence-based interventions like motivational interviewing, behavioral activation, or problem-solving therapy to patients screened for common mental disorders by PCPs. Though BHPs/care managers are typically clinical social workers, counselors, or psychologists, they may come from other cadres as well. For example, in South Africa the United Kingdom-funded Programme for Improving Mental Health Care (PRIME) model used professional nurses as care managers.[13] BHPs and PCPs have regular meetings with psychiatric consultants to systematically review their caseloads. Patients who have had little or no clinical improvement are prioritized for discussion. Psychiatric consultants can join such meetings by distance, as they are usually not based at the facility where the care integration is occurring.

Collaborative Care therefore diversifies the roles of the mental health specialist—in this case a psychiatric consultant—to include provision of support, supervision, and mentorship to non-specialists at a distance. The model uses a *stepped-care* approach, reserving higher levels of care for more complex and severe cases.[14] Figure 6.2 describes the relationships between providers for a hypothetical, simplified approach to stepped care. Treatments begin at lower levels of the hierarchy, within primary care, *stepping up* when necessary to higher levels of specialization.

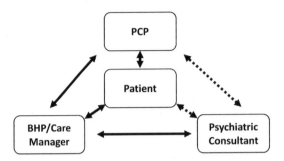

Figure 6.1 Interactions between team members in a Collaborative Care Model.

Solid lines represent frequent contacts and dotted lines show infrequent contacts between team members. Source: Figure used with permission from University of Washington; © 2019 University of Washington AIMS Center.

Figure 6.2 Hierarchical representation of Stepped Care, where most patients are at the lower levels, and those who need intensive care are stepped up to more specialized settings.

Source: Figure used with permission from University of Washington; © 2019 University of Washington AIMS Center.

Collaborative Care applies the principles of the chronic care model to incorporate evidence-based behavioral health treatment into primary care or medical specialty settings.[11] It has five core principles: (1) a patient-centered, team-based approach to supporting care for behavioral health disorders; (2) population-based care, using a registry to actively track patients and ensure none fall through the cracks; (3) measurement-based treatment to target, where patient outcomes are tracked and regularly reviewed by the team, with timely treatment modifications until targets are achieved; (4) evidence-based pharmacotherapy and brief behavioral therapies; and (5) account-able care where providers are reimbursed for quality of care and improved clinical outcomes.[15]

The patient-centered, team-based approach allows providers to collaborate in the delivery of effective care, rather than being limited by rigid delineation by role or title. The team comes together to ensure that patients receive the optimal care necessary to accomplish symptom improvement. PCPs and BHPs meet regularly with psychiatric consultants to maintain the provision of evidence-based, validated medication treatment and behavioral interventions, by reviewing patient cases in detail and adjusting or tailoring treatment plans as needed. These systematic case review (SCR) meetings are held routinely—weekly is recommended—regardless of caseload size, with the time required for individual SCR meetings depending on the complexity of the patient population, the rate of caseload turnover, and the level of experience of the team. These meetings may occur in person, over video conference, or by phone.[16] Primary care providers therefore conduct the bulk of patient-related activities while being in direct and regular communication with mental health specialists to ensure that quality of care is maintained. Measurement-based care means that decisions are informed by data: patients are actively tracked through registries to ensure that the clinical team monitors the patient's response to treatment. Workload and case management are also tracked using routine data. This usually implies the presence of a comprehensive electronic health record (EHR): building or transforming an EHR system for use with Collaborative Care can be an implementation challenge requiring up-front and ongoing investment of substantial person-time and financial resources.[17] At each visit, patient symptoms, side effects, and other key factors are measured using validated instruments, such as the Patient Health Questionnaire-9 (PHQ-9) for depression. Using structured and validated instruments at each visit helps the team use data to inform their clinical decisions, as well as to feed into quality improvement and accountable care standards. At the facility and health system levels, quality improvement approaches are also used to examine data from patient engagement, workload, registries, charts, and validated patient-level instruments to drive progress in patient outcomes. Patients, PCPs, BHPs, psychiatric consultants, and other administrative or consultative staff must have shared goals, trust, clarity on roles and workflow, and be mutually accountable.[18]

More than 80 randomized controlled trials have demonstrated the effectiveness of Collaborative Care for the treatment of depression and anxiety in primary care in high-resource settings across a range of ages, patient populations, and payers.[19,20] In these studies, Collaborative Care has led to improved patient outcomes (increased rates of depression response and remission, larger reductions in depression and anxiety symptoms, and more depression-free days), reduced costs, and increased patient satisfaction, when compared to usual care.[20–22]

Recent and ongoing trials suggest that Collaborative Care may be robust in low-resource settings or with low-income or vulnerable patients. The Depression Among Women Now (DAWN) study suggested that Collaborative Care for depression actually had greater impact among women in the United States with no insurance or with public coverage compared to higher-income women with commercial insurance.[23] Meanwhile, the INtegrating DEPrEssioN and Diabetes treatmeENT (INDEPENDENT) randomized controlled trial evaluated the effectiveness of a multi-component intervention combining Collaborative Care with decision support technology to provide population health management for patients with diabetes and depression in four diabetes specialty clinics in India. Care coordinators—locally based, bilingual allied health professionals with backgrounds in dietetics or diabetes education—supported participants in depression and diabetes self-care and monitoring to help them reach PHQ-9, fasting blood glucose, HbA1c, blood pressure, and LDL cholesterol targets.[24] In this trial, the Collaborative Care intervention led to greater improvements in depressive symptoms and cardiometabolic indices, as well as reductions in anxiety symptoms among participants with anxiety, compared to usual care.[25,26] Similar positive effects were observed in the Healthier Options through Empowerment (HOPE) cluster randomized trial of Collaborative Care, which enrolled patients with co-morbid depression and diabetes and/or cardiovascular conditions,[27] and promising effects have been observed in an uncontrolled implementation study of Collaborative Care in Nepal.[28] Collaborative Care models have even proven to be effective when involving non-allopathic and traditional care providers;

for example, the COllaborative Shared care to IMprove Psychosis Outcome (COSIMPO) cluster randomized trial established the effectiveness and cost-effectiveness of Collaborative Care for psychosis when delivered by traditional and faith healers, in partnership with primary care providers, in Ghana and Nigeria.[29]

Other approaches to integrated care

Collaborative Care, as typically implemented, is distinguished by the nexus of BHP/care manager, PCP, and patient, with oversight by a psychiatric consultant. Its hallmark is the SCR meeting, attended by the BHP/care manager, PCP, and psychiatric consultant. Other approaches to integrated care, like stepped-care models, do not incorporate all these components. Several have demonstrated promising effectiveness through clinical trials.

In the MANAshanti Sudhar Shodh (MANAS) trial, a large (n=1360) cluster randomized trial in India, primary care patients with depression or anxiety disorders who received treatment through a stepped-care model were significantly more likely to recover at six months when compared to those receiving standard care (risk ratio 1.22; 95% CI 1.00–1.47). This multi-component intervention offered case management and psychosocial interventions provided by a trained lay health counselor, supplemented by antidepressant medications prescribed by a PCP with supervision by a mental health specialist. It was particularly effective among patients who received care in public facilities.[30]

Similarly, a stepped-care approach was effective among women with depression in antenatal clinics in Santiago, Chile. In a clinical trial of n=240, 70% of those receiving the intervention recovered from depression, compared to 30% of patients receiving usual care. The multi-component intervention in this study included structured psychoeducational groups led by nurses or midwives; a structured pharmacotherapy protocol for patients who needed antidepressant medication treatment, to be provided by physicians; systematic monitoring of clinical progress and treatment adherence; training of doctors about identification and treatment of depression; and weekly one-hour supervision of the nurses or midwives by a psychiatrist.[31]

However, not all findings have been uniformly positive. For example, the Stepped Care Intervention for Depression in Primary Care in Nigeria (STEPCARE) trial was a clustered randomized controlled trial testing the effectiveness of a stepped-care intervention for primary care adult patients with depression in 11 local government areas, using a version of the mhGAP Intervention Guide (mhGAP-IG) contextualized and adapted for the Nigerian health system.[32] The trial found that the stepped-care intervention was not more effective than enhanced usual care, though it did appear to lower overall health system costs.[33]

Key considerations for implementation of integrated care models

In this section, we will discuss key considerations that are common among integrated care models. We outline several below, with a focus on task-sharing, supervision, and workforce.

Task-sharing

Integrated care models rely on *task-sharing*, regardless of the resource level of the implementation context. The question of how to operationalize task-sharing in integrated care is therefore critical. We distinguish the approach described in this chapter, used in clinical settings, from task-sharing approaches used in community settings.[34] Although recently developed integrated care models are incorporating community components (e.g., interventions delivered by community health workers at or near patients' homes), our focus is on facility-based task-sharing. We also need to distinguish between *task-shifting* and *task-sharing*. The World Health Organization (WHO) defines task-shifting as: "the name now given to a process whereby specific tasks are moved, where appropriate, to health workers with shorter training and fewer qualifications."[35(p.7)] This can be contrasted with the term task-sharing, which the National Academy of Medicine defines as a practice that is: "needs-based, not hierarchical or territorial, and allows roles to expand or contract according to need [and] is the most appropriate approach to health care delivery in low-resource environments."[36(p.115)] An important difference between task-shifting and task-sharing is that the latter provides a more equitable approach to address the workforce. However, we must acknowledge here that clinical healthcare settings in both high- and low-resource contexts inherently contain hierarchies across professions, and thus, task-sharing is often an aspirational concept.

Another necessary distinction is among the types of healthcare workers sharing tasks within the integrated care team across high- and low-resource settings. The aforementioned health workforce shortages mean that membership within integrated healthcare teams is shaped differently across contexts. Integrated care teams typically involve physicians with varying degrees of specialty alongside nurses or other allied health professionals. However, integrated care team members in low-resource settings may have fewer skills than their high-resource counterparts. For example, integrated care models in diabetes contexts in the United States work with highly experienced medical nurses as care managers to help patients learn cognitive behavioral techniques.[37] In contrast, in India, where an acute nursing shortage exists, nutritionists and other allied health professionals were identified as being available to provide care coordination and brief psychotherapies for depression.[24,38] In South Africa, HIV adherence counselors were trained and supervised to provide counseling drawing on cognitive behavioral psychotherapy techniques.[39] In Nepal, care coordination is provided by counselors who have only six months of behavioral health training and no medical background. This has required close support and supervision from the psychiatric consultant.[40] Ultimately, it is the resources within each context that determine which team members are involved in provision of services within integrated care models.

Supervision

A key issue is how to implement adequate systems for ongoing supervision as part of integrated care.[41] Supervision is widely recognized as necessary to foster the development of a provider's skills in mental health service delivery.[42] A lack of ongoing supervision can result in low intervention fidelity and provider competency.[43] Traditional one-off trainings are a necessary but insufficient step toward building the confidence and competence of mental health service providers.[41,44–46] Indeed, the type of training seems to be less important than the dosage of supervision in predicting provider adoption and fidelity of evidence-based practices.[47] Without supervisory support, established programs experience significant declines in service delivery within two years.[48] Systematic reviews and cross-country studies of integrated care and task-sharing programs in low-resource settings emphasize the importance of ongoing supervision to help service providers meet patient needs, though there have been few formal evaluations of supervisory models to determine which are the most effective.[34,49,50]

Supervision is a cyclical process in which senior members of the health system set expectations for the practice of healthcare workers reporting to them, observe and audit that practice, evaluate practice against expectations, and offer guidance for corrective action.[51] So-called "traditional supervision," which was and continues to be the norm in many post-colonial and lower-resourced health systems, focuses on oversight with the goal of identifying problems, without emphasizing guidance or support, assuming that corrections can only be made through punitive measures. Traditional supervision is reactive and episodic, rather than proactive and continuous, occurring through short supervisory visits and the completion of routine forms and checklists.[52,53] In contrast, *supportive supervision* focuses on continuously identifying and resolving problems, optimizing resource allocation, and promoting teamwork.[51] It incorporates self-assessment, peer-assessment, and community input, using a system of objective measures to drive improvements in processes at primary care facilities.[54] Supportive supervision has led to improved health worker performance in low-resource settings.[51] In sub-Saharan Africa, it has been shown to increase job satisfaction and worker motivation.[55] Supportive supervision is the model specifically recommended in the context of task-sharing; WHO guidelines state that supportive supervision should be provided to all task-shared health workers, and that supervisors should have appropriate supervisory skills.[35]

The literature describing supervision of integrated mental health care in low-resource settings is sparse. In low-resource areas of high-income countries, studies emphasize the importance of ongoing supportive supervision, and describe methods for ensuring fidelity of service delivery at a distance. For example, in rural Australia, one program trained aboriginal mental health workers for three years, followed by weekly in-person or telephone-based supervision.[56] In rural Alaska, Behavioral Health Aides working in remote clinics were trained, supervised, and supported from a distance, which was necessary given the geography of the area.[57] The literature is even sparser in LMIC settings. One early report, published in 2001, briefly summarized supervisory structures for integrated primary mental healthcare services in India, Iran, Nicaragua, and Guinea-Bissau, and emphasized ongoing supportive supervision beyond the period of training.[58] A more recent series of case studies from sub-Saharan Africa, Latin America, and the Caribbean highlighted the importance of support and supervision in helping community health workers who had reported feeling depressed or stressed when they first started delivering mental healthcare interventions, and reported that a minimum number of mental health specialists were required to provide supervision of non-specialists as well as specialized referral treatment services.[59,60]

Models of supervision clearly vary in the number, type, and level of expertise of supervisors available, though they also vary in several other ways. For example, they may vary in the frequency and duration of supervision. In Nepal, a non-governmental organization has developed a model of supervision in which a psychiatrist based in the capital travels to the rural site every few months to train and offer clinical supervision. While in the capital, he performs a weekly case review with health workers via telephone.[61] Models of supervision may also vary in the communication method. Researchers in Pakistan have developed a technological solution to training and supervision, using tablet-based multimedia manuals to deliver training modules, and applying a cascade model to supervise remotely by phone, given considerable distances between sites.[62] Supervision may also be at the individual or group levels. Researchers in Zimbabwe have developed a group-based method of supervision, facilitating WhatsApp groups that allow providers to share problems and offer peer support.[63] Few studies offer evidence of the comparative effectiveness of the various combinations of each of these variables.[64,65] No ideal frequency or duration of supervision has been identified, though the quality of supervision appears to be more important than its dosage.[66] Peer supervision promotes collaboration and empathy outside of the traditional supervisory hierarchy, and may be less costly than other forms of supervision.[67,68] Group supervision can increase supervision coverage at reduced cost.[66] Decision support tools and job aids reduce supervisor reaction time to shifts in supervisee behavior, while checklists improve supervisee performance.[53,66] Supervisors clearly need and benefit from training in supervisory skills, though again no ideal dosage or method of supervisor training has been identified.[66]

Among programs delivering Collaborative Care, formal supervisory relationships between psychiatric consultants, PCPs, and BHPs are rare.[15] Rather, the relationship between specialists and primary care providers tends to be consultative; PCPs and BHPs may or may not implement the advice of the psychiatric consultant. Most programs delivering Collaborative Care do not establish formal supervisory relationships to support the delivery of psychotherapeutic interven tions by the BHPs, and this may limit the capacity of BHPs to deliver interventions with fidelity, especially in low-resource settings where other support for psychotherapeutic intervention may not be available. However, process evaluations of Collaborative Care models implemented in high-income settings suggest that regular face-to-face interactions between PCPs and BHPs are critical for effective collaboration.[69,70]

The Apprenticeship Model is a well-studied collection of training and robust supervision methods adopted by an affiliated group of researchers and implementers developing and pilot-ing mental health services in a variety of low-resource settings (Figure 6.3).[71] To date, the Apprenticeship Model has primarily been used in community contexts. In this model, counselors may be any type of mental health service provider, including community members trained to deliver an intervention, while supervisors are counselors with the expertise or skills necessary to support other counselors. Counselors and supervisors from projects using the Apprenticeship Model have tended to be employed by community-based organizations or schools, rather than by the health sector. Trainers have most often been experts from outside the service delivery con-text; in many cases, these have been individuals with doctoral-level training in clinical psychology based at large research universities in high-resource settings.[71]

The Apprenticeship Model has five steps: (1) selection of counselors and supervisors, (2) training, (3) practice groups, (4) supervised expansion of skills, and (5) mutual problem solving. In the first step, the researchers or implementers choose counselors and supervisors with a mini-mum high school-equivalent education, strong interpersonal skills, an interest in working with mental health, and supported time at a relevant organization or public institution (e.g., school).[71] In the second step, counselors and supervisors receive extensive training in the intervention, including didactic and experiential learning. For every 30 minutes of passive learning, trainees are exposed to one hour of active learning through role-playing or practice. Supervisors receive additional training in supervision. In the third step, both counselors and supervisors practice pro-viding the intervention under observation by trainers. The goal is to ensure that supervisors are adept at the intervention so that they can later supervise the counselors. In the fourth step, both counselors and supervisors practice their skills on a small group of patients. Supervisors and train-ers meet weekly as supervisors take an apprentice role to become "local experts," and supervise

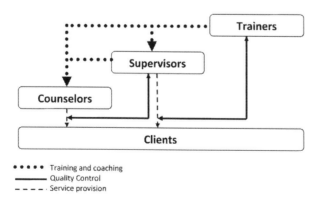

Figure 6.3 Apprenticeship Model.

Source: Figure reproduced based on open access provision from BioMed Central[71]

the counselors together. Throughout this process, all three groups come together regularly to address emergent problems.

Though the Apprenticeship Model has been most frequently applied at the community level, there have been recent efforts to expand its use into clinical settings via integrated care models. As part of the five-country, UK-funded PRIME study, researchers evaluated the implementation of integrated care packages incorporating versions of the Apprenticeship Model in South Africa and Nepal.[5] In South Africa, the PRIME team used master's-level clinical psychologists as trainers and bachelor's-level psychologists as supervisors to develop cadres of health facility-based lay counselors. Lay counselors delivered group- and individual-based counseling for common mental disorders at the level of primary care, as part of chronic disease services.[39] The clinical psychologists supervised the bachelor's-level psychologists who in turn supervised the lay counselors. As this approach was fully integrated into routine primary care, implementers had to adjust the Apprenticeship Model to accommodate the demands and limitations of the health system. For example, the lay counselors were not only responsible for the delivery of mental health services; they were also responsible for delivering HIV counseling and testing. Trainers and supervisors had to recognize this and work with counselors to support the delivery of both services. Evaluations are ongoing to assess the acceptability and feasibility of this approach.

In Nepal, the PRIME team trained all primary care staff in pilot facilities to assess and manage priority mental health disorders as part of an integrated care model.[40] Two different approaches of the Apprenticeship Model were used: one for prescribing physicians, and one for non-prescribing nurses and other health workers delivering psychosocial interventions. Prescribers were supervised at a distance by a psychiatrist living in the capital, with infrequent opportunities for *in vivo* supervision or ongoing training. Non-prescribers were supervised monthly, as a group, by a community counselor.

Workforce

Another challenge of implementing these models has centered upon the cadre of workers who perform and/or supervise mental health service delivery. As noted above, in high-resource settings, Collaborative Care BHPs are often social workers or nurses trained with an emphasis on behavioral health. In low-resource settings, these types of healthcare workers may be scarce or non-existent at health facilities. Feasible models for integrated care will therefore require training of and supervision by *existing* cadres of workers in clinical settings, at least in the short term. Indeed, there have been lengthy discussions among Ministries and Departments of Health of several countries about which cadres of workers may be available and suitable for this purpose. For example, the South African Department of Health has supported the training of HIV lay counselors to deliver integrated mental health counseling as part of the PRIME model, after negotiations between the directorates responsible for HIV testing and treatment, non-communicable disease management, and the health workforce. These lay counselors are funded by the US President's Emergency Plan for AIDS Relief (PEPFAR) and are present in most primary care facilities in the country. However, the issue of supervision by existing cadres of mental health specialists remains largely unresolved, even in South Africa. In countries lacking even the availability of lay counselors at health facilities, it is unclear which healthcare workers can feasibly and sustainably provide and/or supervise integrated mental health care.

Even if suitable cadres of healthcare workers are available to provide or supervise integrated mental health care, these new roles must be carefully delineated and financially supported. Appropriate remuneration that corresponds to job demands, complexity, numbers of hours worked, training, and roles undertaken will be critical to the sustainability and effectiveness of large task-sharing programs.[72] Healthcare workers engaged in task-shared service delivery may justifiably seek increased recognition or pay in exchange for the increased workload from addressing mental health issues with their patients, alongside reductions in their other job duties. Failure to address these issues may result in elevated staff turnover, draining valuable financial and human resources and limiting program effectiveness.

Other considerations

Integrated care models face additional challenges during implementation in low-resource settings. Mental health may not be prioritized by health system leadership; most LMICs spend far less than needed on the provision of mental health services, and many lack the governance, mental health policy frameworks, or regulatory environments necessary to support and enforce the provision of high-quality care.[6,7] Essential psychotropic medications may not be readily available at primary care facilities.[7,73-75] Measurement-based care relies on clinicians having continuous access to real-time, longitudinal data on patient care and health outcomes, though health data in LMICs is frequently of poor quality, mismanaged, underused, and siloed within specific disease areas.[76] EHR systems may out-perform paper-based systems and alleviate some of these challenges, though they cannot function in health facilities without electricity.[77] Finally, integrated models often assume continuity of care and the ability of patients and providers to have repeated interactions at regular intervals over time, though low socioeconomic status, lack of available transport, distance from health facilities, out-of-pocket fees, and other factors are often significant barriers to patient access and utilization of primary care in LMICs.[78]

Future directions for integrated care in low-resource settings

Across low- and high-resource settings, more work is needed to identify the optimal strategies for leveraging scarce human and financial resources to provide mental health services where they are needed the most. What are the preferred models or setting for each population? What is the best way to provide ongoing training, supervision, and mentorship? How can such care models be sustained? The answers lie in continued attention to scale-up of sustainable, integrated care models. Combining models may be one solution, for example, employing psychiatric consultants to act as supervisors in clinical contexts, designating care manager roles to primary care nurses, and adding care coordination meetings to bring all staffing components together to discuss patients who do not improve. Combining elements of both models can ensure a high quality of psychiatric medication provision and counseling services.

There will be an advantage in strengthening ties between clinics and communities. Strong community partnership and training of community health care workers can capture patients who are lost to follow-up from clinics. Similarly, leveraging technological innovation can strengthen communication and linkages between patients residing in communities, community healthcare workers, supervisors based anywhere, and staff located in facilities. Strong ties to community leadership can also help to ensure local relevance and cultural appropriateness of interventions.

Lastly, more research is needed on the appropriateness and adequacy of scale-up of integrated care models. The National Institute of Mental Health (United States), Department of International Development (United Kingdom), US Agency for International Development, and others have funded various randomized clinical trials to establish effectiveness of these integrated care models in low-resource contexts. However, scale-up and science around the penetration of the interventions, adoption of the models by facilities, quality of supervision, and sustainability of these models is just beginning. These studies will provide invaluable evidence around methods to navigate through implementation bottlenecks. While the National Institutes of Health,

Global Alliance for Chronic Diseases, and others have earmarked funding for such projects, large amounts of resources, further study, system-wide change, interdisciplinary cooperation, and more will be needed to improve the overall health of populations worldwide.

References

1. Vos T, Lim SS, Abbafati C, et al. Global burden of 369 diseases and injuries in 204 countries and territories, 1990–2019: a systematic analysis for the global burden of disease study 2019. *The Lancet.* 2020;396(10258):1204–22. doi:10.1016/S0140-6736(20)30925-9

2. Demyttenaere K, Bruffaerts R, Posada-Villa J, Gasquet I, Kovess V, Lepine JP, et al. Prevalence, severity, and unmet need for treatment of mental disorders in the World Health Organization World Mental Health Surveys. *JAMA.* 2004;291(21):2581.

3. Thornicroft G, Chatterji S, Evans-Lacko S, et al. Undertreatment of people with major depressive disorder in 21 countries. *The British Journal of Psychiatry.* 2017;210(2):119–24. doi: 10.1192/bjp.bp.116.188078

4. Lancet Global Mental Health Group, Chisholm D, Flisher AJ, et al. Scale up services for mental disorders: a call for action. *The Lancet.* 2007;370(9594):1241–52. doi:10.1016/S0140-6736(07)61242-2

5. Lund C, Tomlinson M, De Silva M, et al. PRIME: a programme to reduce the treatment gap for mental disorders in five low- and middle-income countries. *PLOS Medicine.* 2012;9(12):e1001359. doi:10.1371/journal.pmed.1001359

6. Saxena S, Thornicroft G, Knapp M, Whiteford H. Resources for mental health: scarcity, inequity, and inefficiency. *The Lancet.* 2007;370(9590):878–89. doi:10.1016/S0140-6736(07)61239-2

7. World Health Organization. *Mental health atlas 2017.* 2018. Geneva: World Health Organization; 2018.

8. GBD 2019 Demographics Collaborators. Global age-sex-specific fertility, mortality, healthy life expectancy (HALE), and population estimates in 204 countries and territories, 1950–2019: a comprehensive demographic analysis for the Global Burden of Disease Study 2019. *The Lancet.* 2020;396(10258):1160–203. doi:10.1016/S0140-6736(20)30977-6

9. Woltmann E, Grogan-Kaylor A, Perron B, Georges H, Kilbourne AM, Bauer MS. Comparative effectiveness of collaborative chronic care models for mental health conditions across primary, specialty, and behavioral health care settings: systematic review and meta-analysis. *The American Journal of Psychiatry.* 2012;169(8):790–804.

10. Bower P, Gilbody S, Richards D, Fletcher J, Sutton A. Collaborative care for depression in primary care: making sense of a complex intervention: systematic review and meta-regression. *The British Journal of Psychiatry.* 2006;189(6):484–93. doi:10.1192/bjp.bp.106.023655

11. Wagner EH, Austin BT, Von Korff M. Organizing care for patients with chronic illness. *Milbank Quarterly.* 1996;74(4):511–44.

12. Joshi R, Alim M, Kengne AP, et al. Task shifting for non-communicable disease management in low and middle income countries–a systematic review. *PLoS ONE.* 2014;9(8):e103754. doi:10.1371/journal.pone.0103754

13. Fairall L, Petersen I, Zani B, et al. Collaborative care for the detection and management of depression among adults receiving antiretroviral therapy in South Africa: study protocol for the CobALT randomised controlled trial. *Trials.* 2018;19(1):193. doi: 10.1186/s13063-018-2517-7

14. Katon W, Von Korff M, Lin E, et al. Stepped collaborative care for primary care patients with persistent symptoms of depression: a randomized trial. *Archives of General Psychiatry.* 1999;56(12):1109–15. doi:10.1001/archpsyc.56.12.1109

15. Raney LE. Integrating primary care and behavioral health: the role of the psychiatrist in the collaborative care model. *Focus (American Psychiatric Publishing).* 2017;15(3):354–60. doi:10.1176/appi.focus.15305

16. Bauer AM, Williams MD, Ratzliff A, Unützer J. Best practices for systematic case review in collaborative care. *Psychiatric Services.* 2019;70(11):1064–7. doi:10.1176/appi.ps.201900085

17. Wolk CB, Last BS, Livesey C, et al. Addressing common challenges in the implementation of collaborative care for mental health: the Penn integrated care program. *Annals of Family Medicine*. 2021;19(2):148–56. doi:10.1370/afm.2651

18. Ratzliff A, Unützer J, Katon W, Stephens KA. *Integrated care: creating effective mental and primary health care teams*. John Wiley & Sons; 2016. 288 p.

19. Archer J, Bower P, Gilbody S, et al. Collaborative care for depression and anxiety problems. *Cochrane Database of Systematic Reviews*. 2012;10:CD006525. doi:10.1002/14651858. CD006525.pub2

20. Katon WJ, Lin EHB, Von Korff M, et al. Collaborative care for patients with depression and chronic illnesses. *The New England Journal of Medicine*. 2010;363(27):2611–2160doi:10.1056/NEJMoa1003955

21. Simon GE, Katon WJ, VonKorff M, et al. Cost-effectiveness of a collaborative care program for primary care patients with persistent depression. *The American Journal of Psychiatry*. 2001;158(10):1638–44. doi:10.1176/appi.ajp.158.10.1638

22. Simon GE, Katon WJ, Lin EHB, et al. Cost-effectiveness of systematic depression treatment among people with diabetes mellitus. *Archives of General Psychiatry*. 2007;64(1):65–72. doi:10.1001/archpsyc.64.1.65

23. Katon W, Russo J, Reed SD, et al. A randomized trial of collaborative depression care in obstetrics and gynecology clinics: socioeconomic disadvantage and treatment response. *The American Journal of Psychiatry*. 2015;172(1):32–40. doi:10.1176/appi.ajp.2014.14020258

24. Kowalski AJ, Poongothai S, Chwastiak L, et al. The integrating depression and diabetes treatment (independent) study: design and methods to address mental healthcare gaps in India. *Contemporary Clinical Trials*. 2017;60:113–24.

25. Ali MK, Chwastiak L, Poongothai S, et al. Effect of a collaborative care model on depressive symptoms and glycated hemoglobin, blood pressure, and serum cholesterol among patients with depression and diabetes in India: the independent randomized clinical trial. *JAMA*. 2020;324(7):651–62. doi:10.1001/jama.2020.11747

26. Kemp CG, Johnson LCM, Sagar R, et al. Effect of a collaborative care model on anxiety symptoms among patients with depression and diabetes in India: the independent randomized clinical trial. *General Hospital Psychiatry*. 2022;74:39–45. doi:10.1016/j.genhosppsych.2021.11.003

27. Srinivasan K, Heylen E, Johnson Pradeep R, Mony PK, Ekstrand ML. Collaborative care compared to enhanced standard treatment of depression with co-morbid medical conditions among patients from rural South India: a cluster randomized controlled trial (HOPE study). *BMC Psychiatry*. 2022;22(1):394. doi:10.1186/s12888-022-04000-3

28. Rimal P, Choudhury N, Agrawal P, et al. Collaborative care model for depression in rural Nepal: a mixed-methods implementation research study. *BMJ Open*. 2021;11(8):e048481. doi:10.1136/bmjopen-2020-048481

29. Gureje O, Appiah-Poku J, Bello T, et al. The effect of collaborative care between traditional/faith healers and primary health care workers to improve psychosis outcome in Nigeria and Ghana (COSIMPO) – a cluster randomized controlled trial. *The Lancet*. 2020;396(10251):612–22. doi:10.1016/S0140-6736(20)30634-6

30. Patel V, Weiss HA, Chowdhary N, et al. Effectiveness of an intervention led by lay health counsellors for depressive and anxiety disorders in primary care in Goa, India (MANAS): a cluster randomised controlled trial. *The Lancet*. 2010;376(9758):2086–95. doi:10.1016/S0140-6736(10)61508-5

31. Araya R, Rojas G, Fritsch R, et al. Treating depression in primary care in low-income women in Santiago, Chile: a randomised controlled trial. *Lancet*. 2003;361(9362):995–1000. doi:10.1016/S0140-6736(03)12825-5

32. Gureje O, Oladeji BD, Araya R, Montgomery AA. A cluster randomized clinical trial of a stepped care intervention for depression in primary care (STEPCARE)–study protocol. *BMC Psychiatry*. 2015;15:148. doi:10.1186/s12888-015-0542-6

33. Gureje O, Oladeji BD, Montgomery AA, et al. Effect of a stepped-care intervention delivered by lay health workers on major depressive disorder among primary care patients in Nigeria

(STEPCARE): a cluster-randomised controlled trial. *The Lancet Global Health.* 2019;7(7):e951–60. doi:10.1016/S2214-109X(19)30148-2

34. Padmanathan P, De Silva MJ. The acceptability and feasibility of task-sharing for mental healthcare in low and middle income countries: a systematic review. *Social Science and Medicine.* 2013;97:82–6. doi:10.1016/j.socscimed.2013.08.004

35. World Health Organization. PEPFAR, UNAIDS. Task shifting: rational redistribution of tasks among health workforce teams: global recommendations and guidelines. Published online 2007. Accessed April 28, 2016. http://www.who.int/iris/handle/10665/43821

36. Institute of Medicine (US) Committee on Envisioning a Strategy for the Long-Term Burden of HIV/AIDS: African Needs and U.S. Interests. *Preparing for the Future of HIV/AIDS in Africa: A Shared Responsibility.* Washington (DC): National Academies Press (US); 2011. 374 p.

37. Katon W, Lin EH, Von Korff M, Ciechanowski P, Ludman E, Young B, et al. Integrating depression and chronic disease care among patients with diabetes and/or coronary heart disease: the design of the TEAMcare study. *Contemporary Clinical Trials.* 2010;31(4):312–22.

38. Garner SL, Conroy SF, Bader SG. Nurse migration from India: a literature review. *International Journal of Nursing Studies.* 2015;52(12):1879–90.

39. Petersen I, Fairall L, Bhana A, Kathree T, Selohilwe O, Brooke-Sumner C, et al. Integrating mental health into chronic care in South Africa: the development of a district mental healthcare plan. *The British Journal of Psychiatry.* Published online 2015.

40. Jordans MJD, Luitel NP, Pokhrel P, Patel V. Development and pilot testing of a mental healthcare plan in Nepal. *The British Journal of Psychiatry.* 2016;208(Suppl 56):s21–8. doi:10.1192/bjp.bp.114.153718

41. Kemp CG, Petersen I, Bhana A, Rao D. Supervision of task-shared mental health care in low-resource settings: a commentary on programmatic experience. *Global Health Science and Practice.* 2019;7(2). doi:10.9745/GHSP-D-18-00337

42. Beidas RS, Koerner K, Weingardt KR, Kendall PC. Training research: practical recommendations for maximum impact. *Administration and Policy in Mental Health and Mental Health Services Research.* 2011;38(4):223–37. doi:10.1007/s10488-011-0338-z

43. Massatti RR, Sweeney HA, Panzano PC, Roth D. The de-adoption of innovative mental health practices (IMHP): why organizations choose not to sustain an IMHP. *Administration and Policy in Mental Health and Mental Health Services Research.* 2008;35(1–2):50–65.

44. Beidas RS, Kendall PC. Training therapists in evidence-based practice: a critical review of studies from a systems-contextual perspective. *Clinical Psychology: Science and Practice.* 2010;17(1):1–30.

45. Herschell AD, Kolko DJ, Baumann BL, Davis AC. The role of therapist training in the implementation of psychosocial treatments: a review and critique with recommendations. *Clinical Psychology Review.* 2010;30(4):448–66.

46. McLean KE, Kaiser BN, Hagaman AK, Wagenaar BH, Therosme TP, Kohrt BA. Task sharing in rural haiti: qualitative assessment of a brief, structured training with and without apprenticeship supervision for community health workers. *Intervention (Amstelveen).* 2015;13(2):135–55. doi:10.1097/WTF.0000000000000074

47. Beidas RS, Edmunds JM, Marcus SC, Kendall PC. Training and consultation to promote implementation of an empirically supported treatment: a randomized trial. *Psychiatric Services.* 2012;63(7):660–5.

48. Tibbits MK, Bumbarger BK, Kyler SJ, Perkins DF. Sustaining evidence-based interventions under real-world conditions: results from a large-scale diffusion project. *Prevention Science.* 2010;11(3):252–62.

49. Mendenhall E, De Silva MJ, Hanlon C, et al. Acceptability and feasibility of using non-specialist health workers to deliver mental health care: stakeholder perceptions from the PRIME district sites in Ethiopia, India, Nepal, South Africa, and Uganda. *Social Science and Medicine.* 2014;118:33–42. doi:10.1016/j.socscimed.2014.07.057

50. van Ginneken N, Tharyan P, Lewin S, et al. Non-specialist health worker interventions for the care of mental, neurological and substance-abuse disorders in low- and middle-income countries.

Cochrane Database of Systematic Reviews. 2013;11:CD009149. doi:10.1002/14651858. CD009149.pub2

51. Marquez L, Kean L. *Making Supervision Supportive and Sustainable: New Approaches to Old Problems.* MAQ Papers. Management Sciences for Health; 2002. 28 p.

52. Simmons R *Supervision: the management of frontline performance.* Published Online 1987.

53. Vasan A, Mabey DC, Chaudhri S, Epstein HAB, Lawn SD. Support and performance improvement for primary health care workers in low-and middle-income countries: a scoping review of intervention design and methods. *Health Policy and Planning.* 2016;32(3):437–52.

54. J R. Supportive supervision to improve integrated primary health care. Published online 2006. Accessed April 28, 2016. http://www.popline.org/node/193349

55. Bailey C, Blake C, Schriver M, Cubaka VK, Thomas T, Hilber AM. A systematic review of supportive supervision as a strategy to improve primary healthcare services in Sub-Saharan Africa. *International Journal of Gynecology and Obstetrics.* 2016;132(1):117–25.

56. Bartik W, Dixon A, Dart K. Aboriginal child and adolescent mental health: a rural worker training model. *Australasian Psychiatry: Bulletin of Royal Australian and New Zealand College of Psychiatrists.* 2007;15(2):135–39. doi:10.1080/10398560701196745

57. Hoeft TJ, Fortney JC, Patel V, Unützer J. Task-sharing approaches to improve mental health care in rural and other low-resource settings: a systematic review. *Journal of Rural Health.* 2018;34(1):48–62.

58. World Health Organization Mental Health Policy and Service Development Team & Cohen, Alex. *The effectiveness of mental health services in primary care: the view from the developing world.* Geneva: World Health Organization; 2001. 37 p.

59. Razzouk D, Gregório G, Antunes R, Mari JDEJ. Lessons learned in developing community mental health care in Latin American and Caribbean countries. *World Psychiatry.* 2012;11(3):191–95.

60. Petersen I, Ssebunnya J, Bhana A, Baillie K. Lessons from case studies of integrating mental health into primary health care in South Africa and Uganda. *International Journal of Mental Health Systems.* 2011;5(1):8. doi:10.1186/1752-4458-5-8

61. Acharya B, Maru D, Schwarz R, et al. Partnerships in mental healthcare service delivery in low-resource settings: developing an innovative network in rural Nepal. *Globalization and Health.* 2017;13(1):2. doi:10.1186/s12992-016-0226-0

62. Zafar S, Sikander S, Hamdani SU, et al. The effectiveness of technology-assisted cascade training and supervision of community health workers in delivering the thinking healthy program for perinatal depression in a post-conflict area of Pakistan - study protocol for a randomized controlled trial. *Trials.* 2016;17:188. doi:10.1186/s13063-016-1308-2

63. Chibanda D, Verhey R, Munetsi E, Cowan FM, Lund C. Using a theory driven approach to develop and evaluate a complex mental health intervention: the friendship bench project in Zimbabwe. *International Journal of Mental Health Systems.* 2016;10:16. doi:10.1186/s13033-016-0050-1

64. Bosch-Capblanch X, Garner P. Primary health care supervision in developing countries. *Tropical Medicine and International Health.* 2008;13(3):369–83.

65. Bosch-Capblanch X, Liaqat S, Garner P. Managerial supervision to improve primary health care in low-and middle-income countries. *Cochrane Database of Systematic Reviews.* 2011;9. CD006413

66. Hill Z, Dumbaugh M, Benton L, Källander K, Strachan D, ten Asbroek A, et al. Supervising community health workers in low-income countries–a review of impact and implementation issues. *Global Health Action.* 2014;7(1):24085.

67. Strachan DL, Källander K, ten Asbroek AHA, et al. Interventions to improve motivation and retention of community health workers delivering integrated community case management (iCCM): stakeholder perceptions and priorities. *American Journal of Tropical Medicine and Hygiene.* 2012;87(5_Suppl):111–19.

68. Kim YM, Putjuk F, Basuki E, Kols A. Self-assessment and peer review: improving Indonesian service providers' communication with clients. *International Perspectives on Sexual and Reproductive Health.* 2000;24(1):4.

69. Coupe N, Anderson E, Gask L, Sykes P, Richards DA, Chew-Graham C. Facilitating professional liaison in collaborative care for depression in UK primary care; a qualitative study utilising normalisation process theory. *BMC Family Practice.* 2014;15:78. doi:10.1186/1471-2296-15-78

70. Oishi SM, Shoai R, Katon W, et al. Impacting late life depression: integrating a depression intervention into primary care. *Psychiatric Quarterly.* 2003;74(1):75–89. doi:10.1023/a:1021197807029

71. Murray LK, Dorsey S, Bolton P, et al. Building capacity in mental health interventions in low resource countries: an apprenticeship model for training local providers. *International Journal of Mental Health Systems.* 2011;5(1):30. doi:10.1186/1752-4458-5-30

72. Colvin CJ, Hodgins S, Perry HB. Community health workers at the dawn of a new era: 8. Incentives and remuneration. *Health Research Policy and Systems.* 2021;19(3):106. doi:10.1186/s12961-021-00750-w

73. Wagenaar BH, Stergachis A, Rao D, et al. The availability of essential medicines for mental healthcare in Sofala, Mozambique. *Global Health Action.* 2015;8:27942. doi:10.3402/gha.v8.27942

74. Acharya B, Ekstrand M, Rimal P, et al. Collaborative care for mental health in low- and middle-income countries: a WHO health systems framework assessment of three programs. *Psychiatric Services.* 2017;68(9):870–72. doi:10.1176/appi.ps.201700232

75. Rahman MA, Babaye Y, Bhat A, Collins PY, Kemp CG. Availability of two essential medicines for mental health in Bangladesh, the Democratic Republic of Congo, Haiti, Nepal, Malawi, Senegal, and Tanzania: evidence from nationally representative samples of 7958 health facilities. *Journal of Global Health.* 2022;12:04063. doi:10.7189/jogh.12.04063

76. Ndabarora E, Chipps JA, Uys L. Systematic review of health data quality management and best practices at community and district levels in LMIC. *Information Development.* 2014;30(2):103–20.

77. Puttkammer N, Baseman JG, Devine EB, et al. An assessment of data quality in a multi-site electronic medical record system in Haiti. *International Journal of Medical Informatics.* 2016;86:104–16. doi:10.1016/j.ijmedinf.2015.11.003

78. Peters DH, Garg A, Bloom G, Walker DG, Brieger WR, Rahman MH. Poverty and access to health care in developing countries. *Annals of the New York Academy of Sciences.* 2008;1136:161–71. doi:10.1196/annals.1425.011

Chapter 7

Educational Partnerships

Addressing Challenges in Meeting Trainee Goals with Established or New Global Mental Health Educational Programs

Carla Marienfeld, Xinran Hu, Yang Yang, Zhening Liu, Eve Lasswell, and Robert M. Rohrbaugh

Summary points

- Long-term, collaborative relationships among faculty, departments, and academic institutions promote consistent, high-quality, mutually beneficial training and lead to partnerships that are durable and strong; in this chapter, these partnerships are referred to as "deep."
- Trainees may have background, interest, and expertise in settings not covered in existing, long-term (deep) partnerships. Academic institutions then face the dilemma of having all global mental health (GMH) trainees work within existing partnerships versus enabling motivated trainees to develop new partnerships; partnerships that add breadth and may be new or transient are referred to in this chapter as "wide" since they expand the variety of options.
- The presence of long-term, deep partnerships, as well as an ethical approach to GMH training, can help to turn new trainee-initiated partnerships into ongoing engagements that lead to a wide range of opportunities for future trainees.
- Projects sponsored by the Yale-China Association, the Xiangya-Yale medical school partnerships, and the Yale Global Mental Health educational program exemplify the value of both deep and wide partnerships.
- Lessons, experiences, and interpretations from these efforts are generalizable across different types of partnerships, from academic collaborations to public–private partnerships (PPPs), both within and across institutions in high-income countries (HICs) and/or low- and middle-income countries (LMICs).

Introduction

Global mental health (GMH) education programs are a relatively new component of the global health education portfolio; many academic institutions are still building new HIC-LMIC or LMIC-LMIC partnerships around the world for mutually beneficial work in the GMH field.[1,2] As the development of education programs in GMH unfolds, there is often a tension between developing fewer, long-term institutional partnerships (we will call these "deep" partnerships) and creating a wide range of *ad hoc* or transient engagements across various locations, projects, and topic areas (we will call these "wide" partnerships). Using case examples, we will discuss the advantages and disadvantages of developing deep, simultaneously deep and wide, and wide partnerships for GMH education programs. The Yale Global Mental Health Program (YGMHP) (Box 7.1) and its partners, including the Yale-China Association and the Xiangya-Yale medical school partnership programs, are described as examples of these types of partnerships. The YGMHP focuses on residents completing academic GMH projects; this emphasis has fostered several collaborations that range from short-term, transient projects in various parts of the world to deep engagements with the Xiangya School of Medicine in Hunan Province, China.

DOI: 10.4324/9781315160597-10

BOX 7.1 THE YALE GLOBAL MENTAL HEALTH PROGRAM (YGMHP)

The Yale Global Mental Health Program (YGMHP) has defined core residency didactics, a regularly scheduled GMH elective, and funded and supported global academic experiences with facilitated mentorship leading to scholarly productivity. Descriptions of these experiences and their outcomes (i.e., an increased number of presentations on GMH issues in both the core and elective didactic programs, an increased number of global academic experiences, and the academic productivity of the residents) have been published elsewhere.[3] This impact is mediated through having a specific GMH track, publicity about GMHP events through email and on the departmental website, involvement of faculty in attending and presenting at the GMH elective and mentoring residents, and discussion of GMH funding and initiatives at the highest levels of the department. The long-term investment of faculty in supporting resident involvement in the GMHP and the ingenuity of both faculty and residents in developing funding for international experiences have promoted the success of the program. The deep and wide partnerships across institutions developed by Yale faculty and the Yale Department of Psychiatry have facilitated the opportunities for residents interested in GMH.

An important consideration HIC academic institutions may face is the tension between the benefit of long-standing institutional collaborations and the interests of trainees who have specific interests, backgrounds, or expertise who want to engage in GMH experiences in settings outside the institution's existing partnerships. The dilemma is whether to ask the trainee to adjust their work to fit into an existing deep partnership or to permit a wider experience in a one-time interaction with limited oversight or confidence about the experience. HIC- or LMIC-based academic institutions—which are often in urban and high-resourced regions—face this dilemma when seeking partnerships with community-based organizations or healthcare delivery systems in rural and under-resourced regions within or outside their respective countries.

In this chapter, we describe the experience of the Yale GMH Program to illustrate an example of an approach that balances these competing priorities. Our approach has successfully integrated these priorities and resolved this tension by using the following strategies: a) continually building on deep partnerships as a foundation and extending them to encompass a wide range of opportunities for trainees, and b) drawing on institutional experience with deep partnerships to apply successful organizing principles and existing resources in establishing new institutional relationships and experiences. With respect to the latter, these might range from repurposing pre-departure planning materials and protocols with site-specific adjustments to tapping faculty members with established expertise in GMH and mentoring trainees as part of the mentorship team for trainees engaging in the new experience. In addition, setting key parameters (such as designating a faculty sponsor for trainees at each of the partner institutions) to ensure that these new partnerships provide strong learning environments for trainees and mutually benefit the partner institutions adds to the wide range of partnerships that academic institutions can offer for future trainees.

Goals and ethical considerations for partner development

Among the first steps in developing partnership programs is having a clearly defined ethical framework for collaboration. The guidelines from the Working Group on Ethics Guidelines for Global Health Training (WEIGHT) provide a comprehensive set of ethical considerations in global health training.[4] The YGMHP, using the WEIGHT guidance, decided that trainees should not engage in clinical work in international settings due to several ethical considerations. Firstly, residents providing clinical care in GMH settings outside of the region where their residency is located would be unfamiliar with the specific service delivery system, nuances in the local language, and presentations of psychiatric illness, and they would not be able to provide longitudinal care for the patient. Secondly, depending on local credentialing requirements, trainees may require local clinical oversight, in addition to context-specific and routine clinical supervision. Depending on the local context and needs, their clinical contributions may not fully offset the drain on human resources. As a result, in many low-resource settings, this additional clinical supervision by busy clinicians who may already be overburdened would not be feasible. Lastly, there is uncertainty about the level of supervision trainees would receive versus the supervision they may need. This risks that the trainee may participate in patient care that they are unprepared for and could result in adverse outcomes for patients, which would be an unacceptable outcome for both patient care and supporting a trainee.

For these reasons, the YGMHP has chosen to develop training experiences that support Yale psychiatry residents in developing an academic project in lieu of providing supervised clinical care. The project is designed to provide them with an opportunity to closely observe the system of healthcare delivery, even though they are not participating in patient care at the partner site. For this academic project, the Yale psychiatry residents are also required to identify a faculty sponsor from the partner site to ensure a mentored partnership and bilateral experience. This approach has facilitated the development of academic projects between trainees and faculty at both Yale and their partner sites and has helped in the development of partner faculty academic and mentorship skills, partner site research capacity-building, partner faculty development, and trusted partnerships between Yale and institutions across the world.

In addition, the focus on research and scholarly activities provides opportunities for trainees to learn about research ethics in international settings, opportunities to observe clinical work and the healthcare system without being responsible for patient care, pre-existing structures for supervision and mentorship, and reciprocal research opportunities.

In addition to the experiential component of a collaborative GMH project (time spent abroad), preparation of the trainee prior to the experience abroad and continuation of project-related commitments upon return are critical. Well-developed institutional collaborations facilitate engagements where trainees are well informed about the local context to support their personal safety and to develop meaningful learning experiences. Moreover, such collaborations can establish a mutual understanding that supports reliable and high-quality learning environments that meet trainee and site-based needs. Having a deep understanding of the partner site leads to an enhanced pre-experience orientation and safety awareness, assurance of effective mentorship for the project, and access to training on site-specific ethical issues. With such preparation, trainees will be part of a community that values the history of the institutions and countries they work with and be inspired to contribute to the mission of the collaboration.

Educational partnership development

Widening partnerships

A trainee's goals, interests, and background may not always be a good match for existing, long-term partnerships. Relying solely on deep collaborations may stifle trainee initiative to explore their areas of interest for their career (especially if that interest cannot be accommodated at the site). It is helpful to provide dedicated mentorship and support for the trainee to develop a feasible project that enhances their career interests. These projects can result in a range of new, wide partnerships, but, as they are facilitated by faculty and mentors from each site, they can promote more long-term, potentially career-spanning relationships among the trainee, faculty, and partner site.

Having a trainee be the primary coordinator of their experience in a new site—with faculty mentorship—provides the trainee with the opportunity to learn about the culture, language, and systems of care in a part of the world that is most interesting to them. New and short-term projects, which result in a wide range of partnerships, can benefit from the infrastructure developed with existing deep partnerships. Pre-departure preparation can focus on general principles of ethics and clinical care that the site mentors can further contextualize.

Deepening partnerships

Deep, long-term partner sites have long-standing relationships both among faculty and also between the institutions. Such strong relationships are best achieved and maintained through direct faculty collaborations, as institutional collaborations in the absence of faculty collaborations are unlikely to be sustained. Additional institutional support, such as providing trainee elective time or supporting bilateral faculty exchange, can be extraordinarily important to sustain the collaboration. Collaborative exchange of trainees enhances these relationships and can further the goals of faculty for professional development, research collaboration, and capacity-building.

There are many financial and administrative barriers to overcome to provide field-based GMH experiences, and it is understandable that many training directors, who often face increasing regulations and decreasing budgets, may be reluctant to develop new opportunities. Administrative barriers are often highest initially; once platforms and processes are established, logistical challenges and costs associated with deep partnerships are usually much lower than those for short-term and new programs. An advantage of cultivating and utilizing deep institutional partnerships is that financial barriers may be partially overcome by existing infrastructures. In addition, utilizing faculty grant support for trainee projects that fit within the scope of the grant (that presumably already involves the "deep" partner site) can offset costs to the training program to cover trainee salary and benefits during the international experience.

The goal of such long-term partnerships is to explicitly seek active collaborative relationships, and often these relationships involve trainees, or can be easily adapted to do so. This process of collaborative exchange of trainees between institutions with deep relationships can avoid the start-up time and infrastructure investment required to develop numerous short-term partnerships.

By design, the goal of deep partnerships is a bidirectional exchange of experiences, knowledge, and resources, wherein exchanges of trainees can form or augment the relationship. Using the Xiangya and Yale School of Medicine partnership as an example, we see how the Chinese and American psychiatry trainees and medical students are provided with an opportunity to personally experience undergraduate and graduate medical training at each institution and its affiliated hospital systems (see Box 7.2). In addition to observing in the hospital, trainees follow a strict system of training consistent with each hospital's policies. They learn about a variety of training mechanisms provided at each program that can facilitate career growth, and they engage in collaborative projects when they return to their home institution. They also learn about a variety of patient care responsibilities carried out by residents under attending physicians' supervision. The similarities and differences of medical education between China and the United States are often discussed, focusing on topics such as the quality and cost of medical education, healthcare reimbursement, and diagnostic and treatment approaches. This level of deep engagement, resource-sharing, and long-term bidirectional learning in both clinical and research settings is only possible through long-term partnerships.

BOX 7.2 THE XIANGYA SCHOOL OF MEDICINE AND THE YALE SCHOOL OF MEDICINE

Short-term clinical exchange of medical students typically lasts for one month, and in many years, approximately 10% of the Yale School of Medicine (SOM) graduating class have had an experience at Xiangya Medical School in Hunan, China. Yale psychiatry residents also typically elect 4–6 weeks for the global academic experience if they choose to focus on a project with Xiangya partners.

Approximately ten Xiangya medical students come to Yale for a one-month clinical experience each year; because Yale SOM wanted to ensure provision of a bidirectional exchange experience, Yale pays travel costs for several low-income Xiangya students to have this experience. These individuals, and other Xiangya students who were able to pay for the experience themselves, are all hosted by Yale.

In another program whose goal is to develop the next generation of academic leaders at Xiangya, six Xiangya MD/PhD students complete a two-year research experience to develop a deep understanding of the importance of ethically conducted and well-designed research, as well as to gain the experience necessary to continue academic projects and collaborations when they return to China.

Xiangya psychiatry residents come to Yale SOM for one month, and their experience has included observation in adult, geriatric, and child and adolescent services as well as the interventional psychiatry service at Yale New Haven Hospital. They have opportunities to attend daily morning rounds with attending physicians in a team-based learning environment. The residents are able to observe new patient admissions with the on-call resident and inpatient rehabilitation activities, as well as attend grand rounds and clinical case conferences.

Deep academic collaboration facilitates GMH education and develops a wide range of clinical, research, and training experiences

The collaboration between investigators, students, and residents can result in ongoing projects that build on deep partnerships to create a wide range of educational opportunities. In this section, we provide examples of resident and faculty collaborations through the deep, ongoing collaboration between Yale and China. A major focus of the authors' work has been on educational programs to improve China's mental health workforce development, ensure a sustainable supply of psychiatrists and allied mental health professionals, and narrow the significant gap between mental health service coverage and the need for these services. This range of activities builds on a century of collaboration facilitated by the Yale-China Association (see Box 7.3). The initial goals of this collaboration were a lot more limited than the wide range of current projects that are now supported. The current GMH projects build on this deep partnership and provide several opportunities for trainees from both Yale and China. There are several examples that illustrate the diversity of these experiences (see Boxes 7.4 and 7.5). Most of these projects have involved trainee collaborations and have spanned many years and many individuals. The long-standing relationship and strength of the overall partnership allow them to flourish by engaging in activities ranging from brief, time-limited experiences with small scholarly products to larger bodies of work with a larger-scale impact.

BOX 7.3 THE YALE-CHINA ASSOCIATION

Since 1901, the private, non-profit Yale-China Association has been committed to health and education work in China through building bridges between Yale University and Chinese institutions. Among its legacies is the founding of iconic health institutions such as Xiangya Hospital (1906), Xiangya School of Nursing (1911), and Xiangya School of Medicine (1914), through the pioneering efforts of Dr. Edward Hume, his Yale-China colleagues, and local Chinese partners. Health program activities between Yale and Chinese institutions facilitated by the Yale-China Association span medicine, nursing, and public health disciplines. Beginning over 100 years ago, the Xiangya-Yale program is an example of a deep training experience in Hunan Province of the People's Republic of China. Dr. Edward H. Hume came from India to Changsha, China, and joined the Yale-China Association. In 1906, Dr. Hume rented a house to start the first western medicine clinic in Hunan Province, the Yale-China "Yali" clinic. In the summer of 1913, members from the Yale-China Association and the Chinese Society for the Promotion of Medical Education formed a joint board of directors to start a new medical school in Hunan Province. The name of this consortium, consisting of medical and nursing schools as well as the affiliated hospital, was the Xiangya Medical Educational Association. Here "Xiang" refers to Hunan in Chinese, and the "Ya" is for Yale. The partnership was revitalized in the late 1980s when the bilateral political situation allowed for such collaborations. Over the last 30 years, many Yale and Xiangya faculty in nursing, medicine, and public health have had the opportunity to work in the partner organization for periods that range from one month to one year, and in the past decade, these experiences have been extended to other health professions' trainees.

BOX 7.4 EXAMPLE EXPERIENCES AND PROJECTS BETWEEN YALE AND XIANGYA

One project examined stigma among Chinese medical students at different levels of training, surveying them with a questionnaire addressing attitudes and beliefs about people with mental illness. Attitudes were assessed for: (a) social acceptance of people with mental illness, (b) supernatural causes of mental illness, (c) biopsychosocial causation, (d) rehabilitation, and (e) social integration. Areas of most stigmatization were low social acceptance and little favor for social integration. Students with more individual experiences such as planning to continue clinical psychiatric training, believing psychiatry should be more valued, and having friends with mental illness had less stigmatized attitudes than others.[5] Further study demonstrated that a single formal psychiatry course may improve understanding of the biopsychosocial causes of mental illness, but did not affect other attitudinal domains among Chinese college students.[6]

Another project involving a Xiangya resident assessed China's Psychiatry Major Curriculum (PMC), which is an effort to improve the quality of undergraduate psychiatry education, and compared it to undergraduate psychiatry education programs at Yale. PMC provides more comprehensive exposure to psychiatry than conventional curricula in China, with more preclinical experiences and psychiatry clerkship course hours, greater diversity of clinical sites, and exploration of subspecialties. PMC employs a variety of teaching methods and offers mentoring for students, with similar preclinical content and course hours as programs in the United States. The study was designed with aims to highlight areas for improvement and to recommend implementation of concrete measures to improve psychiatric education in Chinese medical schools.[7] An ongoing project aims to assess a one-year education program, being implemented nationwide, to certify community primary care providers (PCPs) as practicing psychiatrists in local settings.

BOX 7.5 GMH ACTIVITIES BETWEEN YALE AND XIANGYA

Yale and Xiangya faculty have collaborated on the development of other education projects, health services research, and the phenomenology of mental disorders. A major decade-long effort resulted in the creation of a competency-based model for residency training at Xiangya, including but not limited to psychiatry residency training. This model has significantly influenced the model adopted by the Chinese central government for all of China's residency education. Xiangya faculty adopted a Yale program using music appreciation to strengthen discernment of auscultated heart sounds. Mental health service delivery projects have included one Yale resident's investigation into access, timely diagnosis, and treatment in rural areas.[8] Another Yale resident used snowball-sampling methods to provide an assessment of barriers to China implementing community-based, recovery-oriented mental health care. Additional work has examined the association of the internal migration, for example from rural to urban settings, within China, and the risk of subsequent hospitalization for schizophrenia, as well as the age of onset of symptoms and their severity.[9]

Faculty collaborations also extend to the nursing and public health schools. Re-established in the 1990s, a deep and long-standing collaboration exists between faculty at the Xiangya and Yale schools of nursing. NIH R01 grant funding for HIV care and for other topics like training nurses in psychotherapy has resulted in the development of a PhD program in nursing at Xiangya. This collaboration has also facilitated service improvement in clinical roles in novel areas of care, has increased the academic and independent scope of work, and has contributed to Xiangya School of Nursing being rated among the very best schools of nursing in China. There is a bidirectional exchange of faculty in public health, including an NIH R25 grant that facilitated teaching and development of a model research ethics review process at Xiangya. This allows trainees in public health, medicine, and nursing fields to come to Yale for exposure to our system of ethical review of research while sharing their own methods and culture of work.

Through these examples, we have learned that having faculty with deep experiences in the institution and having organization staff committed to the training experience help to prepare students for their field-based training experience and troubleshoot challenging situations when the student is on site. Based on the feedback from trainees, such support improves the quality of their experience. This is especially important for sites in LMICs, where there may be little infrastructure on site and the trainees may have limited familiarity with the location.

Collaboration through public–private partnerships (PPP) to facilitate education in GMH

Public–private partnership (PPP) is often loosely defined as cooperative institutional arrangements between public (government) and private (non-government) sector actors.[10] Development of institutional collaborations can be significantly augmented and enhanced through public–private partnerships, which can include non-governmental organizations, consortiums, multilateral organizations, and other groups. These organizations can be the partners themselves, or can be the mediator to facilitate collaboration. The private, non-academic organization Yale-China Association has played a critical role in developing the relationship between Yale and Xiangya. There are several examples of how this relationship can foster collaboration (see Box 7.6).

BOX 7.6 EXAMPLES OF PUBLIC–PRIVATE PARTNERSHIP COLLABORATION

The inauguration of the Yale-China Association represented cooperative agreement between public and private partners from China and the United States to develop a western school of medicine in China. It enjoyed the advantage of both western support from the Yale-China Association and local Hunanese support. The Yale-China Association, serving as a trusted cultural broker between two larger academic institutions, catalyzes collaborations with infusions of staff and financial resources. Bidirectional exchange facilitated by public–private partnerships offers opportunities for both parties to learn from each other and to continue building programs and partnerships. Efforts facilitated by the Yale-China Association to develop competency-based models of residency training, which began with three programs in psychiatry, pediatrics, and internal medicine, have now grown into more than 80 residency programs at Xiangya's three affiliated hospitals. This collaborative model of residency training developed at Xiangya continues to be one of the top residency training models in China, and will include fellowship training to build upon its previous efforts to strengthen graduate medical education in China. In addition, the Yale-China Association has provided fellowship training opportunities for women in the health professions for nearly 20 years through the Chia Fellowship Program. This unique fellowship program not only provides training opportunities for professionals in the medicine, nursing, and public health disciplines at Central South University and Kunming Medical University to come to Yale for six months, it also brings women health professionals from rural western Hunan to Central South University (Xiangya) for five months of training, thereby investing in rural health professionals' career development.

Partnerships can also facilitate community and ongoing opportunities to develop the partnership to be deeper over time, and wider over multiple groups. The Chia Fellowship Program through the Yale-China Association also convenes an annual academic conference for former fellows to share their research results, and provides community grants opportunities that former fellows can apply to for health education and intervention projects in underserved communities. Perhaps best illustrating the value of deep and wide partnerships, the legacy of the Yale-China Association's health work in China has endured more than a century of prosperous and challenging times in China, through periods of peace and war, ultimately giving rise to tremendous health institutions.

Global health training programs and experiences are also facilitated by the development of public–private partnerships, often with support from leadership at the top or the vision that results from relationships that are being established. The partnership with the Hunan Health and Family Planning Commission provides a model of public–private partnerships in China. National and regional health agencies in China are sometimes interested in partnerships with trusted non-governmental organizations (NGOs), in particular when additional support would be needed to address health challenges in rural and underdeveloped areas. Working with the Yale-China Association, the Hunan provincial government provides policy guidance in alignment with national health goals, infrastructure and personnel support, as well as medications. A similarly successful partnership model in global mental health is the Nepal partnerships network developed with the Nepal Ministry of Health (MOH) which became interested in working with Possible, a non-profit healthcare organization, to add mental healthcare services to rural public health services through a public–private partnership.[1]

Lessons learned

International institutional partnerships also confer a significant benefit on recruitment of residents. In our experience, many talented applicants to psychiatry residency programs have had formative GMH experiences during medical school or have participated in a global health track or certificate program and may wish to build on these experiences during residency training. Many residency programs are also committed to recruiting applicants from diverse backgrounds, who have had diverse life experiences, and who have demonstrated commitment to care of underserved populations. Having a set of opportunities that have depth and a wide range of foci can demonstrate commitment to these principles and is attractive to prospective applicants.

Many academic institutions have existing partnerships for global health educational experiences. As GMH programs are developed in academic centers, the most obvious approach is to build on existing, long-term partnerships. However, the disadvantage of developing GMH training experiences restricted to only pre-existing, deep relationships is that it may not meet the education objectives for all trainees. The Yale experience demonstrates that a deep partnership can continue to evolve and can lead to an expansion of opportunities for additional health professional training (nursing, research, teaching, clinical, public health, etc.). Notwithstanding challenges inherent to developing GMH-oriented training opportunities, our experience has taught us that building from the foundation of a deep institutional collaboration reduces initial infrastructure barriers and enables efficiency in maintaining these partnerships as compared with development of new short-term experiences. It does take time to develop and apply for funding that allows for these programs to grow. A "one-size-fits-all" approach may not meet the GMH educational needs and interest for all trainees. For those who have specific objectives or for those who have had previous experience at a particular site, it may be important to support the development of one-time experiences. However, these can be built on existing partnerships, and by ensuring availability of mentorship and other resources, these new programs can be turned into ongoing collaborations that can provide a wide range of opportunities for future trainees.

References

1. Acharya B, Maru D, Schwarz R, Citrin D, Tenpa J, Hirachan S, et al. Partnerships in mental healthcare service delivery in low-resource settings: developing an innovative network in rural Nepal. *Globalization and Health.* 2017;13(1):2.

2.   Kelly E, Doyle V, Weakliam D, Schönemann Y. A rapid evidence review on the effectiveness of institutional health partnerships. *Globalization and Health.* 2015;11(1):48.

3.   Marienfeld C, Rohrbaugh RM. Impact of a global mental health program on a residency training program. *Academic Psychiatry.* 2013;37(4):276–80.

4.   Crump JA, Sugarman J, Working Group on Ethics Guidelines for Global Health Training. Ethics and best practice guidelines for training experiences in global health. *American Journal of Tropical Medicine and Hygiene.* 2010;83(6):1178–82.

5.   Zhu Y, Zhang H, Yang G, Hu X, Liu Z, Guo N, et al. Attitudes towards mental illness among medical students in China: impact of medical education on stigma. *Asia-Pacific Psychiatry.* 2018;10(2):e12294.

6.   Sun B, Fan N, Nie S, Zhang M, Huang X, He H, et al. Attitudes towards people with mental illness among psychiatrists, psychiatric nurses, involved family members and the general population in a large city in Guangzhou, China. *International Journal of Mental Health Systems.* 2014;8:26.

7.   Jing L, Chang WC, Rohrbaugh R, Ouyang X, Chen E, Liu Z, et al. The psychiatry major: a curricular innovation to improve undergraduate psychiatry education in China. *Academic Psychiatry.* 2018;42(3):376–81.

8.   Hu X, Rohrbaugh R, Deng Q, He Q, Munger KF, Liu Z. Expanding the mental health workforce in China: narrowing the mental health service gap. *Psychiatric Services.* 2017;68(10):987–9.

9.   Zhang W, Zhu Y, Sun M, Guo R, Wu G, Wang Z, Xue Z, Shi J, Ouyang X, Pu W, Liu Z, Chiu HFK, Rosenheck R. Longitudinal trajectories of psychotic-like experiences and their relationship to emergent mental disorders among adolescents: A 3-year cohort study. *The Journal of Clinical Psychiatry.* 2019;80(4):18m12437. doi: 10.4088/JCP.18m12437. PMID: 31347795.

10. Hodge GA, Carsten G. Public-private partnerships: an international performance review. *Public Administration Review.* 2007;67.3:545–58.

Mobilizing a Range of Resources to Advance Research and Service in Global Mental Health Training

*Pamela Scorza, Brian Neff, Tahilia J. Rebello,
LeShawndra N. Price, Matias Irarrazaval, Lidia Goveia,
David M. Ndetei, Victoria Mutiso, André Fiks Salem,
Liza Magill, Victoria Leonard, Milton Wainberg, and
Kathleen M. Pike*

Summary points

- The extreme scarcity of resources for mental health care in most low- and middle-income countries has resulted in research being neglected in favor of providing clinical care.
- Rather than being framed as competing priorities, research and clinical training can be integrated to capture synergies that improve service delivery.
- Global mental health (GMH) practitioners and educators need to better recognize and allocate inherent resources all partners bring to education and research, including financial, government, cultural/community, human, and technology resources.
- We describe examples of programs that have effectively mobilized these resources to build successful GMH training initiatives, ultimately leading to improved GMH research and clinical care.

Introduction

Neuropsychiatric disorders represent the leading cause of disability worldwide, yet only a fraction of individuals with mental disorders receives treatment.[1] This is especially true in low- and middle-income countries (LMICs) where care is scarce.[2] Limited financial resources to close this treatment gap in LMICs has fostered a belief that generating scientific knowledge must take a backseat to providing treatment in global mental health (GMH) training. With so many individuals needing care, the thinking goes, why divert precious resources to research? However, the authors' experience as GMH researchers, educators, and clinicians is that allocating resources to research can improve treatment in real time and significantly contribute to capacity-building that translates into lasting enhancements in mental health treatments and systems.

Research advances evidence-based clinical care, builds a vocabulary across geography and disorders, connects local clinical practice with global guidelines, and validates local clinical practice for its efficacy within various cultural contexts. This work advances the GMH field toward an enhanced understanding of etiology, treatment, and prevention of mental health disorders. It legitimizes mental conditions and diseases worldwide, thereby decreasing stigma and increasing treatment access. The "either-or" choice between research and clinical services—that is, that one must choose between strengthening research capacity or building clinical service capacity—in LMICs is a false one. Research findings in dissemination and implementation design are now being used globally to strengthen health systems capacity to manage mental disorders and improve treatment outcomes, as well as to consider cost-effectiveness and examine how

DOI: 10.4324/9781315160597-11

evidence-based clinical and prevention interventions can be adapted, scaled up, and sustained in community-based settings or service delivery systems.[3,4]

There is an ongoing shift toward recognizing the importance of research in GMH training. In 2010, the US National Institutes of Health (NIH) declared global health research to be one of the agency's five major priorities, and in an influential commentary in 2013, Francis Collins (the NIH director at that time) and colleagues[5] note the importance of increasing research investment on non-communicable diseases that substantially contribute to the high burden of mortality and morbidity, particularly in LMICs. They go on to urge global health practitioners to expand research capacity and training opportunities, especially for investigators from LMICs. The World Health Organization (WHO) has also specifically identified the development and strengthening of research capacity in its Mental Health Action Plan 2013–2020,[6] highlighting the importance of strong research and data collection infrastructure for equipping communities to collect and utilize locally generated data to meet their mental health targets, identify public health priorities, and build clinical, scientific, prevention, and promotion programs. In 2018, the *Lancet* Commission on Global Mental Health and Sustainable Development also reaffirmed the need for GMH research and expanded the focus from reducing the treatment gap to addressing gaps in prevention and quality of care.[7]

This chapter presents case studies of effective research training partnerships between institutions in LMICs and HICs to demonstrate how such partnerships can surmount admittedly daunting resource constraints and advance the GMH agenda to improve mental health outcomes. These discussions will be beneficial for diverse stakeholders navigating the balance between research and care: academic leaders committed to building capacity in GMH, funders considering the most rational investment in GMH, and trainees seeking strategies to combine research and clinical care in their careers.

There has been an impressive increase in attention to GMH research training in the past decade among students, researchers, and clinicians in both LMICs and HICs. Groundbreaking collaborative training models between and among institutions in LMICs and HICs show great promise in advancing best practices in service delivery. However, challenges remain. It is difficult for some LMIC partners to invest resources into conducting empirical studies when faced with overwhelming clinical loads. HIC partners often have more funding opportunities for GMH research, which can require LMIC partners to pursue a research agenda that is out of line with local needs and on-the-ground realities to meet funders' requirements. There is also limited geographic distribution of GMH research, with most of this research focused in LMICs that have strong existing research collaborations with HIC universities. In addition, there are persisting inequities in opportunity for LMIC investigators to contribute to GMH research, which perpetuates an unfortunate asymmetry in perceived contributions and authorship credit in some LMIC-HIC collaborations. Moreover, LMIC-HIC partnerships can be fraught with complex cultural differences and power dynamics influenced by historical contexts and resource discrepancies (see Chapter 1). These obstacles can make equitable, two-way exchange difficult, and they also can undermine the quality of GMH treatment. Throughout this chapter we share lessons learned on how to navigate these challenges while balancing research and clinical training priorities.

We begin with an explanation of why resource recognition and deployment are the most important parts of developing successful GMH research training partnerships. This section will outline the types of resources stakeholders bring to collaborations, and the need to appreciate each of these resources while strategically and creatively leveraging them to build sustainable, effective GMH research capacity-building initiatives. At the end of this section, we will introduce the five types of resources that will be addressed in this chapter and have been effectively utilized by collaborative GMH training programs. The chapter is organized by these resources—financial support, government partnership, community engagement, health professional human capacity, and technology—with each one paired with a case study of a training program.

The first case focuses on how to use financial resources effectively to prioritize capacity-building and the needs of local partners for research. The US National Institute of Mental Health's (NIMH) Collaborative Hubs for International Research on Mental Health demonstrates how a program tasked with expanding research activities in LMICs has effectively utilized research funding to build research and clinical capacity in GMH at centers around the world. The projects that this NIMH initiative has funded promote strong partnerships with local governments, ensure that local priorities are addressed, and have resulted in research training that can produce culturally relevant findings that are directly applicable to mental health systems and positively impact the delivery of care.

We continue with an examination of the case of the Paises Africanos de Lingua Oficial Portuguesa (PALOP) Mental Health Implementation Research Training Program in Mozambique as an example of effective allocation of local government resources for GMH research training. This initiative demonstrates how involving policymakers in research training leads to integration of evidence-based practice into national policy. PALOP serves as compelling evidence that, with the support of Ministries of Health, practice-based research training can be integrated into clinical work in such a way that it is complementary rather than competing.

We next address one of the most undervalued resources in GMH training: community and cultural expertise. Using the case of the Africa Mental Health Research and Training Foundation's (AMHRTF) Multi-sectoral Stakeholder Team Approach to Scale-Up Community Mental Health in Kenya (TEAM) studies, we demonstrate the essential foundation of community and cultural expertise as a resource that makes it possible to engage community stakeholders and advance mental health on the ground.

The fourth resource that we focus on is health professional human resource capacity in GMH research training programs. One of the research hubs supported by the NIMH, the Regional Network for Mental Health Research in Latin America (RedeAmericas), has effectively promoted capacity-building activities that create sustainable pathways to develop effective mentor relationships for researchers. This project's focus on capacity-building through mentorship has led to trainees' successful completion of pilot studies and academic publishing, highlighting the potential of leveraging professional human resources to strengthen both research and clinical care.

We conclude with the resource of technology, using the example of the World Health Organization's Global Clinical Practice Network (GCPN) to illustrate how technological resources can multiply the reach and collaboration potential of GMH work. The International Classification of Diseases—11th version (ICD-11) was informed by a Field Studies Research Program that was hosted on the GCPN, an online network consisting of over 17,000 clinicians from 164 countries around the world that continues to grow. This tool was used to elicit real-time global expertise that informed the newest edition of global clinical guidelines, ultimately improving diagnosis and treatment of mental health disorders around the world.

The past decade has seen an exciting launch of some of the first large-scale collaborative programs for GMH training. These programs have the potential to catalyze major advances in GMH research that will produce innovative solutions for closing the GMH treatment gap. High-quality LMIC-HIC research training collaborations can help to foster long-term support for GMH research in low-resource settings worldwide. Further, both LMIC and HIC institutions benefit in the course of establishing a strong foundation of collaboration that reflects the needs and interests of the partners. We hope that outlining the types of resources that must be leveraged for effective GMH research and sharing examples of successful research capacity-building initiatives will encourage institutions and funders to invest in expanding GMH capacity-building worldwide.

Resources for GMH research

Implementation of GMH research capacity-building programs requires a set of diverse resources. Space must be acquired to develop and conduct the research. Staff must be fairly compensated for their contributions. Further, research training often necessitates material and other resources such as transportation, medical technology, training tools, and office supplies. The lack of supplementary resources needed to support effective international collaboration, such as travel for conferences and meetings, web-based conferencing tools, and trainings in cross-cultural competency and leadership, leaves many eager researchers discouraged by the barriers to conducting effective GMH research training. In the face of these daunting challenges, the first step to building GMH research capacity is to take stock of existing resources from all collaborating partners that can be leveraged to develop research capacity.

The word "resource" is often assumed to imply financial resources only. Unfortunately, this leads to the erroneous assumption that HICs bring more "resources" to LMIC-HIC research collaborations, due to the larger pool of government and philanthropic funds available to the HIC-based partners. We do not deny—nor wish to ignore—that this financial resource disparity exists, and that entrenched resource disparities persist between LMICs and HICs. In fact, we affirm these are problematic and should be redressed. Our focus here, however, is on making the argument that these resource disparities are not insurmountable obstacles to GMH research. We also note that resource disparities exist within LMICs and HICs, respectively. In addition, some sites that may be financially well resourced may lack other types of resources, such as community buy-in, cultural knowledge, or government partnership, which are also essential to conducting high-quality research. Indeed, we argue that every site has resources that can be leveraged to improve mental health and that effective GMH research training programs recognize and value the unique capacity of each partner to advance their objectives: no type of resource is more, or less, important to the overall goal of advancing research capacity and reducing the GMH treatment gap. In the next sections, we will provide examples of how research teams have performed GMH research that increases capacity and strengthens clinical care by identifying and leveraging financial, government, cultural, human, and technology resources.

Financial resources: The case for investing in GMH research capacity-building

It is well understood that financial resources are essential to conducting effective research in GMH. To form collaborations, complete training activities, and build research programs, large-scale and sustainable funding support is required. Yet, there is a dearth of funding directed at GMH research, especially in LMICs. Most low-income countries invest less than 1% of their health budgets in mental health services, and less than 1% in health professional human resource capacity and research.[8] Even development assistance for health from the world's richest countries has spent less than 1% on mental health since 2007.[1] If garnered and leveraged strategically, there are numerous types of financial resources that can promote GMH capacity-building, including government or non-governmental grant funding, intergovernmental organization funds, non-profit organization and foundation donations, and individual philanthropic contributions. Although most global financial resources for GMH come from donor HICs, LMICs also contribute to financial resources for research collaborations directly through grant or individual monetary support, as well as indirectly through in-kind donations such as salary support for staff time during their engagement in research, community space, or medical supplies.

The US National Institute of Mental Health (NIMH) is an example of a federal agency that has strategically utilized its financial resources to support GMH capacity-building. NIMH recognized the need to address the GMH "treatment gap"—the proportion of people who need, but do not receive care—when it refined its research priorities to emphasize four areas: 1) addressing acute disparities in access to mental health care through research on the treatment gap in LMICs; 2) building research capacity by creating sustainable pathways to research careers in GMH within the United States and in LMICs; 3) anticipating global public health needs based on both epidemiologic and demographic transitions; and 4) prioritizing research settings in which existing research infrastructure can be leveraged. Following this priority setting, NIMH dedicated significant financial resources to GMH research capacity-building across its grant-recipient institutions in LMICs. In 2010, NIMH launched an initiative called Collaborative Hubs for International Research on Mental Health in Low- and Middle-Income Countries (CHIRMH).[9] This funding initiative focused on two of the most pressing mental health treatment gap challenges: the dearth of specialized mental healthcare providers capable of delivering evidence-based interventions, and the need to build a cadre of researchers around the globe capable of conducting innovative mental health research across diverse social contexts. This NIMH-funding initiative supported integration of research and clinical capacity-building aims toward improving mental health outcomes. CHIRMH (Box 8.1) has aimed to increase the research base for mental health interventions in LMICs by integrating research findings from clinical, translational, epidemiological, and policy spheres. With the goal of reducing the mental health treatment gap through building research infrastructure and developing local research capacity, CHIRMH has promulgated essential knowledge, tools, and sustainable strategies for use by government agencies, non-governmental organizations, and healthcare institutions.

BOX 8.1 DEVELOPMENT OF COLLABORATIVE HUBS FOR INTERNATIONAL RESEARCH ON MENTAL HEALTH IN LOW- AND MIDDLE-INCOME COUNTRIES (CHIRMH) INITIATIVE

CHIRMH applicants needed to meet three requirements for acceptance into the hub. First, applicants needed to demonstrate a partnership with a local and/or regional governmental or non-governmental organization, a research institution, or a mental health service user advocacy group in a LMIC. This was to ensure that both service provider and service user perspectives were considered and that local priorities were addressed by the research agenda put forth by the applicant, who could be from a HIC or LMIC. Such partnerships increase the likelihood that any research findings would be culturally and contextually relevant and disseminated to key stakeholders, as well as could be meaningfully taken up by local policymakers and implemented into practice. Second, applicants were required specifically to address whether and how they engaged the process of "task-sharing," i.e., distributing mental health tasks appropriately throughout health workforce teams as a method of more efficiently utilizing the scarce healthcare providers trained specifically in evidence-based mental health care. By invoking this requirement, the NIMH sought to stimulate research that would test strategies for reducing the treatment gap by increasing human capital resources for delivering quality care. Third, applicants were required to develop research capacity-building activities within the conduct of the research. The goal of this requirement was twofold: to establish resources and infrastructure for research that would benefit the region in which the research was being conducted, and to increase the number of qualified scientific and technical personnel capable of conducting mental health research.

The CHIRMH initiative funded the development of five regional centers for mental health research, education, training, and practice that incorporated the needs and perspectives of local populations and emphasized building research capacity for the benefit of their respective regions. Each center focused on fostering multiple, sustainable pathways to research careers—including, but not limited to, conventional academic routes—along with training personnel at NGOs and government ministries to conduct high-quality research. This multifaceted approach promised a significant impact on enhancing human capital for conducting research because it eliminated some common barriers to developing research capacity. For instance, CHIRMH capacity-building centers offered multiple types of training and career development activities rather than a single, traditionally academic pathway to a research career. A more detailed description of the five research capacity-building centers has been published elsewhere.[10]

By providing organized, well-defined pathways to research, the centers helped refine and standardize a career development process that had previously often been haphazard and dependent upon individual relationships. And through its broad array of research capacity-building activities, CHIRMH centers successfully increased the numbers of professionals capable of conducting mental health research within each region, resulting in an expanded global network of investigators. Understandably, each region was at a unique stage of readiness to conduct research and engage in such research capacity-building efforts. Thus, each hub, with its aggregation of resources from multiple institutions and organizations, fostered beneficial South-South and North-South collaborations, bidirectional learning, and seeding of research activities, especially in countries with more limited research infrastructure. Because the hubs were required to integrate research capacity-development activities within treatment intervention studies implemented in collaboration with local players, CHIRMH prioritized a convergence of the two goals of conducting research and expanding access to treatment. NIMH, through its support of GMH training initiatives and creation of CHIRMH, illustrates the power of financial resources in GMH research to build training capacity that expands research initiatives and strengthens clinical care delivery across all hubs.

Government resources: Government partnership for policy integration

Building sustainable mental health research and clinical care training infrastructure in LMICs is impossible without leveraging government resources. As leaders responsible for the wellbeing of their constituents, governments have a mandate to invest in promoting mental health. Government resources include political will, local expertise, a national platform, funding, and legislative power. No systemic change is possible without a combination of these resources. Policy change is often stymied because mental health research findings frequently do not reach the decision makers responsible for creating public health initiatives. Partnership between researchers and government actors bridges this information gap, empowering policymakers with the knowledge to create evidence-based policy. GMH practitioners can leverage government resources by recognizing the necessity of national buy-in, local expertise, and policymaking as vehicles for sustainable change.

Paises Africanos de Lingua Oficial Portuguesa Mental Health Implementation Research Training Program in Mozambique (PALOP) was designed and implemented in partnership with the government of Mozambique, demonstrating effective leveraging of government resources by capitalizing on political will to build mental health training structures into national policy. PALOP is the Mozambican arm of the NIH-funded Partnerships in Research to Implement and Disseminate Sustainable and Scalable Evidence Based Practices in Sub-Saharan Africa

(PRIDES SSA) program.[10] Because Mozambique's mental health system was in its infancy at the time PRIDES SSA was launched in 2014, this context offered a unique opportunity to design mental health program strategy from scratch using state-of-the-art implementation research that fosters evidence-based practices, potentially creating a template for other countries to follow. The seventh poorest nation in the world—where more than 70% of the population lives in rural areas and where there are currently only 13 psychiatrists and 75 psychologists serving approximately 25 million people—Mozambique was the site of an implementation science mental health training program funded by the Fogarty International Center and the NIMH.[11] The program included a two- to three-year scholarship that offered research courses, hands-on research activities, and PhD study options to Mozambican clinical psychologists and psychiatrists with varying levels of training and expertise. The initiative's partnering institutions are the New York State Psychiatric Institute/Columbia University, Vanderbilt's Institute for GMH, and the University of Pennsylvania in the United States; the Universidade Federal de São Paulo (UNIFESP) and Rio de Janeiro (UFRJ) in Brazil; and the Universidade Eduardo Mondlane School of Medicine, the Mozambique Institute for Health Education and Research, and the Mozambique Ministry of Health.[12]

BOX 8.2 USING IMPLEMENTATION AND DISSEMINATION RESEARCH TO SCALE UP EVIDENCE-BASED PRACTICES IN MOZAMBIQUE

Further bolstering implementation science research in LMICs, the new Partnerships in Research to Implement and Disseminate Sustainable and Scalable Evidence Based Practices in Sub-Saharan Africa (PRIDES SSA) has the dual aim of expanding the evidence base for effective task-sharing in Mozambique and training multi-disciplinary research teams in four other African countries. The first goal is to expand mental healthcare coverage by leveraging the task-sharing already in place for psychiatric technicians, while also devising other cost-effective service delivery pathways—that is, working to mobilize other already existing workforces to be employed in mental health care. The PRIDES SSA study aims to create an implementation "template" that might inform future efforts to establish task-sharing in Mozambique as well as in similar countries. The second goal is to train research "seed teams," professionals from Botswana, Malawi, South Africa, Zambia, and Mozambique who will commit to return to their home countries and conduct mental health implementation research, inform policymakers to leverage evidence from local scientific research, prepare providers to deliver evidence-based practices, and develop programs at local universities and other sites of higher education to mentor the next generation of investigators. They will be empowered by their degree and training to adapt validated mental health programs into their low-resource settings, further contributing to reducing the global mental health treatment gap.

Improving implementation science research capacity and clinical practice simultaneously in Mozambique was only possible because of the steadfast support of the Mozambique Ministry of Health. Many professionals in the Ministry already held evidence-based practices in high regard due to their education in mental health and so stood behind the Fogarty/NIMH training initiative from the start. Moreover, the program granted academic titles that conferred respect and authority on local mental health professionals, who therefore felt more empowered to propose evidence-based programs to policymakers and other health authorities. As early as 1996, the Mozambique Ministry of Health had been enlarging its mental health services by increasing the number of providers using task-sharing. Its clinical training program for "psychiatric technicians"—mid-level health professionals who are trained for 30 months to identify mental disorders, provide mental health care, and prescribe psychotropic drugs—has led to a great increase in service provision throughout the country.[11] There are now at least one or two psychiatric technicians in every district, though coverage in rural areas is still low.[12] Whereas initially, technician training efforts focused on raising awareness of epilepsy, the focus is now on using practices validated by implementation science to cover a wider range of mental disorders.

The PRIDES SSA initiative in Mozambique illustrates that training new local mental health researchers in LMICs and disseminating innovative, integrated, and community-based best practices to treat and prevent mental illness are complementary efforts. The two goals can be united when healthcare strategies are guided by implementation science research, which increases efficiency and reduces costs by being aware of the local context. The program is also a sterling example of why leveraging government resources in GMH research, training, and practice is essential. The current structure of PRIDES SSA[13] ensures the production of mutually defined, locally relevant, evidence-based research is supported by the government of Mozambique, and that its findings are accessible to policymakers. The result is a fertilized national landscape, primed to close the mental health research and treatment gap.

Cultural/community resources: Local partnership in each stage of research

Community resources encompass local cultural expertise. This expertise involves knowledge of cultural norms, socioeconomic structures, key players, and how they interact in each community. In the mental health context, local expertise illuminates how information is communicated, how treatment barriers are reinforced, how stigma operates, and much more. Community and cultural resources are pivotal to developing research capacity that benefits the local community, as well as gaining effective buy-in from community stakeholders who can inform priorities and support sustainability of research initiatives.

Successful GMH capacity-building programs must make use of community resources in research development and respect the local context by considering cultural and geographic factors, resource limitations, and competing health priorities in research design. Community involvement can be promoted through various methodologies such as community-based participatory research,[11,12] theory of change,[14] participatory action research,[15] empowerment evaluation,[16] participatory rural appraisal,[17] and awareness campaigns. These methodologies provide a structured way to involve the community in defining research priorities and long-term goals, mapping the pathways to achieve these goals, identifying context-specific barriers and opportunities, and mutually defining metrics to assess research outcomes.

In addition to ensuring research is feasible and appropriate in the community cultural context to improve outcomes, there is also an ethical imperative to integrate community resources into GMH research. Considering the history of global colonialism and the continued systemic inequalities perpetuated along class, racial, gender, and sexual orientation lines, researchers must be mindful to not perpetuate cultural imperialism. That is, outsiders to a community should approach work there as a guest, being careful to avoid imposing "right/wrong" judgments formed outside of the local cultural context. Likewise, researchers must be aware of the power dynamics at play between themselves and the community, taking steps to minimize any action that could manifest as coercion. In short, research design should be responsive to the needs and norms dictated by the community. In addition, research collaborators from the high-resource settings should be aware of how their work may strain community resources and take steps to mitigate and offset these impacts.

The impact of community involvement in research is manifold. When local partners feel ownership of the project, it can result in a stronger communal understanding and appreciation of the benefits and utility of the research, and a stronger appreciation of the impact of research on practice, patient outcomes, and health systems. Community buy-in may subsequently foster a culture of research and increase demand for research activities. This demand may be subsequently recognized and met by the public or private sectors, resulting in increased funding for mental health research and training activities. It may also lead to the integration of research activities into the national health agenda and health budget. Furthermore, engagement of policymakers and the public sector in nascent and ongoing phases of research may diminish the bureaucratic and political barriers to successful implementation of research initiatives and enhance financial support from the public sector. Community engagement could also contribute to the adoption or integration of research into national strategies resulting in ongoing political and financial support to research initiatives.

Developing a strong foundation of collaboration that reflects the needs and interests of the involved partners benefits both HIC and LMIC institutions, alike. This can be seen clearly in the example of the Africa Mental Health Research and Training Foundation (AMHRTF). AMHRTF is a research center based in Nairobi, Kenya. It systemically prioritizes community partnership and integration of culturally relevant practices in its research. This approach demonstrates highly effective leveraging of community resources. AMHRTF's work establishing research and clinical care infrastructure in rural Kenya provides a case study that demonstrates the positive impact of engaging community stakeholders in building sustained research capacity.

BOX 8.3 USING THE TEAM PROJECT TO CREATE COMMUNITY PARTNERSHIP AND SUSTAINABILITY FOR GMH RESEARCH IN KENYA

In collaboration with the Columbia GMH Program, the Africa Mental Health Research and Training Foundation received a scale-up grant in 2015 from Grand Challenges Canada to establish an initiative in rural Makueni County, Kenya called: "Multi-sectoral Stakeholder TEAM Approach to Scale-Up Community Mental Health in Kenya: Building on Locally Generated Evidence and Lessons Learned" (TEAM). TEAM was an 18-month research project aimed at addressing the barriers of lack of trained human resources and the challenges of stigma to mental health care in Kenya. The TEAM initiative partnered with primary care centers and the informal healthcare structure of traditional and faith healers to gain direct access to the Kenyan rural population, creating a referral program to ensure that individuals who were identified by these partners as in need of mental health care received treatment by providers trained in mental health care. In the early phases of developing and implementing TEAM, AMHRTF engaged with key players via a stakeholder analysis, using several of the community engagement methodologies. The goal of this stakeholder analysis was to engage the research team, community, and local government to foster collective ownership and successful integration of the research initiative into healthcare seeking and referral practices in the community and healthcare system. They adopted both a top-down and bottom-up approach of community engagement, including political and administrative leaders from the county government, community leaders and advocates, users and their families, local clinicians, community health workers, traditional healers, and faith healers.

By engaging government officials and cultivating a community demand for their mental health research and services, the TEAM partners were able to secure political support for their work. Through continuous engagement, they convinced the Makueni County government to provide matching funds to support the research. The county government also agreed to integrate TEAM research staff in government health centers, cover the costs of medications and consultations fees, and provide salary support for public healthcare workers participating in the research. Because of early engagement of the community and county government, mental health services and data collection activities, based on TEAM, are now fully integrated into other health services at the facility level as per official policy.[18-22]

The TEAM study's impact on clinical care in Kenya and other low-resource settings would have been severely limited without AMHRTF's systemic engagement of community resources. Its approach demonstrates how these resources bolster the quality of GMH research and support sustained adoption of evidence-based clinical treatment.

Human resources: Building health professional human resource capacity for GMH

Expanding mental health treatment globally is simply not possible without increasing the number of professionals able to administer care in LMICs. However, training mental health specialists requires time, money, and a robust clinical training infrastructure. Both LMICs and HICs struggle to overcome these resource barriers in expanding the ranks of service providers. Moreover, the training of new researchers, especially in low-income settings, is often overshadowed by the urgent need to increase treatment delivery.[23]

GMH training programs initiated by HICs must be responsible for emphasizing capacity-building in research through collaborative research partnerships that create mentorship opportunities and hands-on research experience for potential researchers. In 2004, the Global Forum for Health Research, in collaboration with the WHO, mapped research capacity in LMICs to raise awareness of global disparities in research capacity. Over half of the mental health researchers or stakeholders had not received formal training in epidemiology, public health, or basic sciences, suggesting a need for dedicated training programs for professionals.[24] This chapter highlights an example of a successful research capacity-building program for research professionals in LMICs: The Regional Network for Mental Health Research in Latin America (RedeAmericas).

RedeAmericas—one of the CHIRMH hubs—was a network of mental health professionals in Latin America and at Columbia University that aimed to promote mental health research through pilot service delivery projects and the training of mental health researchers in Latin America.[25] The capacity-building cornerstone of RedeAmericas was its mentorship program, which offered support and opportunities to a broad range of professionals with high potential to conduct essential mental health research in Latin America. Mentorship conveyed crucial benefits on these professionals by facilitating their career selection, enhancing their career advancement and productivity, influencing their selection of academic specialty, and providing financial support and mentorship for research projects, theses, and publications. Key to the mentorship program, mentees learned actively through mental health service delivery projects, gaining the capacity to conduct implementation research that could directly improve mental health service delivery.

To best leverage the resource of professional human capacity, RedeAmericas used a targeted mentorship model to effectively support and encourage the professional development of health professionals to become GMH researchers while addressing challenges to cross-cultural mentorship. Although it is important to acknowledge that cultural differences may impact the effectiveness of mentor-mentee relationships, programs such as RedeAmericas illustrate the possibilities for research mentorship that enhances capacity in both LMICs and HICs. The successful cross-cultural mentorship employed by RedeAmericas shares four major lessons, described below.

Utilize a strengths-based approach to develop trust in cross-cultural mentorship

An effective cross-cultural mentorship program must remain cognizant of the delicate interpersonal dynamics involved in mentorship; that is, a mentor must strike a balance between communicating nurturing support to trainees on the one hand and challenging them intellectually and technically on the other. In other words, a mentor aims to guide and advise mentees by deploying their own expertise without conveying a patronizing attitude. Establishing trust is, unsurprisingly, perhaps the most salient component in building rapport with a mentee. Some mentees may be nervous about working with a mentor from a HIC academic institution, so anything a mentor can do to convey a sense of honesty and reliability will strengthen the relationship. Mentors can empathize with a mentee's challenges, share knowledge without being patronizing, and remain nonjudgmental. Moreover, social identities such as ethnicity and race likely impact many aspects of the mentoring relationship. For example, identity can play a salient role in a mentee's selection of mentor, in the ways mentees and their mentors relate, and benefits that may result from same- or cross-identity matches. Mentoring programs should pay close attention to facilitating the development of each mentor-mentee relationship. Our experiences with RedeAmericas suggest that program mentors should take a *strengths-based* approach that focuses on the positive qualities of mentees instead of the problems they may be experiencing. Mentees should be aware of the historical context of local engagements that may contribute to mistrust. Mentors should be self-reflective and mindful about the ways in which they, themselves, respond to multiple characteristics of the mentee, including aspects of a mentee's racial identity and cultural values, but should not create a relationship that is patronizing or overprotective in the name of sensitivity. In the end, mentoring outcomes are impacted by mentor-mentee social identities but depend on far more than a simple racial or ethnic match.

Contain a strategy for addressing inherent barriers to international collaboration

A mentoring program must also have a strategy for addressing barriers that are inherent in any international collaboration, including language difficulties (especially communication in scientific English), limited resources (e.g., limited access or lack of access to sophisticated statistical analysis packages), and suboptimal infrastructure (e.g., slow Internet access in some LMICs). Particularly in the case of clinician-researcher mentees from LMICs, high-income country mentors must understand and effectively work with the high competing demands of clinical service provision on the mentee's time. In RedeAmericas, language difference was one major barrier. Barriers to effective communication with Latin American mentees were overcome substantially through computer-mediated communication, which was used to initiate and sustain both peer-to-peer and mentor-mentee relationships. Internet-based communication alleviated barriers to traditional communications due to time and schedule limitations and physical distances, and for clinician-research mentees, electronic communication was even used for clinical supervision and support. Both mentors and mentees reported positive experiences using the Internet as a regular communication tool, saying that it allowed them to interface with peers and mentors they would not otherwise have been able to connect with; opened access to a rich collection of international resources, such as scientific journals, seminars, and networking opportunities; and provided opportunities to learn and contribute to international research that advances the goals of the global GMH agenda. There are many challenges to utilizing the Internet to overcome barriers to international collaboration, and not all RedeAmericas' mentees were able to connect easily with their mentors due to intermittent Internet access or limitations in their access to necessary communication tools. However, RedeAmericas anticipated and created a plan for the distance-related barriers inherent in international collaboration, allowing the program to create an alternate strategy to maintain effective mentorship.

Carefully weigh ethical principles considering locally applicable research ethics frameworks

GMH research presents some unique ethical considerations, which are important to introduce to trainees to support their understanding of international standards for ethical research and particular vulnerabilities that may disproportionately affect study populations they plan to serve. For example, it may be difficult to create a randomized controlled study design in low-resource settings that is ethical given that "treatment-as-usual" may be equivalent to "no treatment at all." Preventing coercion among research participants in settings with high poverty and low literacy is an essential aspect of research in LMICs. The lack of capacity for institutional ethical or research review in some under-resourced settings may require additional effort to establish a framework for research review and incorporation of local perspectives and guidance. In addition to ensuring ethical conduct of human subjects research—which applies to any setting—targeted research training must aim to ameliorate the historic tendencies of researchers from high-income countries to paternalistically "take the lead" in work conducted with LMIC partners (see Chapter 3). There should be safeguards in place to ensure balanced bidirectional collaboration. Through effective mentorship, RedeAmericas mentees from Chile learned how to apply and develop strategies to confront these ethical challenges in a workshop held in Santiago, where they discussed the importance of research ethics from a global health perspective and learned about sequencing designs, using historical controls, and building in protections for vulnerable subjects. These research training concerns are not only imperative from an ethical perspective, but they also ensure that research will lead to sustained improvements in clinical care because carrying out health research that respects research participants will build provider and community trust in health services and therefore helps to build engagement with health services.

To highlight various strategies that capacity-building initiatives might employ to ensure the ethical acceptability of GMH research while also expanding access to treatment for underserved populations, we turn now to a case study of one RedeAmericas research project (Box 8.4).

BOX 8.4 PROVIDING CROSS-NATIONAL RESEARCH MENTORSHIP IN THE CONTEXT OF A RESEARCH STUDY TO IMPLEMENT AND TEST A PSYCHOSOCIAL INTERVENTION

Critical Time Intervention Task Shifting (CTI-TS) is a psychosocial intervention for people with severe mental disorders developed by Dr. Ezra Susser and his colleagues at Columbia University.[26] Designed to support the recovery and facilitate the full participation in society of individuals in treatment for serious mental illness, CTI-TS is a time-limited, community-based psychosocial intervention designed to complement existing health services. CTI-TS is based on a community mental health model, seeking to improve patients' continuity of care, social integration, and overall quality of life. A team of CTI-TS workers (community mental health workers and peer support workers), trained and supervised by mental health professionals, collaborate with participants to identify specific factors that are impeding recovery and continuity of care.[27] Together, they create a feasible plan to address these obstacles and expand the patient's support networks.

CTI-TS employed a variety of best research practices to ensure the project's robustness and ethical acceptability. Before the program was piloted in Santiago, Chile, and Rio de Janeiro, Brazil, mentees conducted a comprehensive literature review to identify any existing studies that might offer lessons that the team could apply to this population. No substantial research on this type of initiative was uncovered; though this meant the team had few templates from which to work, it did ensure that any potential research findings would be useful to the GMH community. Additionally, the CTI-TS team worked together to identify and minimize the ethical risks of this initiative through thoughtful sampling decisions, intensive local engagement, and non-stigmatizing communication. Going beyond what was required by local Institutional Review Board (IRB) review requirements, the team created community-based advisory boards to solicit and consider participant input, ensure protection of participants, and adequately assess study risks by fully examining potential threats to and vulnerability of the participating communities. The pilot study elicited local conceptions of and terminology for mental health topics and sought to clarify the local relevance of psychosocial interventions for people with severe mental disorders.[28] The CTI-TS team used these findings, together with knowledge of context, adherence to ethical guidelines, and ethical review structures, to improve the appropriate informed consent procedure and to accurately assess and explain potential benefits to participants.

Ensure all partners are receiving fair credit in research collaboration outputs

An important product of any research collaboration is the writing and publication of findings in the scientific literature that can advance the field. Because scholarly publications are also the currency of evaluation and promotion for academic advancement, mentorship in HIC-LMIC collaborations should ensure that LMIC collaborators and trainees have opportunities to develop and utilize academic writing skills and receive appropriate credit for their contributions. Although providing opportunities for authorship and fair attribution of authorship credit may be regarded as routine issue for research mentors to address, mentors working in the global health domain should be aware that the Global South is underrepresented in scientific publications. In addition to the inherent value to supporting equitable opportunities for LMIC collaborators and mentees, RedeAmericas found that collaborative authorship—throughout the entire research and writing process—has numerous scientific benefits. These include more accurate description of study methods, context, and limitations; greater linguistic proficiency in explaining language use and cultural adaption of instruments and interview guides; more appropriate interpretation of findings; more realistic assessment of feasible applications of findings; and advancement of career goals for all research partners. Expeditious publication of study findings may be important for both scientific and career advancement goals, but these goals should not compromise equitable access to career advancement opportunities or academic capacity-building. It is therefore essential for GMH collaborators and mentors to safeguard and facilitate bilateral participation in the scientific process; in addition to promoting ethical engagement within North-South collaboration, this investment in supporting academic career development through training and authorship can have long-term benefits for mental health systems.

As RedeAmericas demonstrates, strengthening research capacity through mentorship programs in LMICs while delivering care is both feasible and impactful: a powerful, cost-effective, and sustainable means of advancing GMH.

Technology: Building research networks to leverage expertise from clinicians worldwide

The advancement of technological resources, including online networks, online training platforms, telemedicine and teletherapy, and instant translation, has begun to transform GMH research and practice. These tools improve collaboration between international partners, who can benefit from virtual meetings and the ability to live-edit documents online. In addition, technological resources can inform and improve research by allowing for the input of mental health stakeholders from around the world, thereby supporting research on global standards and vocabulary for the advancement of GMH treatment.

Technology in GMH research can simultaneously improve research capacity and clinical services by engaging clinicians in local and global research networks.[29] Research networks represent a collective of individuals and/or groups and serve to link researchers, practitioners, public health professionals, and other relevant stakeholders, such as policymakers and members of civil society. These linkages are usually forged through an online platform for communication and collaboration. The features of research networks often include a clear mission and statement of purpose that consist of a commitment to research, channels for communication among network participants, a governing body responsible for administration of the network, and support staff. Network members are unified by their research interests, discipline, field of study, and/or geographic location, although some networks do cut across research domains and global regions.

Research networks are a powerful tool to improve GMH research and training capacity-building, especially in their ability to provide members with longitudinal access to the resources required to lead, conduct, and/or participate in research studies. Some resources that research networks share to inform GMH capacity-building include online, on-demand trainings on relevant areas such as research design/methodology/analysis and research ethics, opportunities to participate in learning collaboratives, access to statistical and other technical expertise, and administrative support. These provisions may be especially important in engaging researchers working in low-resource settings who may not otherwise have access to the human, financial, or logistical requirements to initiate or participate in research activities. Research networks also have the capacity to provide members opportunities to develop research agendas that are relevant to their interests/regions of practice, submit collaborative grant proposals with other members, and co-author research presentations and/or publications. In these ways, research networks can provide the communication and collaboration streams and the structural and technical support and resource access to help develop sustained engagement in research activities.

Practice-based research networks (PBRNs) are one type of research network in which individual clinicians, academics, and/or practices work together to engage in research that is directly relevant to clinical practice and can lead to enhancements and quality improvements in care.[30,31] PBRNs facilitate the translation of research into changes in clinical practice and catalyze the implementation of new knowledge into often measurable changes in clinical care and patient outcomes.[32] The World Health Organization's Global Clinical Practice Network (GCPN) is the world's largest practice-based research network in the mental health field.[33] It aims to bring together global knowledge and local expertise to advance mental health worldwide. The GCPN uses an Internet-based platform, where mental health practitioners of any discipline can complete free membership and subsequently participate in Internet-based research related to GMH. Through this online site, researchers have disseminated surveys for research to thousands of practitioners across the world, ensuring that the perspectives of clinicians from all global regions inform global vocabulary, diagnostic tools, and treatment guidelines to advance mental health care.

BOX 8.5 GLOBAL CLINICAL PRACTICE NETWORK

Established in 2005, the GCPN (https://gcp.network) currently has over 18,000 members, which makes it more than 15 times larger than any other registered PBRN. It is also one of the only international PBRNs with members from 164 countries representing all global regions, with 40% of members residing in LMICs. The GCPN has diverse disciplinary and language representation with over ten mental health disciplines represented in the network (e.g., medicine, psychology, nursing, social work, occupational therapy) and registration available in nine languages. The GCPN has a history of longitudinal research engagement with its members, who have been consistently collaborating in a rigorous scientific research program of studies focused on testing and enhancing the diagnostic guidelines for mental and behavioral disorders for the eleventh edition of WHO's International Classification of Diseases (11th Revision; ICD-11).[33-35] Beyond the ICD-11, the GCPN is transforming into a network that facilitates local, regional, and global research collaborations with the objective of advancing scientific and clinical knowledge and translating these findings into improved clinical care. Its goal is substantial, sustained, data-driven improvements in mental health care globally.

The GCPN could not exist without its robust, technologically enabled infrastructure. It is but one example of the power of technology to connect thousands of people and transform mental health research, diagnosis, and treatment.

Conclusion

The examples in this chapter show that implementing collaborative mental health research training programs that consider local realities while upholding rigorous and impact-driven methods is possible. In fact, such collaborative training programs can transcend seemingly impossible resource barriers and catalyze mental health research in low-resource settings while simultaneously improving service delivery. Such programs, whether training researchers in HICs or LMICs or both, will invariably face challenges, including the false premise that research training and clinical service delivery are mutually exclusive priorities. Successful mental health research capacity-building programs will integrate research within clinical care, with each strengthening the other to improve GMH outcomes.

Building sustainable GMH research training programs requires identifying and leveraging financial, governmental, human resource, community, and technological resources. Although available current funding resources are inadequate to respond to the vast need for GMH research, the NIMH's Collaborative Hubs for International Research on Mental Health demonstrate strategic allocation of existing grant funding to support GMH research capacity-building. Through strong partnerships with LMIC governments and universities, hubs were designed to reflect local priorities and be applicable to clinical practice. As seen in the case of the Paises Africanos de Lingua Oficial Portuguesa Project, designing research training programs in partnership with government stakeholders increases the likelihood of the adoption of evidence-based legislation.

Programs centering community resources and cultural expertise, such as the AMHRTF's TEAM program, benefit from community and government buy-in and more findings that can be implemented within local health system realities. Ongoing relationships between HIC mentors and LMIC mentees, as seen in the example of the Latin American NIH-funded hub RedeAmericas, can effectively utilize professional human resources by being sensitive to the needs and capacities on each side of the relationship. This requires investing time in building trust, engaging with local resources to ensure the research plans and implementation meet both local and international ethical standards, and developing capacity and opportunities for commensurate contributions toward publications by HIC and LMIC authors. Finally, the example of the Global Clinical Practice Network shows how a practice-based online research network can utilize technology as a resource to support clinicians in delivering better mental health care while advancing knowledge about mental health diagnosis and treatment.

The goals of GMH research and clinical care are complementary, not competing. The resources described in this chapter, when leveraged correctly, will improve GMH research capacity at the same time as informing clinical guidelines and treatment. As mental health clinical intervention science advances, we must also continue to prioritize research on optimizing the means for dissemination, uptake, and implementation of evidence-based interventions. In other words, building implementation science research capacity is requisite to expanding the capacities for mental health service delivery. The opportunity is to move away from an either-or mindset to a both-and frame so that we can more effectively attend to effectiveness and implementation concurrently.[36-38] Innovative training programs that build research capacity within the context of implementation science research by leveraging key resources for GMH can help to forge strong partnerships within and across LMICs and HICs that advance the evidence base and improve mental health services so that we continue to move forward in closing the global mental health treatment gap.

References

1. World Health Organization. *World mental health report: transforming mental health for all*, 2022. Available from: https://www.who.int/publications/i/item/9789240049338
2. Global Burden of Disease Collaborative Network. Global burden of disease study 2017 (GBD 2017): burden by risk 1990–2017. Seattle, WA: Institute for Health Metrics and Evaluation (IHME); 2018. Available from: http://ghdx.healthdata.org/record/ihme-data/gbd-2017 -burden-risk-1990-2017
3. Brown CH, Curran G, Palinkas LA, Aarons GA, Wells KB, Jones L, Collins LM, Duan N, Mittman BS, Wallace A, Tabak RG. An overview of research and evaluation designs for dissemination and implementation. *Annual Review of Public Health*. 2017;38:1–22.
4. Levin C, Chisholm D. Cost-effectiveness and affordability of interventions, policies, and platforms for the prevention and treatment of mental, neurological, and substance use disorders. In: *Mental, Neurological, and Substance Use Disorders: Disease Control Priorities*, 3rd ed. (Vol. 4). Washington, DC: The International Bank for Reconstruction and Development; 2016. pp. 219–36.
5. Collins PY, Insel TR, Chockalingam A, Daar A, Maddox YT. Grand challenges in GMH: integration in research, policy, and practice. *PLoS Medicine*. 2013;10. doi:10.1371/journal. pmed.1001434
6. WHO. Comprehensive mental health action plan 2013–2020. Geneva; 2013. Available from: apps.who.int/gb/ebwha/pdf_files/WHA66/A66_R8-en.pdf
7. Patel V, Saxena S, Lund C, Thornicroft G, Baingana F, Bolton P, Chisholm D, Collins PY, Cooper JL, Eaton J, Herrman H,. The Lancet Commission on global mental health and sustainable development. *The Lancet*. 2018;392(10157):1553–98.
8. WHO. *2014 Mental Health Atlas*. Geneva: World Health Organization; 2015.

9. Pilowsky DJ, Rojas G, Price LN, Appiah-Poku J, Razzaque B, Sharma M, et al. Building research capacity across and within low- and middle-income countries: the collaborative hubs for international research on mental health. *Academic Psychiatry.* 2016;40:686–91. doi:10.1007/s40596-016-0493-3

10. Wainberg ML, Lovero KL, Duarte CS, Fiks Salem A, Mello M, Bezuidenhout C, Mootz J, Feliciano P, Suleman A, Fortunato dos Santos P, Weissman MM. Partnerships in research to implement and disseminate sustainable and scalable evidence-based practices (PRIDE) in Mozambique. *Psychiatric Services.* 2021;72(7):802–11.

11. Dos Santos PF, Wainberg ML, Caldas-de-Almeida JM, Saraceno B, Mari JDJ. Overview of the mental health system in Mozambique: addressing the treatment gap with a task-shifting strategy in primary care. *International Journal of Mental Health Systems.* 2016;10(1):1–9.

12. Sweetland AC, Oquendo MA, Sidat M, Santos PF, Vermund SH, Duarte CS, Arbuckle M, Wainberg ML. Closing the mental health gap in low-income settings by building research capacity: perspectives from Mozambique. *Annals of Global Health.* 2014;80(2):126–33.

13. Wainberg ML, Lovero KL, Duarte CS, Salem AF, Mello M. et al. Partnerships in Research to Implement and Disseminate Sustainable and Scalable Evidence-Based Practices (PRIDE) in Mozambique. *Psychiatric Services.* 2020;71(12):1257–1260. doi: 10.1176/appi.ps.202000090.

14. Israel BA, Schulz AJ, Parker EA, Becker AB. Review of community-based research: assessing partnership approaches to improve public health. *Annual Review of Public Health.* 1998;19(1):173–202.

15. Centers for Disease Control and Prevention. Community-based participatory research. CDC. Available from: https://www.cdc.gov/pcd/issues/2007/jul/06_0182.htm. Accessed November 16, 2018.

16. MacQueen KM, Bhan A, Frohlich J, Holzer J, Sugarman J. Evaluating community engagement in global health research: the need for metrics. *BMC Medical Ethics.* 2015;16(1):44.

17. Baum F, MacDougall C, Smith D. Participatory action research. *Journal of Epidemiology and Community Health.* 2006;60(10):854–7.

18. Israel BA, Checkoway B, Schulz A, Zimmerman M. Health education and community empowerment: conceptualizing and measuring perceptions of individual, organizational, and community control. *Health Education Quarterly.* 1994;21(2):149–70.

19. Chambers R. Participatory rural appraisal (PRA): analysis of experience. *World Development.* 1994;22(9):1253–68.

20. Mutiso VN, Musyimi CW, Nayak SS, Musau AM, Rebello T, Nandoya E, et al. Stigma-related mental health knowledge and attitudes among primary health workers and community health volunteers in rural Kenya. *International Journal of Social Psychiatry.* 2017;63(6):508–17.

21. Mutiso VN, Pike KM, Musyimi CN, Rebello TJ, Tele A, Gitonga I, et al. Changing patterns of mental health knowledge in rural Kenya after intervention using the WHO mhGAP-Intervention Guide. *Psychological Medicine.* 49(13), 2018;2227–2236.

22. Mutiso VN, Musyimi CW, Rebello TJ, Gitonga I, Tele A, Pike KM, et al. Patterns of concordances in mhGAP-IG screening and DSM-IV/ICD10 diagnoses by trained community service providers in Kenya: a pilot cross-sectional study. *Social Psychiatry and Psychiatric Epidemiology.* 2018;53(11):1277–87.

23. Mutiso VN, Gitonga I, Musau A, Musyimi CW, Nandoya E, Rebello TJ, et al. A step-wise community engagement and capacity building model prior to implementation of mhGAP-IG in a low-and middle-income country: a case study of Makueni County, Kenya. *International Journal of Mental Health Systems.* 2018;12(1):57.

24. Global Forum on Health Research. Research capacity strengthening (RCS): progress and perspectives. In: Davey, S. *10/90 Report on Health Research 2003–2004.* Geneva: GFHR; 2004.

25. Yang L, Pratt C, Valencia E, Conover S, Fernández R, Burrone MS, Cavalcanti MT, Lovisi G, Rojas G, Alvarado R, Galea S. RedeAmericas: building research capacity in young leaders for sustainable growth in community mental health services in Latin America. *Global Mental Health.* 2017;4 https://www.ncbi.nlm.nih.gov/pmc/articles/PMC5454783/.

26. Silva TFCD, Lovisi G, Cavalcanti MT, Dahl C, Conover S, Valencia E, Susser E. Critical time intervention: task shifting: a new psychosocial intervention for people with severe mental illness in Latin America. *Archives of Clinical Psychiatry*. 2013;40:243.

27. Agrest M, Le PD, Yang LH, Mascayano F, Alves-Nishioka S, Dev S, Kankan T, Tapia-Muñoz T, Sawyer S, Toso-Salman J, Dishy GA. Implementing a community-based task-shifting psychosocial intervention for individuals with psychosis in Chile: perspectives from users. *International Journal of Social Psychiatry*. 2019;65(1):38–45.

28. Baumgartner JN, Silva TFCD, Valencia E, Susser E. Measuring social integration in a pilot randomized controlled trial of critical time: intervention-task shifting in Latin America. *Cadernos Saude Coletiva*. 2012;20:436–9.

29. Mutiso VN, Pike K, Musyimi CW, Rebello TJ, Tele A, Gitonga I, et al. Feasibility of WHO mhGAP-intervention guide in reducing experienced discrimination in people with mental disorders: a pilot study in a rural Kenyan setting. *Epidemiology and Psychiatric Sciences*. 2018;28(2),: 1–12.

30. Green LW, Ottoson JM, Garcia C, Hiatt RA. Diffusion theory and knowledge dissemination, utilization, and integration in public health. *Annual Review of Public Health*. 2009;30, 151–174.

31. Adams J. Collaborations: The rise of research networks. *Nature*. 2012;490(7420):335.

32. Simon GE. PBRNs or RBPNs or both? *Psychiatric Services*. 2015;66(11):1129. doi:10.1176/appi.ps.661102

33. Reed GM, Rebello TJ, Pike KM, Medina-Mora ME, Gureje O, Zhao M, et al. WHO's global clinical practice network for mental health. *The Lancet Psychiatry*. 2015;2(5):379–80.

34. Williams RL, Rhyne RL. No longer simply a practice-based research network (PBRN) health improvement networks. *Journal of the American Board of Family Medicine*. 2011;24:485–8.

35. Keeley JW, Reed GM, Roberts MC, Evans SC, Medina-Mora ME, Robles R, et al. Developing a science of clinical utility in diagnostic classification systems: field study strategies for ICD-11 mental and behavioral disorders. *American Psychologist*. 2016;71(1):3.

36. First MB, Rebello TJ, Keeley JW, Bhargava R, Dai Y, Kulygina, M, et al. Do mental health professionals use diagnostic classifications the way we think they do? A global survey. *World Psychiatry*. 2018;17(2):187–95.

37. Reed GM, Sharan P, Rebello TJ, Keeley JW, Elena Medina-Mora M, Gureje O, et al. The ICD-11 developmental field study of reliability of diagnoses of high-burden mental disorders: results among adult patients in mental health settings of 13 countries. *World Psychiatry*. 2018;17(2):174–86.

38. Curran GM, Bauer M, Mittman B, Pyne JM, Stetler C. Effectiveness-implementation hybrid designs: combining elements of clinical effectiveness and implementation research to enhance public health impact. *Medical Care*. 2012;50(3):217.

Chapter 9

Student Engagement in Global Mental Health

Perspectives on Curricular, Extracurricular, and Advocacy Opportunities

Brendan Eappen, Nick Seymour, Matthew Basilico, Georgina Miguel Esponda, Concilia Tarisai Bere, and Helen Jack

Summary points

- Students are well positioned to contribute to positive social change addressing global mental health given the salience of mental illness among youth; the emergence of social norms that make talking about mental health more routine and less stigmatized; mental health service availability in some universities; their eagerness to take on new projects and novel approaches while in training; and the unique opportunities for early career development.
- Integration of local and global mental health efforts can provide a foundation for student action that is motivated by both personal relevance and global concern.
- Mentored curricular and extracurricular opportunities for student engagement are necessary to develop a pipeline of new members into the global mental health workforce.
- Student activism has strong historical roots that can inform action promoting global mental health.

Introduction

Given that students are the future of the mental health workforce, this chapter is written from the perspective of current and recent global mental health (GMH) trainees as an invitation to educators and peers to reflect upon the importance of—and possibilities associated with—well-supported, active student engagement in the field. It should be acknowledged that several of the authors are affiliated with a single (and admittedly unrepresentative) university in a high-income country (HIC), limiting the generalizability and utility across contexts of the perspectives shared here. Nonetheless, the authors hope to use their varied and aggregate experience in GMH to provide a trainee-centered point of view and practical suggestions for both senior career mentors who support students and trainees across the educational spectrum as well as students who seek opportunities for meaningful action. The authors of this chapter are themselves trainees and young professionals from the United States, Mexico, and Zimbabwe and draw from their respective experiences in the areas of social sciences, clinical psychology, medicine, research, and activism.

Educators and implementers should know that many students may not see a clear career path in GMH ahead of them despite deep personal motivations to work in the field, such as witnessing the experience of a loved one living with mental illness, managing their own condition, or being drawn toward innovative responses to the suffering of fellow human beings. The growing depth and breadth of the field of GMH—as well as the substantial burden and complexity of mental illness globally—merits the development of additional GMH training programs and broad integration of GMH topics into courses in related fields. Furthermore, we believe that GMH programs should provide preferential access and support to students from low- and middle-income

DOI: 10.4324/9781315160597-12

countries (LMICs), who may be particularly well positioned to improve global mental health equity.

In addition to inviting students to participate in scholarly projects and focused coursework, mentors can help students navigate opportunities to gain experience in clinical, policy, non-profit, research, and advocacy arenas relevant to GMH and connect students with professionals across these fields. Educators should empower trainees to promote mental health beyond the confines of their particular field of study. Given the global stigma of mental illness and overall low levels of funding for and attention to GMH, all trainees in GMH should be prepared to advocate for more equitable and progressive systems of mental health care, leveraging the political capital, professional network, humanistic perspective, and technical expertise gained in their training for broader social impact.

Why are students important to global mental health?

The shortage of mental health professionals is considerable around the world, but particularly in LMICs, and perpetuates the GMH treatment gap.[1-5] The field needs not only skilled and committed health practitioners but also researchers, innovators, implementers, and managers who can address the many system-level challenges in GMH. Helping students recognize the GMH-relevant depth of need and injustice could create a stronger pipeline into careers in the field. Engaging students in thinking about how GMH connects with coursework in related fields (for example, by introducing GMH concepts through a history course's session on deinstitutionalization of persons living with mental illness) may build a generation of professionals across various fields who make mental health integration a priority, rather than an afterthought.

Strengthening GMH education is an investment in the future of the field; moreover, students can already make meaningful contributions. Although students may lack the professional expertise of senior actors in the field, they bring enthusiasm, new ideas, and flexible career aspirations. Students are in an excellent position to be advocates and champions for the field of GMH. The impact of student advocacy can be local or international, whether through movement building, protests, letter-writing campaigns, or lobby meetings with policymakers. Advocacy can also be very personal, insofar as it can involve sharing experiences of mental illness with teachers, friends, and family, speaking to the value of high-quality mental health services, and promoting help-seeking behaviors to reduce the stigma of mental illness and help others to access available care and support.

Why is global mental health important to students?

Mental health topics are highly salient to students, especially those who experience or observe psychological distress firsthand. The onset and persistent suffering of mental illness are common among adolescents.[6-8] Globally, nearly half of mental disorders begin by age 18, with a peak age of onset at 14.5 years of age.[9] When young people seek help, they often turn to their peers. Unfortunately, generalizable data about the prevalence of seeking peer support in response to psychological crises has not been well documented in college students. One study in the United States found that over half of high-school-aged participants would likely share their suicidal ideation with peers, but were unlikely to contact professionals.[10] Further, the poor accessibility of mental health professionals in low-resource settings often makes treatment-seeking difficult even when desired. In addition to accessibility barriers, stigma may influence young people to seek a friend's support instead of seeking help from family or professionals. Setting aside whether professional services are accessible or not, many students are attuned to the suffering of their peers and want to provide support. The authors contend that many young people who have witnessed or experienced mental illness are motivated to act to improve mental health care—this is energy that can be directed toward their engagement with GMH.

Increasing mental health awareness may offer untapped potential for advocacy, but it is important to recognize that the availability of services and acceptability of discussing treatment vary widely across countries, campuses, and even social groups within a single campus. Even so, at least on some university campuses in the United States, addressing mental health is becoming more socially normative. For instance, there has been increased utilization of college counseling services over the past couple of decades, with the exception of 2020–2021 when the COVID-19 pandemic brought a decrease in counseling utilization, likely due to fewer students living on campus and a decrease in clinical capacity.[11] While student mental health services in the United States may have grown in visibility and popularity, there remain vast unmet needs in the United States.[12,13] Box 9.1 contrasts the culture of help-seeking for mental health and available services at two institutions known to the authors. Although these are not globally representative examples, they do illustrate the range of attention given to mental health possible in the university setting.

BOX 9.1 LOCAL INSTITUTIONAL CULTURE OF MENTAL HEALTH HELP-SEEKING AND SERVICES AT TWO UNIVERSITIES KNOWN TO THE AUTHORS

At Harvard College, about 40% of undergraduate students accessed mental health services at some point during their undergraduate career, according to a 2015 article published in the student newspaper, which has a steady stream of articles written by students both praising access to mental health services and critiquing the university's offerings.[14] Nearly every bulletin board around campus has a poster advertising mental health services at the university clinic or a peer counseling service. Harvard College has six peer counseling groups, several open since the 1980s. Some have a specific focus, such as relationships, eating concerns, sexual orientation, and contraception. A newer group, founded in 2016, invites students to come with concerns about race or class, targeting first-generation as well as racial minority students, who have customarily sought care from university health services at much lower rates.[13,15] Even with this attention given to mental health, the authors understand there is much room for improvement.

In contrast, Universidad Iberoamericana, a private university in Mexico City, does not have any peer counseling services and, although the university offers psychological support, it has not always been widely publicized. This is perhaps unsurprising in a country where fewer than 20% of individuals living with a mental disorder receive treatment (compared to 40% in the United States).[16] National surveys in Mexico show that approximately a quarter of young people (18–29 years old) are affected by mental disorders.[17] Although this prevalence is similar to that of other age groups, young people in Mexico have the lowest odds of accessing treatment.[16,18] Increasing awareness and conversations about mental health within school communities in LMICs is potentially one of the most important activities to overcoming barriers to care.

Stressors associated with attending college—including intensified academic and social pressures, relocating away from family supports, or navigating unfamiliar social settings—can provide fertile ground for mental illness to develop. These challenges may particularly affect some students from LMICs studying in a HIC. Having to adjust to a completely new environment and a foreign education system can prove to be challenging. Students from non-majority racial and religious backgrounds and students who grew up in other countries have expressed how campus mental health services do not always meet their needs.[19] Some worry that they will not feel connected with a provider who comes from a background so different from their own, or that friends or family will criticize them for seeking help.[19] Indeed, some evidence suggests that individuals who are white are more likely to access university mental health services when they have needs.[20] Academic institutions should be leaders in assuring that students have equitable access to mental health care. Some of these same students from LMICs who experience challenges adapting to a foreign university may be particularly motivated and well positioned to engage with global mental health, having knowledge of their personal experience and how it relates to, perhaps, distinct cultural conceptions of mental illness. Personal experience can illuminate unmet needs wherever healthcare systems and social discourse are inadequate to address the burden of mental illness.

Given the considerable prevalence of mental illness among students of university age and opportunities for discourse to emerge from shared experiences, peer support, and student associations, students may be well attuned to mental health needs in local communities and globally. By definition, GMH is global and includes the local communities from which students originate and where they may be able to work toward meaningful change. Local disparities and structural inadequacies in HICs and LMICs relevant to mental health must be understood and addressed by GMH actors. Where mental health is stigmatized on a local level, students may find university environments motivating or empowering as they transition into adulthood and join new communities. Raising awareness of mental illness and providing better support for affected students could be an effective form of local activism. For universities at which mental health discourse is common, relating local mental health efforts to other local and global efforts—possibly revealing associated health and social inequities—could be a natural progression for students in developing concern for the mental health of the most vulnerable populations.

Curricular engagement

The pipeline for a skilled, robust mental health workforce starts with the integration of GMH into existing educational offerings and training programs. Notably, GMH training will look very different for college students, who may have a lecture on GMH as part of a broader global health course, than it will for master's degree-level students who are learning relevant research methods to prepare them for careers in the field or medical trainees who are building clinical skills and cultural competencies to treat patients and design health delivery systems. Although there are no readily accessible data on the number of GMH programs, 99 member institutions listed on the Consortium of Universities for Global Health's (CUGH) portal maintained at least one global health program (whether graduate, undergraduate, certificate, or unspecified) as of 2019.[21] CUGH developed a set of core competencies for interprofessional education in global health that form a basis for education for trainees in all disciplines.[22] GMH education can build off this existing competency framework and develop mental health-specific applications and examples. These competencies, and possible mental health applications of them that feel important to the authors, are shown in Table 9.1. Chapter 4 in this volume describes strategies to identify GMH competencies, as part of a framework to develop a curriculum for specific learners.

From the authors' perspective as trainees, curricular offerings should prepare students with multidisciplinary perspectives and expertise, attitudes of humility and curiosity, an inspiring sense of possibility for the poorest and sickest people, socially critical analytical lenses, and models of equitable partnership. These suggestions are relevant both to designing courses dedicated to

Table 9.1 Consortium of Universities for Global Health's Basic Global Health Competencies—Proposed application to mental health for student curricula and training

Global health competency domain	Application to mental health
"Global burden of disease"	Understand the contribution of mental illness to global morbidity and mortality, how the global community has addressed this burden, and the benefits and limitations of burden of disease modeling.
"Globalization of health and healthcare"	Compare the systems that different countries use to deliver mental health services and describe how global forces, such as immigration or climate change, may shape mental health outcomes and services.
"Social and environmental determinants of health"	Describe how poverty, culture, and other social determinants affect access to mental health services and mental health outcomes. This should highlight the centrality of social determinants to mental health, whether through local or global examples.
"Collaboration, partnering, and communication"	Discuss the interdisciplinary mental health care delivery team, including traditional medicine practitioners, and build skills in bringing together diverse perspectives to solve GMH problems.
"Ethics"	Apply basic bioethics frameworks to issues that frequently arise in mental health, including involuntary treatment and resource scarcity.
"Professional practice"	Describe gaps in mental health services worldwide and, depending on trainee level, begin to develop skills that could help address unmet needs.
"Health equity and social justice"	Understand the global inequity in access to mental health services and the fundamentals of a human rights-based approach to healthcare.
"Sociocultural and political awareness"	Identify the key institutions involved in the field of GMH and how broader global institutions affect mental health care.

Source: Adapted for GMH from a partial list of the competencies developed by Jogerst and colleagues[22]

GMH as well as to integrating GMH topics into courses in related fields. In either case, coursework may highlight the burden and manifestation of various mental illnesses, data on differential access to care, and case studies of evidence-based programs that address mental illness in various cultural contexts. These case studies can serve as a platform for engaging students while presenting key concepts through examples of policy change, task-shifting, task-sharing, capacity-building for training and care delivery, non-profit interventions, and other approaches. Dedicated GMH coursework should include an introduction to active areas of inquiry and advocacy in the field, as well as exposure to diverse ideological frameworks guiding this work. Anthropological accounts and personal narratives should be presented to students to empower them with both a sense of urgency to promote GMH and the humility necessary to engage with the complex and often distinct experiences of mental illness across cultures. Comprehensive GMH education should draw from complementary fields including psychology, neurobiology, anthropology, implementation science, medicine, epidemiology, economics, public health, political science, history, human rights, and ethics.

Currently, GMH curricula are disproportionately taught in HICs. Hence, partnerships with universities around the globe will be key to increasing local capacity, making programs more accessible and affordable for students from low-resource backgrounds and particularly those in LMICs, where there is a high need for mental health professionals. Students from LMICs, moreover, are often the best informed to design interventions and policy with their local contexts in mind and to bridge the global mental health resources with the needs in their own communities. Providing students mentored field-research opportunities can support the development of projects relevant to where they practice and contribute to local capacity-building (such as is done at Harvard Medical School's MMSc Program in Global Health Delivery, for example).[23] Similarly, Box 9.2 describes a promising collaboration between a non-governmental organization (NGO) and an undergraduate psychology program in Mexico, which facilitates experiential learning and helps expand access to mental health services. Higher education programs have an important role in increasing student awareness of the mental health needs of vulnerable populations and ensuring students develop what Metzl and Hansen term "structural competency"[24]: a better understanding of how structural issues, like poverty, exclusion, low literacy, and violence, cause and aggravate mental illnesses.[24] Student advocacy, in turn, could also ensure that principles of equity and justice are prioritized in access to and in the structuring of GMH training. As such, the socially critical curricula developed by GMH educators and the advocacy community enlivened by GMH trainees can be mutually reinforcing. Placement in settings of care delivery—with appropriate supervision and accommodation to avoid imposing a burden to local resources—can provide a unique experience for students training in well-resourced settings to see firsthand the complex causes of mental illness or distress and the barriers to access to care present in diverse communities. These placements need not necessarily be in distant regions, however; placements at a local clinic, refugee resettlement organization, or homeless shelter, for example, also have high educational value. Prior training in structural competency can help students approach placements with humility and further work in global mental health. Such training can also be enhanced by the inclusion of faculty experienced in implementation, as perspectives on challenges encountered in research and care delivery settings are essential augmentation to classroom-based learning about methods, data management, and intervention development.

In addition, training programs should provide students with the tangible skills that will help them find and be successful in careers in both academic and non-academic settings. These skills could span research methods, project management practices, team-building approaches, fundraising, and writing, for example, among many others. The collaboration described in Box 9.2 presented an opportunity to offer students a perspective on the many contextual factors that influence the feasibility and effectiveness of interventions and fueled their motivation to continue working with similar populations in the future.

BOX 9.2 AN EXAMPLE OF A STUDENT PLACEMENT THAT SUPPORTED MENTAL HEALTH SERVICE DELIVERY

History of student involvement: The Compañeros En Salud (CES; Partners In Health's sister organization in Mexico) mental health program trains and supervises recently graduated medical doctors to provide mental health services in primary care clinics in rural areas. In order to respond to the mental health needs in the community, CES has involved undergraduate and research degree students to conduct research projects aimed at improving the delivery of mental health services (e.g., studies testing implementation strategies for the delivery of psychoeducation groups or assessing the skills and training needs of community health workers). In addition to a diverse set of technical skills, students have brought initiative, motivation, a desire to learn, and openness to new ideas: all important to delivering services in challenging settings. Drawing on these experiences involving early career professionals, CES has sought to establish collaborations with local universities to recruit regular cohorts of psychology students in their final stages of training to support the delivery of mental health services in primary care clinics.

Pilot placement: In Mexico, health professionals, including psychologists, can deliver health services after completing an undergraduate degree in a relevant discipline. Six undergraduate psychology students from a Mexican university undertook a five-week placement with CES as part of their final year program of study in 2017. Psychology student activities included a) delivering a predesigned two-week workshop based on the Photovoice methodology to a selection of service users diagnosed with depressive or anxiety disorders aimed at empowering users to share their experiences with mental illness, strengthen support networks, and combat stigma, and b) providing feedback to primary healthcare workers following observation of their consultations with patients with depression or anxiety.

Results: Medical doctors expressed that students made valuable contributions to the diagnosis and treatment of service users with mental illness, and workshop participants reported having established positive relationships with students as well as feeling better able to discuss their illness with others after the workshop. However, this placement required extensive support and resources from the mental health team, which had to ensure students had appropriate supervision at all times since this was the first time most of them had lived and worked in remote and rural communities. The experiences and environments to which Mexico's university-educated health professionals are accustomed often differ from the realities of rural and low-resource communities, so they encountered many linguistic and cultural barriers. Supervision was key to improving communication between students and members of the communities and in guiding clinical decisions. Students also became familiar with differences between psychology offices in urban areas and primary care clinics in rural areas. For example, regular appointments are often impractical for patients living in rural and remote communities where they may have to walk for hours to get to a clinic. Lengthy sessions are restricted by the unavailability of healthcare professionals, as doctors see an average of 20 patients per day. This is in stark contrast to the psychology practice that students had observed in urban settings within Mexico, where appointments are typically 50 minutes in length and occur regularly (often weekly or biweekly). During the placement, medical doctors and students could engage in dialogue about the complexities of providing physical and psychological treatments in a single consultation, and students were able to understand the need to adapt to these conditions.

Extracurricular engagement

In order to overcome the pervasive stigma and resource gaps associated with GMH, the field particularly needs people who feel empowered to speak up. Although students may not yet be able to provide direct services or lead research efforts, they can be impactful through advocacy by raising awareness, persuading policymakers and legislators with the moral case for mental health care, and mobilizing political will through writing letters and organizing and participating in protests. Such advocacy is not only powerful in effecting change in the near term, but it can encourage a mindset that prepares students and trainees to be lifelong, vocal advocates for mental health as well. The field of GMH needs a generation of clinicians, scientists, and policymakers who can act as champions for the cause. As a critical complement to a university education, advocacy empowers students to be engaged thinkers and apply their learning to real-world issues across disciplines and sectors, including in the fight for global mental health equity. Advocacy in GMH requires a solid understanding of relevant issues, well-informed goals and priorities, and a sense of identity and community associated with the cause. These critical elements can be provided through curricular and extracurricular initiatives and also supported by academic mentors.

Of course, there are valuable extracurricular opportunities for students to engage in GMH in addition to advocacy, including service learning, peer counseling, interest groups, and research. Service-learning opportunities may include indirect work that bolsters GMH actors, for example, through fundraising. They may also include direct service such as in short-term field-based experiences in global health[25] or in working with marginalized populations close to home, such as in shelters or clinics serving people experiencing homelessness. Peer counseling groups supervised by campus health services can provide structure and guidance to leverage the already central role of caregiving in many students' identities. Interest groups provide a forum for discussion and reinforce the legitimacy of the field and related career paths. Research opportunities could include collaboration on existing projects tailored to particular students' level of experience as well as guidance on student-driven projects. Mentors should make efforts to ensure that students understand the theories of change underlying their work, given that research can often be quite removed from actual beneficiaries' lives. A complementary set of opportunities for extracurricular engagement that includes advocacy, direct service, community building, and science may offer trainees the most insight into the interrelatedness of these domains and the best opportunity to find their place in the GMH movement.

The authors urge leaders in the field involved in academia, policy, advocacy, and implementation to engage students. This may take the form of meeting with interested students, offering perspective from their field-based work, recommending reading materials, or connecting trainees with faculty and programs within their professional network. It could also entail securing grant funding for student workers and protected mentorship time. Professors can encourage participation in the wide-reaching global mental health community, say, by connecting students to organizations such as the Mental Health Innovation Network[26] and the Movement for Global Mental Health,[27] which have newsletters and websites that include internship opportunities, discussion forums, recommendations for reading, and a catalog of organizations implementing mental health innovations across the world. Students could be invited to join electronic mailing lists to be connected with community resources of universities with relevant initiatives, such as the Alan J. Flisher Centre for Public Mental Health at the University of Cape Town and Stellenbosch University,[28] the Centre for Global Mental Health based out of the London School of Hygiene and Tropical Medicine and King's College London,[29] the Columbia University Global Mental Health Programs,[30] and GlobalMentalHealth@Harvard.[31] Opportunities for well-designed summer fellowships focused on GMH, structured around research, implementation, familiarity with academic literature, and community building could also engage student interest and encourage exploration of GMH advocacy. Stigma associated with mental illness may present additional barriers for students pursuing careers in this field in some professional and social settings, but well-established academic programs and supportive mentors can also counter such stigma and illuminate channels for entry into the field. The interdisciplinary nature of global mental health is certainly a strength, and students benefit from understanding that there are multiple possible career paths into the field. Unfortunately, the complexity of the field can leave students uncertain about how to enter. Without opportunities for productive engagement while exploring their interest in GMH, students could be drawn into fields with more easily accessible opportunities and miss opportunities in the domain of GMH. As students, we are making a plea for more concrete opportunities for student involvement.

Student advocacy: Relevance of HIV activism to global mental health

This chapter concludes with a call to action: students can and should engage in advocacy today. Advocacy builds essential skills, provides a natural structure for mentorship, harnesses motivation, and is an opportunity for impact even before students develop deep expertise. The main reason to engage in student advocacy is that it works. Mental health activism can benefit from the strategies employed by HIV/AIDS activists. The global HIV/AIDS movement provided lessons where youth and other non-professionals used the resources available to them—self-learning, mobilization, strategic planning, and moral conviction—to change the tide of major domestic and global policies. Indeed, histories of the global HIV/AIDS response note that many of the critical policy victories came on the back of advocacy efforts led by student and grassroots activists, with some academics going as far as to say that HIV/AIDS advocacy and activism spurred an unprecedented process of pharmacological innovation and established international collaboration—all central to the evolution of the field of global health.[32]

The AIDS Coalition to Unleash Power (ACT-UP) is an example of an advocacy effort, in which the mobilization of concerned citizens and students played a pivotal role, that mobilized a social movement and shaped the historic course of a response to the emerging epidemic of HIV/AIDS. Despite their lack of institutional positioning, ACT-UP organizers gained knowledge, devised strategies, and led a series of protest-backed campaigns to influence policies of the National Institutes of Health, the budget of the United States Department of Health and Human Services, and the Catholic Church. One notable campaign identified the policies of the US Food and Drug Administration (FDA) that effectively limited the availability of experimental medicines to patients whose disease course led to certain fatality. ACT-UP members worked to develop ideas—namely, they identified a policy change that would allow individuals suffering from AIDS access to experimental therapies—but they also worked on social strategy, staging protests at the FDA. Their direct actions included protests and civil disobedience, and eventually led to a change in FDA policy that allowed a shortened approval process for key medicines.[33] This policy has withstood over two decades of scrutiny and has been expanded to cover interventions in numerous other categories, speeding the analysis of approximately 400 new technologies from 1998 to 2008.[34]

Key features of AIDS activism appear particularly relevant to mental health advocacy. For example, AIDS was politicized and stigmatized; the political salience of AIDS motivated sufferers and allies to mobilize. Stigma can be destructive to sufferers and to movement building. HIV stigma, however, did not keep activists from working together. Indeed, many people found advocacy efforts to be an important source of solidarity. Although dissimilar in some ways to the HIV/AIDS health crisis, mental health also faces both politicization and stigmatization within many communities globally. Likewise, AIDS affected high-income countries as well as low- and middle-income countries as does mental illness. Many key victories in global AIDS advocacy were aided by alliances between activists in HICs and LMICs. These alliances could also be critical to successful global mental health efforts. The terrible toll exacted by the AIDS pandemic was well known to others and to many evangelical missionaries working in sub-Saharan Africa. When advocacy efforts influenced President George W. Bush to establish a major global AIDS program, the US President's Emergency Plan for AIDS Relief (PEPFAR), these personal connections to the issue proved pivotal on a scale previously unimaginable.[35] Powerful decision makers with personal connections to mental health have in some cases already shared their stories, and the considerable prevalence of common mental disorders means that a substantial fraction of lawmakers will have direct or family experiences with the issue. These personal connections to mental illness, even if not publicly disclosed, can be crucial as efforts are pressed forward; the democratic process depends on the representation of personal narratives, and the ubiquitous nature and challenge of mental illness is highly salient when considered through a personal lens. The solutions to inequities in mental health care should not be conflated with those for inequities in HIV/AIDS, and GMH advocates should be careful not to universalize solutions to complex, context-specific challenges.[36] Nevertheless, there are important commonalities that may suggest reasons for optimism and strategies for an effective approach. Both HIV/AIDS and mental illness are politicized and stigmatized, affect HICs and LMICs, and are frequently personally relevant to key decision makers. Mental health advocates should look to the successful advocacy strategies of the HIV movement for guidance.

We encourage students to organize in promotion of GMH. A basic framework for advocacy strategy is presented in Box 9.3. A number of core features that appear central to the success of HIV/AIDS advocacy efforts may provide valuable guidance to global mental health advocates (see Box 9.4). Clear goals, strategy, willingness to be bold, moral authority, and critical self-reflection are all salient elements of many successful campaigns. History makes clear that students can have a remarkable impact on issues of global health equity. Global mental health could be next. It could start with you, educators and trainees alike.

BOX 9.3 STRATEGY-GUIDING QUESTIONS

1. What is the problem?
2. What can be done concretely?
3. Who can make that change?
4. How can they be influenced to make that change?

Strategy questions and a power mapping of the perceived target are often crucial for designing and implementing a successful advocacy campaign. Asking the questions listed and making the answers concrete helps ensure that limited resources are directed to efforts that maximize likelihood of impact.

(Developed from experience with student advocates from Partners In Health Engage. For a more detailed approach to the topic, see Kim Bobo and colleagues[37])

BOX 9.4 TOOLKIT FOR THE STUDENT ACTIVIST

Strategy	*Explanation*
Begin with the End in Mind	Focusing on a concrete goal (e.g., a policy change) instead of an entire or more general issue can direct efforts in a way that is more effective. Choosing a goal can be difficult, but there will always be further campaigns.
Strategy	Having a clear sense of who holds power over your goal, and how to get them to change, is critical to effective advocacy.
Team Building	Fostering solidarity within the team and with the goal is critical; regular reflection on shared values can be impactful in this regard. Making progress toward the goal can also be one of the most effective ways of team building.

Willingness to Use Non-conventional Tactics	Many successful advocacy efforts involve drawing attention to the issue through marches, civil disobedience, and eye-catching visuals. A common advocacy dictum is that "what is won in the boardroom was first won on the streets," meaning that public pressure is critical to generating change behind closed doors.
Moral Authority	Many advocates are analogous to David against Goliath, and ultimately power rests in a combination of material resources and moral suasion. Demonstrating moral authority is the goal of using non-conventional tactics (i.e., these tactics should be invoked to win over hearts and minds).
Perseverance	Every major advocacy effort had times when it looked impossible, and when people doubted that their objective would be achieved. Perseverance on an issue is necessary to achieve the goal.
Power Generation	Effective advocates are extremely conscious of sources of power, and how to generate their own. Generating public awareness and pressure on elected officials is often a key pathway for effecting change toward a policy goal.
Critical Self-Reflection	Personal motivations and connections with an issue should always be examined. Working with people affected by the issue in question can help to keep all team members grounded. Self-reflection can help to refine and to motivate. But it is also intended to support, not interfere with, the challenging and important work of collective action.

Source: Developed from internal communications with the Harvard chapters of the Student Global AIDS Campaign and Partners In Health Engage.

Conclusion

Tremendous challenges lie ahead in advancing excellence and equity in global mental health, and involving students is key to the present and future of the field. Many students are personally sensitized to the importance of mental health. With the proper structures and relationships in place, they could be well positioned for contributing to the field via their advocacy today and through careers in GMH. Student engagement may initially unfold within educational institutions and local communities. Coursework and dedicated mentorship can establish paths for students to develop and, ultimately, professionalize their interests in GMH, by helping them develop the skills, motivation, and perspectives necessary for contributions both during their training and throughout their careers. Curricular and extracurricular engagement can provide a platform for transdisciplinary introduction to the field, concrete opportunities for invaluable hands-on experiences, and individualized mentorship. Extracurricular engagement may include research, but it should certainly not be limited to it. Across all forms of engagement with GMH, mentors and students should critically consider the complexities of the field as they strive to do good work across distinct cultures and disciplines. Mentors should be mindful of their potential role in inspiring and nurturing academic and advocacy interests in students who are the pipeline of future social scientists, policymakers, and health professionals. These students may go on to build much-needed research, clinical, and other capacities critical to the field. Lest students leave GMH for career paths that are better supported or easier to navigate, educators and mentors should proactively guide students in exploring avenues for a career path within GMH that aligns with their interests. For students and trainees of all levels, advocacy is a particularly promising opportunity to learn and contribute. We call on our peers and on the leaders of the field, at a global and local level, to include and empower students in achieving the aspirations of the global mental health field.

References

1. Fulton BD, Scheffler RM, Sparkes SP, Auh EY, Vujicic M, Soucat A. Health workforce skill mix and task shifting in low income countries: a review of recent evidence. *Human Resources for Health*. 2011;9(1):1.
2. Yasamy MT, Maulik PK, Tomlinson M, Lund C, Van Ommeren M, Saxena S. Responsible governance for mental health research in low resource countries. *PLoS Medicine*. 2011;8(11):e1001126.
3. World Health Organization. *Mental health gap action programme: scaling up care for mental, neurological, and substance use disorders*. Geneva: WHO; 2008. 36 p.
4. Hoge MA, Stuart GW, Morris J, Flaherty MT, Paris M, Goplerud E. Mental health and addiction workforce development: federal leadership is needed to address the growing crisis. *Health Affairs*. 2013;32(11):2005–12.
5. Bruckner TA, Scheffler RM, Shen G, Yoon J, Chisholm D, Morris J, Fulton BD, Dal Poz MR, Saxena S. The mental health workforce gap in low-and middle-income countries: a needs-based approach. *Bulletin of the World Health Organization*. 2011;89:184–94.
6. Hunt J, Eisenberg D. Mental health problems and help-seeking behavior among college students. *Journal of Adolescent Health*. 2010;46(1):3–10.
7. Kessler RC, Angermeyer M, Anthony JC, De Graaf RO, Demyttenaere K, Gasquet I, De Girolamo G, Gluzman S, Gureje OY, Haro JM, Kawakami N. Lifetime prevalence and age-of-onset distributions of mental disorders in the World Health Organization's World Mental Health Survey Initiative. *World Psychiatry*. 2007;6(3):168.
8. Kessler RC, Amminger GP, Aguilar-Gaxiola S, Alonso J, Lee S, Ustun TB. Age of onset of mental disorders: a review of recent literature. *Current Opinion in Psychiatry*. 2007;20(4):359.
9. Solmi, M., Radua, J., Olivola, M., Croce, E., Soardo, L., de Pablo, G. S., et al. Age at onset of mental disorders worldwide: large-scale meta-analysis of 192 epidemiological studies. *Molecular Psychiatry*. 2022;27:281–95.
10. Hennig CW, Crabtree CR, Baum D. Mental health CPR: peer contracting as a response to potential suicide in adolescents. *Archives of Suicide Research*. 1998;4(2):169–87.
11. Center for Collegiate Mental Health. *Annual report: Penn state student affairs center for collegiate mental health*, 2021. https://ccmh.psu.edu/assets/docs/2021-CCMH-Annual-Report.pdf
12. Ketchen Lipson S, Gaddis SM, Heinze J, Beck K, Eisenberg D. Variations in student mental health and treatment utilization across US colleges and universities. *Journal of American College Health*. 2015;63(6):388–96.
13. Hunt JB, Eisenberg D, Lu L, Gathright M. Racial/ethnic disparities in mental health care utilization among US college students: applying the institution of medicine definition of health care disparities. *Academic Psychiatry*. 2015;39(5):520–6.
14. Klein MA. The Harvard condition. *The Harvard Crimson*. October 8, 2015. https://www.thecrimson.com/article/2015/10/8/scrutiny-harvard-condition/
15. Lipson SK, Kern A, Eisenberg D, Breland-Noble AM. Mental health disparities among college students of color. *Journal of Adolescent Health*. 2018 Sep 1;63(3):348–56.
16. Borges G, Medina-Mora ME, Wang PS, Lara C, Berglund P, Walters E. Treatment and adequacy of treatment of mental disorders among respondents to the Mexico national comorbidity survey. *American Journal of Psychiatry*. 2006;163(8):1371–8.
17. Medina-Mora ME, Borges G, Benjet C, Lara C, Berglund P. Psychiatric disorders in Mexico: lifetime prevalence in a nationally representative sample. *The British Journal of Psychiatry*. 2007;190(6):521–8.

18. Medina-Mora ME, Borges G, Lara C, Benjet C, Blanco J, Fleiz C, Villatoro J, Rojas E, Zambrano J. Prevalence, service use, and demographic correlates of 12-month DSM-IV psychiatric disorders in Mexico: results from the Mexican National Comorbidity Survey. *Psychological Medicine*. 2005 Dec;35(12):1773 83.

19. He WM, Kevin CM, Surani S, Yang NY. An AAPI perspective: cultural roots of mental health. *The Harvard Crimson*. 2016; https://www.thecrimson.com/article/2016/1/21/harvard-aapi -mental-health/.

20. Eisenberg D, Hunt J, Speer N. Help seeking for mental health on college campuses: review of evidence and next steps for research and practice. *Harvard Review of Psychiatry*. 2012;20(4):222–32.

21. Consortium of Universities for Global Health. Academic global health programs. Available from: http://www.cugh.org/programs

22. Jogerst K, Callender B, Adams V, Evert J, Fields E, Hall T, Olsen J, Rowthorn V, Rudy S, Shen J, Simon L. Identifying interprofessional global health competencies for 21st-century health professionals. *Annals of Global Health*. 2015;81(2):239–47.

23. Harvard Medical School. Master of medical sciences in global health delivery. Available from: https://ghsm.hms.harvard.edu/education/master-medical-sciences-global-health-delivery/ course-study

24. Metzl JM, Hansen H. Structural competency: theorizing a new medical engagement with stigma and inequality. *Social Science & Medicine*. 2014;103:126–33.

25. Melby MK, Loh LC, Evert J, Prater C, Lin H, Khan OA. Beyond medical "missions" to impact-driven short-term experiences in global health (STEGHs): ethical principles to optimize community benefit and learner experience. *Academic Medicine*. 2016;91(5):633–8.

26. Mental Health Innovation Network. Join the community. Available from: http://www .mhinnovation.net/join-community

27. Movement for Global Mental Health. Benefits of membership. Available from: http://www .globalmentalhealth.org/get-involved/benefits-membership

28. Alan J Flisher Centre for Public Mental Health. 2022. Internet. Available from: http://www .cpmh.org.za/

29. Centre for Global Mental Health. About us. Available from: https://www.centreforglobalment alhealth.org/about-us

30. Columbia University Global Mental Health Programs. CUGMHP news. Available from: https:// www.cugmhp.org/news/

31. Harvard Global Health Institute. GlobalMentalHealth@Harvard. Available from: https:// globalhealth.harvard.edu/mentalhealth

32. Brandt AM. How AIDS invented global health. *New England Journal of Medicine*. 2013;368(23):2149–52.

33. Grossman, LA. AIDS activists, FDA regulation, and the amendment of America's Drug Constitution. *American Journal of Law & Medicine*. 2016 Nov;42(4):687–742.

34. Reichert JM, Rochon SL, Zhang BD. A decade of the fast track programme. *Nature Reviews Drug Discovery*. 2008;7(11):885–7.

35. Farmer P, Kim JY, Kleinman A, Basilico M. *Reimagining global health: an introduction*. Berkeley, CA: University of California Press; 2013.

36. Howell A, Mills C, Rushton S. The (Mis)appropriation of HIV/AIDS advocacy strategies in Global Mental Health: towards a more nuanced approach. *Global Health*. 2017;13(1):44. Published 2017 Jul 1. doi:10.1186/s12992-017-0263-3

37. Bobo K, Kendal J, Max S. *Organizing for social change: Midwest Academy manual for activists*, 4th ed. Santa Ana, CA: Forum Press; 2010. 425 p.

Section III

Additional Areas for Special Focus in Global Mental Health Training

Chapter 10

Training for Humanitarian Crisis Response and Mental Health System Reform

Giuseppe Raviola, Rabih El Chammay, Amruta Houde, Sarah Singer, and Stephanie L. Smith

Summary points

- Frontline teams implementing humanitarian crisis response and new mental health services require key competencies to facilitate needs assessment, program management and service implementation, establishment of sustained training and supervision, data collection with monitoring and evaluation, and analytic and academic skills to evaluate and document completed work. Educators and practitioners in global mental health delivery must seek to attend to all these needs in their training curriculum in order to create sustained career development trajectories for implementers who will work in these kinds of challenging circumstances.
- Foundational knowledge essential to training in humanitarian mental health response and mental health systems strengthening includes: familiarity with international *standards of psychosocial, psychological, and psychiatric care and support* in both humanitarian crises and in developing sustainable services; elements of *health systems* and *clinical services* design; *quality improvement methods* and elements of *training systems* design; and *key concepts in social medicine* as they apply to ethical delivery of mental health care.
- Training curricula should be informed by a proposed care system that can be strengthened and developed according to existing resources—with both *theory of change* and *value chain* approaches (as defined in this chapter) helpful—and should elaborate how care delivery platforms link district hospital, primary care, and community-based components of service delivery following a humanitarian crisis.
- *Internationally endorsed tools for humanitarian response and service planning* include: the Inter-Agency Standing Committee (IASC) Guidelines, the World Health Organization (WHO) model and pyramid of an optimal mix of services for mental health, Psychological First Aid (PFA), Mental Health Gap Action Programme (mhGAP), and the mhGAP Humanitarian Intervention Guide (mhGAP-HIG). Trainings related to humanitarian response and establishment of sustained services following crises should be informed by these tools.
- Integration of planning for both *humanitarian crisis response* and subsequent *mental health system reform* can produce optimal outcomes in settings with constrained resources for mental healthcare delivery.

Introduction

Humanitarian crises—whether due to natural disasters, disease outbreaks, mass violence or other human-made disasters, or technological disasters relating to systems or engineering failures—require comprehensive and timely approaches to mental health and psychosocial support and care. As the impacts of climate change continue unabated—resulting in increased episodic drought, disruption of food and water resources, changes in land use and agricultural conditions, and weakening of

DOI: 10.4324/9781315160597-14

societal infrastructure—conflict, displacement, and migration of human populations are expected to increase.[1] These problems, in turn, will disrupt existing social ties for mobile populations as well as for family and community members who remain in their places of origin.[2] Early and senior career professionals in the allied mental health professions, humanitarian actors, and others working across academic and non-governmental spheres, who are unexpectedly confronted with disaster as well as trauma requiring increasingly complex and multifaceted solutions, must acquire various competencies for mounting safe, effective, evidence-based, and context-appropriate mental health and psychosocial responses. Given a lack of mental health–specific training resources tailored to these needs, their development should be of interest to a wide range of actors: implementers, clinicians, and investigators living and working across low-, middle-, and high-income regions.

The authors of this chapter have worked—in aggregate—in clinical, academic, humanitarian, non-governmental, and governmental sectors to address humanitarian crises that have included earthquakes, floods, fires, lethal disease outbreaks such as Ebola, and post-conflict recovery efforts, with attention not only to emergency-related mental health needs, but also to building capacity for long-term mental health systems development. In their experience, there is insufficient information readily available in either academic or lay literature that can adequately guide planning for response and training program development. This chapter discusses the emerging understanding of best practices and competencies to guide a broad range of actors in developing collaborative and effective responses to mental health needs in the setting of humanitarian crises. In addition to an overview of the leading mental health and psychosocial frameworks for humanitarian crises and mental health system reform, this chapter also addresses how training should be informed by these best practices.

Global mental health delivery and humanitarian crisis response

Whereas global health is broadly concerned with population health and health equity in global contexts, the subfield of global health delivery focuses on resolving treatment gaps that stem largely from geographical, socioeconomic, and political factors that undermine availability and access to quality health care. Global health delivery entails the actual planning, service implementation, and sustained supply of comprehensive, integrated medical and preventive treatments to people living in resource-limited settings. In global health delivery the mere existence of functional, sustained services can arguably, at times, be an innovation relative to care as usual. This is particularly true in global mental health delivery, given the severe resource constraints in the field, and the lack of progress in "scaling up" basic, government-funded services in many global contexts. Since the early twenty-first century, significant progress has been made in articulating interventions and developing platforms to address the mental health treatment gap and to build momentum toward identifying cost-effective, evidence-supported practices and services—including care delivery by non-specialists within a task-sharing model—that could theoretically be made more widely available in resource-limited contexts. Nevertheless, in practice, the implementation, spread, and scale-up of such services is still aspirational. An additional challenge is that, of all clinical domains in global health, mental health continues to receive the least funding in development assistance.[3]

Beyond the difficulty of creating sustainable mental health service programs for even routine care delivery, additional major challenges exist in providing safe, effective, and culturally sound mental health and psychosocial services when disasters, conflict, and displacement occur. Whereas humanitarian crises often inspire non-profit organizations, trainees, and academic centers to contribute to initial recovery efforts, an acute crisis also makes sustained training efforts and establishment of reliable effective supervision of clinical services even more challenging. These difficulties are compounded by the fact that many managers and leaders overseeing crisis responses or health system strengthening in low-resource settings lack experience in clinical mental healthcare delivery or, in some instances, even lack knowledge of the proven effectiveness of mental health treatments. These knowledge and skills deficits result from both an absence of pre-service training in mental health care as well as the absence of functional mental health services in many contexts. Consequently, a prevailing critique of humanitarian mental health efforts is that they marshal resources and planning for only short-term interventions, while failing to provide for, and sometimes even undermining, subsequent longer-term capacity-building, mental health service development, and mental health system reform. This is despite the hugely significant—and often long-standing—impacts on economic, social, and human development made by humanitarian crises. The sequelae of disasters and conflicts elevate risk for poor health in many ways, both proximal and distal to the immediate events. Mechanisms include direct physical injury, exposure to extreme psychosocial stressors, and destruction of infrastructure—including the disruption of primary healthcare services. These proximal impacts, in turn, increase vulnerability to communicable diseases through poor sanitation and lack of preventive resources such as vaccines, and can exacerbate chronic social adversities such as food insecurity and poverty. Crises, thus, broadly disrupt bio-social and human developmental processes, worsening long-term outcomes and promoting risk for mental illness.[4]

Aggregate on-the-ground experience in tandem with an emphasis over the past decade on "building back better" after disasters have demonstrated that qualitative and quantitative assessments of urgent and long-term needs, resource availability, and local context should inform the initial provision of culturally and contextually sensitive, integrated, and coordinated interventions in the aftermath of humanitarian crises.[5] When there are limited resources for psychosocial response and mental healthcare delivery, the integration of planning for both *humanitarian crisis response* and subsequent *mental health system reform* can promote attainment of optimal outcomes and maximal value to service recipients and their communities. Innovative care delivery models such as task-sharing can be combined with conventional interventions such as psychosocial support, psychotherapy, and psychopharmacology delivered by specialists to help build and develop mental health systems of care into long-term services that effectively integrate contemporary, evidence-based biopsychosocial approaches, strong traditional perceptions and beliefs, and religious influences of value to communities.[6,7]

In order to implement humanitarian crisis responses effectively while planning for and developing new mental health services, frontline teams require a number of key competencies that underpin establishment and maintenance of training program infrastructure, as shown in Box 10.1.

BOX 10.1. KEY COMPETENCIES FOR FRONTLINE IMPLEMENTERS IN HUMANITARIAN CRISIS RESPONSE

Assessment skills to analyze contexts via thorough needs assessments and coordinating with partners, with attention to avoiding duplication of efforts.

Strong managerial skills to oversee and build on existing programs and services, both during humanitarian crises and afterwards.

Ability to elaborate sustained clinical training and supervision models that are locally acceptable, feasible, and useful in context.

System design skills for the development of functional data collection systems, with monitoring and evaluation of data used to improve systems and services.

Expertise to facilitate appropriate, well-chosen academic work such as qualitative or quantitative research methods to evaluate and document completed work.

Global mental health educators and practitioners must acquire all of these competencies in order to be effective not only in developing services and building systems, but also in creating sustainable career development trajectories for implementers who work in challenging circumstances. These competencies should be foundational to all global mental health training curricula.

This chapter will draw on the authors' global mental health delivery experiences in a number of settings, with a specific focus on the work of the Ministry of Public Health of Lebanon and the non-governmental organization, Partners In Health (PIH), to illustrate how opportunities can be seized and challenges overcome both in responding to humanitarian crises as well as in strengthening health systems following disasters, conflict, and displacement. Global mental health educators and practitioners can, moreover, deploy their expertise in developing clinical trainings, sustaining supervision, and managing teams in order to develop effective systems to support communities affected by crises, as well as to build long-term clinical capacities.

Humanitarian response practices and training competencies

Frontline teams developing and implementing mental health services and support in the context of humanitarian crisis response require broad training and support in order to integrate sensible, ethical, comprehensive, and cross-sectoral practices. Foundational knowledge to be supported through training spans four key domains: 1) international *standards of psychosocial, psychological, and psychiatric care and support* in both humanitarian crises and in developing sustainable services; 2) *health systems* and *clinical services* design; 3) *quality improvement methods* and *training system* design; and 4) *key concepts in social medicine* as they apply to ethical delivery of mental health care.

Two overarching frameworks that are essential to conceptualizing and underpinning training across humanitarian response and mental health systems reform are the 2007 *Inter-Agency Standing Committee IASC Guidelines*[8] and the World Health Organization (WHO) model and pyramid of an optimal mix of services for mental health.[9] The IASC, created in 1992 by the United Nations (UN), has served as an inter-agency forum for coordination, policy development, and decision-making involving key UN and non-UN humanitarian partners. In the weeks to months following crisis events, planners can seek to implement emerging recommendations as outlined in the 2007 IASC Guidelines, which were developed to help to meet the enormous and diverse needs that present themselves in emergencies. In addition, this organization provides coordination around support, intervention, and training that can mitigate the tendency toward fragmented and often counterproductive activities of various agencies and individuals and can also offset the absence of existing multi-sectoral, inter-agency frameworks.

Simple interventions and mobilization of essential resources outlined in the IASC Guidelines include basic services and security, community and family resources, and articulation of plans for coordinated, multilayered support. These require resources as well as organized training plans. The IASC Guidelines offer critical guidance on "dos and don'ts" in emergency settings, with an emphasis on effective coordination: avoiding duplication of effort; facilitation of community owned and managed programs, local capacity, and use of local practices; organization of a range of supports including Psychological First Aid (PFA) and support for self-help; and limiting the use of psychotropic medications when not clearly indicated. Initial training goals should therefore focus on needs related to the immediate emergency and utilizing proven tools such as PFA. More specifically, the IASC Guidelines divide humanitarian psychosocial and mental health support into four levels, in descending order of prioritization: 1) social considerations in basic services and security (including advocacy for basic services that are safe, socially appropriate, and protect dignity); 2) community and family supports, including communal traditional supports, child-friendly spaces, and social network activation; 3) focused, non-specialized supports, including basic mental health care delivered by primary healthcare clinicians, and basic emotional and practical support provided by community health workers; and 4) specialized services, including mental health care provided by specialists such as psychiatric nurses, psychologists, and psychiatrists. For example, community health workers can support people living in internally displaced persons' (IDP) settlements, providing basic needs and facilitating respectful mourning for those who have died, as well as providing basic psychosocial support informed by PFA, while basic pharmacologic support for those in crisis is also provided by clinicians. This would ideally follow broader and immediate social efforts to ensure safe housing, adequate supplies of food and clean water, and engagement and mobilization of community members in re-establishing family contacts and functional community social networks.

While the four levels of the IASC Guidelines are being enacted in response to an emergency, longer-term planning based on the WHO model (Figure 10.1) can also be considered. The model's organization as a pyramid reflects the recommendation that countries build or transform their mental health services on a foundation of informal services, such as self-care promotion and informal community care, on top of which formal services rest. The latter comprise mental health services integrated into primary health care, community mental health services, mental health services in general hospitals, and circumscribed use of psychiatric services.[9]

Additional priority dimensions underlying the organization of services include accessibility, comprehensiveness, continuity and coordination of care, needs-led care, effectiveness, equity, and respect for human rights.[9] Underpinning successful establishment of such services is the capacity for sectors to collaborate.

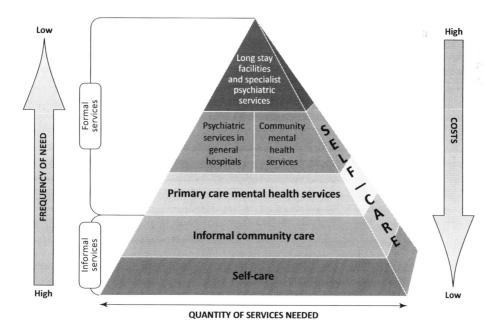

Figure 10.1 The WHO service organization pyramid for an optimal mix of services for mental health.

From: World Health Organization. *Improving health systems and services for mental health.* Geneva: WHO; 2009; p. 22.[9] Used with permission from World Health Organization Press.

Internationally endorsed standards for psychosocial, psychological, and psychiatric care and support

Beyond the basic elements of how systems can and should be organized, a range of psychosocial and clinical interventions is important in order to comfortably layer support and care in a given context. The "real-world" implementation of crisis response leading to sustained mental health services can benefit from specific interventions (as well as frameworks) that guide systems design and planning and also training and supervision decisions. The choice and approach to implementation of interventions, as well as the frameworks, can be relatively flexible and adaptable in terms of the specific clinical content and other salient social and cultural contextual factors. Nonetheless, selection of interventions should also reflect international best practices across psychosocial, psychological, and psychiatric care, which have garnered increasing acceptance. PFA, for example, endorsed by the IASC Guidelines, is an essential package of support that comprises eight Core Actions,[10] and has been repackaged and simplified for use by the World Health Organization.[11] The actions are listed in Box 10.2.

BOX 10.2 EIGHT CORE ACTIONS SPECIFIED BY THE PSYCHOLOGICAL FIRST AID FIELD OPERATIONS GUIDE

1. **Contact and Engagement**
   Goal: To respond to contacts initiated by survivors, or to initiate contacts in a non-intrusive, compassionate, and helpful manner.
2. **Safety and Comfort**
   Goal: To enhance immediate and ongoing safety, and provide physical and emotional comfort.
3. **Stabilization** (if needed)
   Goal: To calm and orient emotionally overwhelmed or disoriented survivors.
4. **Information Gathering: Current Needs and Concerns**
   Goal: To identify immediate needs and concerns, gather additional information, and tailor Psychological First Aid interventions.
5. **Practical Assistance**
   Goal: To offer practical help to survivors in addressing immediate needs and concerns.
6. **Connection with Social Supports**
   Goal: To help establish brief or ongoing contacts with primary support persons and other sources of support, including family members, friends, and community helping resources.
7. **Information on Coping**
   Goal: To provide information about stress reactions and coping to reduce distress and promote adaptive functioning.
8. **Linkage with Collaborative Services**
   Goal: To link survivors with available services and agencies needed at the time or in the future.

> From: Brymer M, Layne C, Jacobs A, Pynoos R, Ruzek J, Steinberg A, Vernberg E, Watson P. *Psychological first aid field operations guide.* 2nd Edition. National Child Traumatic Stress Network. 2006, p. 19.[10]
> Used with permission.

An additional emphasis in the IASC Guidelines underscores the importance of training and supervision of primary healthcare services in good prescription practices and in basic psychological support. Building on these basic principles, Jones and colleagues have described essential knowledge for primary healthcare workers in emergencies, blending PFA with psychological and psychiatric interventions, that can inform *planning of trainings* for care of people living with severe mental disorders in the context of a humanitarian response.[12] The key elements of this include skills in communication, basic problem-solving, PFA, recognition and management of mental disorders (including substance use disorders and neurological conditions such as epilepsy), individual and group psychotherapy approaches, psychotropic medication management, care pathway and referral navigation, and time-management.[12]

Jones and colleagues also offer important *minimal actions* that primary healthcare providers can take to support individuals living with severe mental disorders in the context of a humanitarian crisis.[12] These actions move the humanitarian aid provider from initial engagement with local providers and existing services and agencies to longer-term actions that can promote capacity-building and sustainability. A few examples of key steps include an initial needs assessment, relationship building with community members and local stakeholders, training, development of care pathways and referral systems, psychological and psychiatric care, and reintegration plans—all of which should occur within the existing health system to facilitate sustainable care.[12]

Given the pervasive lack of mental health treatment resources in low- and middle-income countries (LMICs), the WHO has led efforts to adapt and package scalable psychological interventions, such as the essential, evidence-based psychological treatments, cognitive-behavioral therapy (CBT) and interpersonal therapy (IPT).[13] These psychological interventions are viewed as a preferable first line of treatment before pursuing pharmacologic approaches. The WHO developed its Mental Health Gap Action Programme (mhGAP) to enable the scaling up of focused, community-based clinical programs and direct patient care for depression, epilepsy, psychotic disorders, and child and adolescent mental health problems, among other priority conditions. The program's accompanying *World Health Organization's mhGAP Intervention Guide*, initially developed in 2011 and revised in 2016, provides evaluation and treatment guidelines that can be adapted to both provider type and context and includes clinical support tools, protocols, and additional curricular materials for each priority clinical area.[14,15] The guide includes materials for community health workers, schoolteachers, nurses, clinicians, physicians, social workers, and bachelor's degree-holding psychologists. The mhGAP Intervention Guide also provides guidance and clinical algorithms for determining the appropriate intervention and endorses implementing simplified low-intensity psychotherapies such as Problem Management Plus and Thinking Healthy.[16,17]

An additional resource, the *World Health Organization's mhGAP Humanitarian Intervention Guide (mhGAP-HIG)*, was introduced in 2015 and builds upon the original mhGAP Intervention Guide with a particular focus on humanitarian crises. The mhGAP-HIG encompasses guidance for communication, assessment, management, strengthening social support, protection of human rights, and attention to overall well-being, with content emphasis on acute stress, grief, depression, post-traumatic stress disorder, psychosis, epilepsy, intellectual disability, harmful use of alcohol and drugs, and suicide.[18] Organizations such as the International Medical Corps (IMC) and Partners In Health (PIH) have contributed important resources and frameworks for the field around additional guidance on leadership development, building of comprehensive mental health services, and their integration into primary care, as they relate to humanitarian mental health crisis response and the need to "build back better."[19] Such frameworks supplement and build on existing mhGAP resources by providing piloted tools that have been implemented in low-resource settings across both emergency and health systems strengthening contexts. For example, the IMC Toolkit provides a guiding framework and tools for integration of mental health into general health care in humanitarian settings including three steps: assessing and planning for mental health integration; building capacity of general healthcare workers; and strengthening mental health services and systems. The cross-cutting components include monitoring and evaluation, advocacy, and sustainability.[20] Another example is PIH's Cross-Site Mental Health Service Delivery Planning Matrix to Achieve Universal Health Coverage.[21,22] The matrix is a tool to expand service delivery and model effective implementation of mental health services at health centers and community levels. It helps to locally define and achieve consensus on the strategies needed for program development in context, articulating the types of activities that should be prioritized with limited resources to drive management decision-making and systems change.

Effective, scaled-up responses to improve the mental health and psychosocial well-being of populations affected by humanitarian crises therefore requires adaptation of proven, internationally endorsed interventions to specific contexts, with mobilization of multilayered systems of services and supports.[23] The scope of response spans: the provision of food, shelter, water, sanitation, basic health care, and other essential services; actions to strengthen community and family supports (all emphasized in the IASC Guidelines); emotional and practical support through individual, family, or group interventions; ongoing care through community-based outreach and primary healthcare systems that also integrate psychiatric interventions; and capacity-building, program development, and advocacy for strengthened health systems to serve affected populations in the long term.[8]

Case Study 1: The Ministry of Public Health of Lebanon

Lebanon is a small country in the Eastern Mediterranean Region with a total estimated population of 6 million people. Following several decades of civil war, a ceasefire was announced in 2006, and people began returning to their villages in South Lebanon to find their houses completely destroyed. By 2013, after two years of Syrian conflict and crisis, Lebanon had become host to 1.5 million newly displaced persons from Syria, who now comprise more than a quarter of the population of Lebanon. Until 2014, Lebanon's mental health system was weak, characterized by limited availability and accessibility of mental health services. Existing services were mainly in long-stay psychiatric hospitals or in the private sector in the large cities.[24] Building on the Humanitarian Response to the Syrian Crisis, in 2014 the Ministry of Public Health (MOPH) was launched, in partnership with WHO, United Nations Children's Fund (UNICEF), IMC, and the National Mental Health Program. Thereafter, the first Mental Health and Substance Use strategy for Lebanon 2015–2020 was articulated, with the mission, "to ensure the development of a sustainable mental health system that guarantees the provision and universal accessibility of high-quality mental health curative and preventive services through a cost-effective, evidence-based and multidisciplinary approach, with an emphasis on community involvement, continuum of care, human rights, and cultural relevance."[25(p.27)] This mission is in line with the WHO's comprehensive Mental Health Action Plan 2013–2024 and has five domains: 1) Leadership and governance; 2) Reorientation of services; 3) Prevention and promotion; 4) Health information systems and research; and 5) Vulnerable groups.[26]

In order to realize the mission and strategic goals within each of the five domains, the range of different actors in the system—both clinical and non-clinical—will need to acquire new knowledge and skills and, in some cases, new attitudes. Training is thus considered a cross-cutting concern throughout each of these domains, and is conceptualized to engage all relevant actors, from judges to media professionals, teachers, frontline providers, health professionals, mental health professionals, and, importantly, persons with lived experience of mental illness. In an effort to enhance local capacity-building and sustainability toward "building back better," several universities and academics have also been engaged in training. They were specifically engaged at multiple levels, including:

1. Training higher education faculty on mhGAP so that they can teach their students: This was done with the faculty of Public Health at the Lebanese University where there are departments for nursing, midwifery, speech and language therapy, and psychomotor therapy.
2. Training students directly: Master's degree program students in psychology at the Lebanese University were trained on the mhGAP. This training was given directly by a psychologist from the National Mental Health Programme at the MOPH.
3. Inclusion of trainings in selected existing curricula: This included mhGAP in the medical school curriculum at Saint Joseph University in Beirut, Lebanon. This training initially comprised health professionals and has been expanded to include social workers and other allied health system colleagues.
4. Engagement of departments of psychology: This included integration of psychotherapy training (interpersonal therapy—IPT) as part of the regular training of the Master's degree program students. This training was particularly focused on training the teachers in the department in order to ensure a more sustainable model over time.

In order to have a comprehensive view of ongoing training needs, a national capacity-building plan was developed to map all actors (prospective trainees) to their respective roles as articulated by Lebanon's Mental Health Strategy 2015–2020. For each type of actor, a list of competencies was developed (Box 10.3) and aligned with competencies defined by the WHO pyramid-assigned levels (see Figure 10.1).

BOX 10.3 LIST OF COMPETENCIES SPECIFIED IN LEBANON'S COMPREHENSIVE NATIONAL CAPACITY-BUILDING PLAN

	Stigma and discrimination	Mental health literacy	Intervention	Crisis management	Reintegration	Advocacy	Prevention and promotion	Legislation	Self-care
Level 1: Informal community care									
Teachers									
Police officers									
Religious leaders									
Legal professionals									
Prison staff									
Community leaders									
Media professionals									
Level 2: Primary care mental health services									
Frontline providers and humanitarian aid workers									
Midwives									
Gynecologists									
Pediatricians									
PHC staff (GPs, social workers, nurses, family physicians, midwives)									
Level 3: Mental health services in general hospitals									
Emergency Room staff									
Hospital physicians									
Hospital psychiatrists									
General nurses									
Nursing assistants									
Level 4: Community mental health services									
Psychologists									
Psychiatrists									
Social workers									
Mental health nurses									
Occupational therapists									
Level 5: Long-stay facilities									
Psychologists									
Psychiatrists									
Social workers									
Mental health nurses									
Occupational therapists									

From: *Mental health and substance use: Prevention, promotion and treatment, situation analysis and strategy for Lebanon 2015–2020*. Ministry of Public Health, Lebanon, 2018.[25]

Consistent with the aim to integrate capacity-building with pre-service training, mhGAP was integrated into the curriculum of the medical school and department of social work of Saint Joseph University in Beirut. In 2017, 40 professors of nursing, speech therapy, and psychomotor therapy from the Public Health School at the Lebanese University in Beirut were also trained as trainers of mhGAP and have started using it in their teaching. For this training, the material was provided to the teachers who were usually the ones responsible for teaching the mental health course, using it without it being yet formally adopted by the Lebanese University. Finally, a Master's of Mental Health Policy and Service Organization degree is now being developed, reflecting Lebanon's commitment to building the next generation of leaders in mental health who are prepared to develop a collaborative, functional mental health system in the country.

The successful response of the government of Lebanon illustrates that even when responding to a humanitarian crisis with limited resources, much can be achieved by proper planning and clear conceptualization of actions and activities both for the short and long term. Consistent with the IASC Guidelines, response activities must include training of actors outside the health/service delivery sector, integration of trainings within pre-service trainings (for example, integration within the trainings in university curricula of future professionals such as physicians, nurses, social workers, psychologists, and media professionals), and alignment of trainings with overarching national plans, when these exist.

Health system and clinical services design

The actions called for in the guidelines and curricula described in Box 10.2 and in the text above represent emerging international consensus on best practices in psychosocial and clinical care delivered both by specialists and non-specialists. In particular, successfully deploying trainings and implementing mental health services must follow careful planning and requires a high degree of organization, collaboration and coordination, anticipation of future capacity-building needs and budgeting, and follow-through. Thoughtfully developed and shared frameworks for clinical systems design can be very helpful for coordination across actors in developing the actual service delivery platform, and for subsequent budget development and training. However, a major gap in the preparation and readiness of teams in developing functional mental health systems is the lack of knowledge of clinical systems design. Here, by clinical systems design we refer to elements required for comprehensive, quality care delivery including care coordination, training, supervision, and mentorship. Consequently, there is often limited delivery of actual clinical services reflecting proven, evidence-based practices adapted to context that are decentralized from district hospitals to health centers to communities. The most significant obstacle facing global health, and by extension global mental health, is a failure of delivery. In order to deliver maximum value to service recipients, vertical or stand-alone projects, including interventions intended to respond to humanitarian crises, must be integrated into a shared service delivery infrastructure so that personnel and facilities are used wisely toward an optimization of economies of scale.[27]

Two helpful concepts with respect to systems development and design include theory of change and value chain development. A *theory of change* refers to a co-created pathway of change that illustrates the relationships between a variety of outcomes that are each thought of as preconditions of a long-term goal.[28] It includes specific indicators to measure success and a plan for interventions that are used to bring about each of the preconditions of the pathway and at each step of the pathway. It has been used in the global mental health field, for example by the PRIME network, a global consortium of research institutions and ministries of health across five LMICs, to develop a framework guiding the planning and evaluation of mental health systems.[29] The various elements of a theory of change can represent the components viewed by system planners as essential to articulating the processes and practices for the successful design of a mental health system. Thus, it is essential for a theory of change to be co-created along with stakeholders in the system for representation of key perspectives and buy-in.

Kim, Farmer, and Porter have proposed a different "value-based" strategic framework—with a specific focus on measuring overall patient health outcomes by condition and the cost of achieving them—for providing a common structure and language to use in developing a service delivery system that can be improved over time.[27] A *value chain* framework applies a systems-level analysis to the complex processes and interventions that must occur across all levels of a healthcare system over time to deliver high-value care for patients. At its most basic level, a value chain can describe the system elements that are essential for quality care delivery to achieve optimal health outcomes from the time a patient enters the system to the time the patient may leave the system. The specific elements included within a value chain provide a map onto which system builders and implementers can plan for training, monitoring and evaluation, and quality improvement initiatives. It informs value-based systems design, management structures, and operational best practices to be disseminated among those responsible for managing healthcare systems and delivering clinical care, as well as among funders and regulatory bodies evaluating new and existing programs, with greater attention paid to the essential elements of developing systems that may be brought to scale. The value chain supports a shared understanding of how various activities fit together as part of a coherent care delivery process [27] and can be instrumental in guiding clinical planning, training and planning of sustained supervision structures, and quality improvement. The value chain is a helpful tool to outline essential elements of a mental healthcare delivery pathway, including community- and facility-based functions, roles of various stakeholders, and information systems, and can inform integration with the broader health system.

Quality improvement and training systems design

Familiarity with both *quality improvement* (QI) *methods* and *training systems design* are also key to the development of clinical care systems and sustained mental health services in the context of humanitarian emergencies. For example, use of the value chain can be particularly helpful when designing systems to evaluate quality of care, and in developing quality improvement practices that can eventually be linked to data collection systems and even electronic medical records for longer-term practice. With a discrete set of tasks described in the value chain, specific QI projects can be prioritized and targeted by care delivery teams. Now a standard approach in the improvement of health systems, QI methods are characterized by: continuous, ongoing hypothesis testing to address health system challenges; implementation of small-scale demonstrations; collection of data to evaluate improvements; and improvement of communication with and engagement of all participants in the health system.[30] The application of QI methods to both mental health and global health delivery is increasingly appreciated as an important academic discipline and also increasingly accepted as an essential aspect of global health delivery science.

In addition, *training systems design*—the use of emerging methodologies on best practices in training—can ensure that trainings that are developed actually reflect best practices. Knowledge of best practices in the development of training systems is not commonly an area of learning for humanitarian aid workers, nor for medical or mental health professionals, during their formal education or practice in the field. Combining "the *art* of creating engaging learning experiences with the *science* of how the brain works" can ideally be utilized to develop training systems that reflect emerging best practices.[31] Taken together, QI and training systems design can facilitate progressive system improvement, optimal use of limited resources, and development of *collaborative learning networks* so that best practices can be shared across settings and their impacts on training, supervision, mentorship, and service delivery evaluated. Collaborative learning networks have become increasingly important in avoiding one of the great pitfalls of global health, the "reinventing the wheel" phenomenon, whereby organizations and entities, hampered by lack of human resource capacity and working in relative silos, unwittingly replicate materials and practices—including those that do not work well—that have been in use in other contexts, rather than building on existing knowledge and experience in an iterative, context-informed way. For example, the Partners In Health Cross-Site Mental Health Collaborative is a network that includes not only mental health teams across the organization, but community health, monitoring and evaluation, and site leadership, as well as external collaborators to facilitate cross-site discussions, didactics, and sharing of materials. The development of mental healthcare delivery systems informed by exchange of best practices across country sites around training, supervision, monitoring and evaluation, and quality improvement are further described in the case study below.

Case Study 2: The Partners In Health Cross-Site Mental Health Network

Using emerging consensus on best clinical practices, the international non-governmental organization (NGO) PIH has worked to adapt, integrate, and implement the WHO model and pyramid of an optimal mix of services for mental health, the IASC Guidelines, PFA, mhGAP and mhGAP-HIG, the value chain approach, and evidence-based psychosocial, psychological, and psychiatric care in the healthcare delivery sites they operate. This process and utilization have required the development of training structures to ensure successful implementation and care delivery of mental health services across all twelve of PIH's care delivery country sites. This has led to a robust cross-site network of mental health service delivery platforms in collaboration with local ministries of health. From 2016 to 2022 there were more than a quarter of a million visits for mental health conditions across all twelve PIH global sites. The pillars of PIH's model of global mental health delivery include task-sharing, training, supervision, monitoring and evaluation, quality improvement, community-based care, leadership and professional development for front-line implementers, and advocacy and government partnerships. Laying the foundation for these elements during humanitarian crisis responses in the near term therefore ensures a more comprehensive approach to health systems strengthening and "building back better" in the longer term.[5] For example, in the immediate aftermath of the 2010 Haiti earthquake, PIH and partnering local healthcare delivery organization, Zanmi Lasante (ZL), developed a response for individuals with acute and chronic mental health needs, which encompassed best practices outlined in the IASC Guidelines, including implementation of Psychological First Aid.[7,32] This was accompanied by elaboration of a task-sharing pyramid for the development of longer-term services within the PIH/ZL clinical network, intended to serve as a pilot for the country. In contrast to the WHO pyramid, the PIH/ZL version emphasizes a long-term systems-strengthening approach in the context of few existing government-led mental health services and limited resources (Figure 10.2). The adapted pyramid provided a framework for planning and future training. An overarching training structure was articulated by mapping desired skills onto existing cadres of healthcare workers within the system, highlighting the key functions of care providers in the health system, and aligns with a more detailed skills package (Figure 10.3).

The mapping of skills packages enabled PIH to effectively develop trainings in various areas of mental health care and intervention, based on mhGAP. Subsequently, specific care pathways for priority mental health conditions were designed and implemented to deliver care to patients. These priorities have included depression, epilepsy, psychotic disorders, trauma, and child and adolescent mental health conditions. Although mental health services were being delivered across the PIH/ZL system prior to the 2010 Haiti earthquake, the program was formalized and supported by these tools for systems planning and training over the course of the decade following the disaster and the original crisis response.[33] The success of this endeavor is reflected in the scaled-up capacity to care for mental illness in the region: between 2016 and 2021, there were

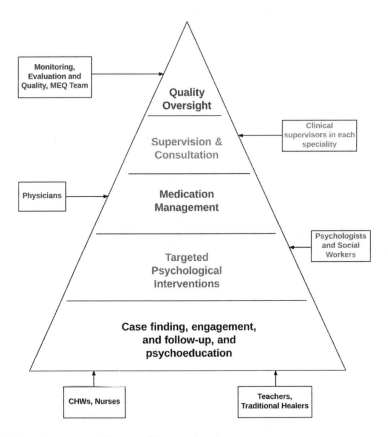

Figure 10.2 Skills package pyramid for post-Haiti earthquake.

From: Raviola G, Eustache E, Oswald C, Belkin GS. Mental health response in Haiti in the aftermath of the 2010 earthquake: a case study for building long-term solutions. *Harvard Review of Psychiatry.* 2012 Feb 8;20(1):68–77. https://journals.lww.com/hrpjournal/pages/default.aspx.[32] Used with permission from Wolters Kluwer Health, Inc.

more than 37,000 visits for a mental health condition within the PIH care system in Haiti, which serves a catchment area with a population of 1.5 million people. This approach, moreover, now serves as a national model in a context of ongoing significant political challenges and resource constraints.[34]

Learning from experience in mental health program design and implementation at various global sites, PIH also implemented a collaborative, cross-national theory of change process that led to the development of a shared, iterative value chain adapted to each PIH country site context based on local preferences (Figure 10.4). The theory of change workshops brought together key implementation stakeholders to further define locally determined change strategies through discussions centered around the value chain, task-sharing pyramid, and skills package described in Figures 10.2 and 10.3.

Core, cross-cutting elements of the system represented in the value chain include sustained training and supervision in clinical, programmatic, academic, and leadership development spheres for local implementation teams. Key elements also focus on quality, comprising patient safety, quality of care, outcomes measurement (including monitoring and evaluation), and the use of data to drive performance improvement. It is these two cross-cutting areas—training and

	Community Leaders	Community Health Workers	Social Workers	Psychologists	Nurses- Health Center- Level	Nurses- District Hospital Level	General Physicians	Specialist Clinicians
MH explanatory models in context of local culture and religion								
Mental health and stigma								
Mental health and human rights								
Familiarity with main symptom groups and disorders								
Priority mental health care pathways								
Basic mental health evaluation								
Screening tool use								
Mental status examination								
Triage rules for priority mental disorders								
Familiarity with learning aids and resources								
Active and empathic listening skills								
Familiarity with accepted treatment approaches								
Relaxation techniques								
Behavioral activation techniques								
Manualized psychotherapies (i.e. IPT, CBT) adapted to context								
Supervision of psychotherapy and mentorship								
Medical management of priority mental disorders								
Medication adherence support								
Main medication types, recognizing side effects								
Managing acute mental health crises and safety								
Supervision of psychopharmacology and mentorship								
Ensuring minimal and safe physical restraint								
Epilepsy evaluation and care								
Specialized psychiatric and neurologic care								
Management of quality improvement								

Skill Package	Color	Skill Package	Color
General Knowledge		Pharmacology	
Triage-engagement-education-support		Specialist care/referral	
Psychotherapy		Quality/oversight	

Figure 10.3 **Mapping skills packages onto the existing system in Haiti post-earthquake, following the IASC-informed emergency response.**

From: Raviola G, Eustache E, Oswald C, Belkin GS. Mental health response in Haiti in the aftermath of the 2010 earthquake: a case study for building long-term solutions. *Harvard Review of Psychiatry.* 2012 Feb 8;20(1):68–77. https://journals.lww.com/hrpjournal/pages/default.aspx.[32] Used with permission from Wolters Kluwer Health, Inc.

Training and Supervision: Clinical, Programmatic, Academic Leadership

Safety, Quality, Outcomes Measurements (M&E) and Performance Improvement

Crisis Response	Prevention	Case-Finding	Assessment	Treatment	Follow-Up	Reintegration
• Use of international guidance • Response coordination team • Team development • Essential needs assessments • Communication and problem solving • Psychological First Aid (PFA) • Basic management of neuropsychiatric disorders • Use of essential psychopharm interventions • Establishment of appropriate lines of referral	**Health Facility Level** • Health system staff stigma reduction and education regarding mental health	• Screening • Referral • Case management	• Diagnosis/ formulation • Enrollment • Mental Status Exam • Medical exam • Laboratory/imaging • Assignment to provider in task-shared system	• Psychoeducation • Choosing treatment plan • Medication management • Psychotherapy • Crisis management • Inpatient hospitalization	• Monitoring of clinical improvement, functioning • Medication adherence support, and monitoring of side effects • Referral back to community with CHW support • Case retention	Individual: • Social skills/work/ vocational training • Self care Household: • Safety • Education/relapse prevention • Caretaker support • Social assistance Community: • Peer support • Stigma reduction/ community activation • Referral • Community leaders involvement System: • Stakeholder engagement with community, local authorities, leaders, government
	Community Level • Poverty reduction activities • Reinforce existing community support networks • Community and family stigma reduction activities • Education on mental health	• Screening • Receiving referrals from community • Case finding (passive and active)	• Crisis management • Referral to health center by community health workers • Enrollment in community activities	• Psychoeducation • Basic psychological support (group, individual) • Social interventions • Psychosocial rehabilitation • Stigma reduction activities	• Case management and care coordination • Monitoring of clinical improvement and functioning • Medication adherence support • Basic psychological support (group, individual) • Referral back to clinic	

Figure 10.4 A mental health service delivery value chain developed for service planning by Partners In Health, with integration of crisis planning for humanitarian emergencies.

Source: Raviola G, Smith S, Rose A, Coleman S, Eustache E. Mental Health Planning Matrix to Achieve Universal Health Coverage. In: PIH Cross-Site Mental Health Strategic Planning Conference; 2016; Boston. Figure used with permission from Partners In Health.[35]

quality—that, in addition to the design of clinical services, have been essential to the expansion of mental health services by the organization in Haiti (following the 2010 earthquake), Rwanda (following the 1994 genocide), Liberia and Sierra Leone (following decades of civil wars and the 2014–2016 Ebola crisis in each of these two nations), and elsewhere. The organization developed guidance in each of these key areas for frontline teams based on a uniform training systems design method, the ADDIE (Analysis, Design, Development, Implementation, and Evaluation) Model, in developing learning materials and activities. The ADDIE Model provides a dynamic, flexible guideline for developing effective and efficient instruction that reflects an iterative instructional design process, where the results of the formative evaluation of each phase may lead the instructional designer back to refine any previous phase.[36] A *training process map* provides guidance to implementing teams, who may not operate with the benefit of training experts, to guide the complex process of training model design for various clinical care pathways (Figure 10.5).

A *monitoring and evaluation (M&E) process map*, integrating training components within the system, was also developed for local implementing mental health teams who may operate in isolation from local expertise on monitoring and evaluation (Figure 10.6).

Such tools can be developed, adapted, and iterated over time based on contextual learning, available resources for their actual implementation, and ongoing emerging best practices.

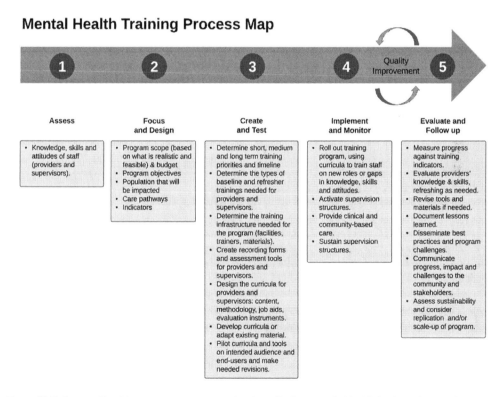

Figure 10.5 A mental health training process map developed by Partners In Health for front-line implementing teams transitioning from humanitarian crisis response to mental health systems development.

Source: Raviola G, Smith S, Manzi A, Forbush L. Training Process Map. In: PIH Cross-Site Mental Health Strategic Planning Conference; 2016; Boston. Used with permission from Partners In Health.[37]

Mental Health Monitoring and Evaluation Process Map

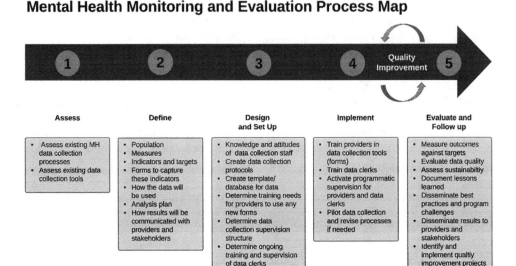

Figure 10.6 A mental health monitoring and evaluation process map developed by Partners In Health for front-line implementing teams transitioning from humanitarian crisis response to mental health systems development.

Source: Raviola G, Manzi A, Rose A, Smith S, Jerome G, Fenelon D. Mental Health Monitoring and Evaluation Process Map. In: PIH Cross-Site Mental Health Strategic Planning Conference; 2016; Boston. Used with permission from Partners In Health.[38]

Although the specifics of any care delivery system in context can vary, it may be helpful for educators and practitioners in global mental health delivery to consider the interconnected roles of training and M&E in systems design, and the use of accepted knowledge in both quality improvement and training systems design.

Key concepts in social medicine and their application to ethical practice in humanitarian settings and in the development of services

The practice of global mental health delivery in the context of humanitarian emergencies has been informed by a number of related subfields and disciplines. These include: *clinical neuroscience*, which through our growing understanding of the brain and the hypothalamic-pituitary-adrenal axis has informed our awareness of the relative roles of acute and chronic stress [39] on the evolution of mental disorders in the context of war and conflict, disease outbreaks, and natural and human-made disasters; *disaster psychiatry*, which through the experience of 9/11 and other crises has broadened our understanding of how disaster-specific interventions[40] (such as PFA) may be helpful and how others (such as Critical Incident Stress Debriefing)[41] can potentially be more harmful than helpful; *global health*, which has revealed the striking burden of mental disorders and the ongoing treatment gap in the care of mental disorders; and *global mental health*, which has clarified the promise of non-specialist-delivered care, a "dimensional" approach to care and support that addresses wellness and distress rather than a purely illness-based approach to care, and emphasizes decentralized care balanced across delivery platforms that include general hospitals, primary health centers, and communities. The field of *social medicine*, that includes drawing from anthropology, history, and other social sciences to examine the roots of health inequities, helps to inform our understanding of illness in context, offering an essential underpinning to ethical practice in global mental health delivery. The importance of a social medicine lens is emphasized here as it relates to the development of training programs in the context of humanitarian response.

Summary

Education and training play a vital role in preparing a broad array of actors—across the spectrum of career development and cadres of providers, as well as across governmental, non-governmental, and academic sectors—to competently and vigorously respond to the mental health and psychosocial problems associated with the now inevitable, increasing frequency of natural and human-made disasters. This chapter has sought to outline core concepts for consideration in seeking to mount a comprehensive approach to training and education as an underpinning to humanitarian response *and the building of systems of care and support* that is also realistic in scope and tailored to the context. Frontline teams implementing humanitarian crisis response and new mental health services require knowledge and competencies to inform and implement needs assessment, program management and service implementation, processes for sustained training and supervision, data collection with monitoring and evaluation, quality improvement, and analytic and academic skills to evaluate and document completed work. It is hoped that new actors operating in this sphere are ready to commit their passion and specific expertise to facing the challenges presented by each new situation, while being open to integrating new areas of knowledge and practice. The improved, future practice of humanitarian mental health and psychosocial response will require the development and nurturing of collaborative teams, which can support the physical, emotional, spiritual and existential challenges faced by front-line workers in the field of action.

BOX 10.4 GLOSSARY OF TERMS USED IN THIS CHAPTER

Community health worker: A community health worker (CHW) is a non-specialist providing frontline care generally in the community in which they live. CHWs serve as bridges between the community and facility.

Inter-Agency Standing Committee (IASC) Guidelines: Guidelines issued by the IASC to enable humanitarian actors to mount an effective, multi-sectoral mental health and psychosocial response in situations of crisis.[8]

Internally displaced person: Internally displaced persons (IDPs) according to the United Nations Guiding Principles on Internal Displacement, are "persons or groups of persons who have been forced or obliged to flee or to leave their homes or places of habitual residence, in particular as a result of or in order to avoid the effects of armed conflict, situations of generalized violence, violations of human rights or natural or human-made disasters, and who have not crossed an internationally recognized State border."[42(p.5)]

mhGAP Humanitarian Intervention Guide (mhGAP-HIG): A planning tool that provides basic management recommendations for care of priority mental health conditions, designed for use by non-specialist providers in humanitarian emergencies.[15]

Non-specialists: Non-specialists include a broad range of health supporters and providers without specialized training, including in mental health. Non-specialists can be referred to as community health workers (CHWs), lay health workers, village health workers, midwives, nurses, primary care providers as well as traditional and religious leaders, among other titles.[6]

Psychological First Aid: Psychological First Aid (PFA) is an evidence-informed modular approach to help children, adolescents, adults, and families in the immediate aftermath of disaster and terrorism. PFA is designed to reduce the initial distress caused by traumatic events and to foster short- and long-term adaptive functioning and coping. PFA is designed for delivery by mental health and other disaster response workers who provide early assistance to affected children, families, and adults as part of an organized disaster response effort.[10]

Quality Improvement: Quality Improvement (QI) is a framework used to systematically improve the way care is delivered to healthcare service users. QI involves measuring, analyzing, and improving care delivery processes, to inform continuous efforts to improve outcomes for patients and healthcare service users.[30]

Task-sharing: Task-sharing involves re-distributing tasks among health workforce teams to make the most efficient use of available health resources. Task-sharing in mental health involves training of non-specialist health workers—individuals with no prior formal training or background in mental health—to deliver mental health care.[6]

Theory of change: A theory of change (ToC) is a helpful tool for developing solutions to complex social problems. It explains how a group of early and intermediate accomplishments sets the stage for producing long-range results. A more complete ToC articulates the assumptions about the processes through which change will occur, and specifies the ways in which all of the required early and intermediate outcomes related to achieving the desired long-term change will be brought about and documented as they occur.[28]

Value chain: A value chain is a comprehensive framework adapted for healthcare delivery outlining interventions required at each level of the health system and roles of various care providers.[27]

World Health Organization (WHO) model and pyramid of an optimal mix of services for mental health: The WHO service organization pyramid describes an optimal mix of services for mental health including informal and formal continuum of services, from primary care to specialist community mental health services to general hospital-based and specialist psychiatric services. The pyramid framework is designed to guide countries on mental health service organization.[9]

References

1.   Hayes K, Blashki G, Wiseman J, Burke S, Reifels L. Climate change and mental health: risks, impacts and policy actions. *International Journal of Mental Health Systems*. 2018;12(28). pp. 1–12.

2.   Torres JM, Casey JA. The centrality of social ties to climate migration and mental health. *BMC Public Health*. 2017;17(1):600.

3.   Vigo D, Thornicroft G, Atun R. Estimating the true global burden of mental illness. *The Lancet Psychiatry*. 2016;3(2):171–8.

4.   Raviola G. Natural and humanitarian disasters, and mental health: lessons from Haiti. In: Davidson L, editor. *The Routledge handbook of international development, mental health and wellbeing*, 1st ed. London: Routledge; 2019. pp. 235–50.

5.   Epping-Jordan J, Van Ommeren M, Ashour H, Maramis A, Marini A, Mohanraj A, et al. Beyond the crisis: building back better mental health care in 10 emergency-affected areas using a longer-term perspective. *International Journal of Mental Health Systems*. 2015;9(1):15.

6. Raviola G, Severe J, Therosme T, Oswald C, Belkin G, Eustache FE. Innovative models in mental health delivery systems: task sharing care with non-specialist providers to close the mental health treatment gap. *Current Psychiatry Reports.* 2019;21(6):44.

7. Raviola G, Severe J, Therosme T, Oswald C, Belkin G, Eustache FE. The 2010 Haiti earthquake response. *Psychiatric Clinics.* 2013;36(3):431–50.

8. Inter-Agency Standing Committee. *IASC guidelines on mental health and psychosocial support in emergency settings.* Geneva: World Health Organization; 2007.

9. World Health Organization. *Improving health systems and services for mental health.* Geneva: World Health Organization; 2009.

10. Brymer M, Layne C, Jacobs A, Pynoos R, Ruzek J, Steinberg A, Vernberg E, Watson P. *Psychological first aid field operations guide.* National Child Traumatic Stress Network (NCTSN) and National Center for PTSD (NCPTSD); 2006.

11. World Health Organization, War Trauma Foundation and World Vision. International. *Psychological first aid: Guide for field workers.* Geneva: WHO; 2011. Available at: https://www.who.int/publications/i/item/9789241548205

12. Jones L, Asare JB, El Masri M, Mohanraj A, Sherief H, Van Ommeren M. Severe mental disorders in complex emergencies. *The Lancet.* 2009;374(9690):654–61.

13. World Health Organization. *Scalable psychological interventions for people in communities affected by adversity.* Geneva: World Health Organization; 2017.

14. World Health Organization. *mhGAP intervention guide for mental, neurological and substance use disorders in non-specialized health settings.* Geneva: World Health Organization; 2011.

15. World Health Organization. *mhGAP intervention guide for mental, neurological and substance use disorders in non-specialized health settings.* Geneva: World Health Organization; 2016.

16. World Health Organization. *Problem management plus (PM+): individual psychological help for adults impaired by distress in communities exposed to adversity.* Geneva: World Health Organization; 2015.

17. World Health Organization. *Thinking healthy: a manual for psychological management of perinatal depression.* Geneva: World Health Organization; 2015.

18. World Health Organization. *mhGAP humanitarian intervention guide (mhGAP-HIG): clinical management of mental, neurological and substance use conditions in humanitarian emergencies.* Geneva: World Health Organization, World Health Organization and United Nations High Commissioner for Refugees; 2015.

19. International Medical Corps. Mental health and psychosocial support. [Internet]. [cited 2019 December 19]. Available from: https://internationalmedicalcorps.org/program/mental-health-psychosocial-support/

20. International Medical Corps. Toolkit for the integration of mental health into general healthcare in humanitarian settings. [Internet]. [cited 2019 December 19]. Available from: https://www.mhinnovation.net/collaborations/IMC-Mental-Health-Integration-Toolkit

21. Partners In Health. Mental health at Partners In Health. [Internet]. [cited 2019 December 2019]. Available from: https://storymaps.arcgis.com/stories/8dca051575aa4dd983e9fe1e21bcff6b

22. Partners In Health. PIH cross-site mental health matrix to achieve universal health coverage. [Internet]. [cited 2022 August 10]. Available from: https://www.pih.org/MHMatrix

23. Marquez P. *Mental health among displaced people and refugees: making the case for action at the world bank group.* Washington, DC: The World Bank; 2016.

24. World Health Organization. *WHO-AIMS report on mental health system in Lebanon.* Beirut: World Health Organization and Ministry of Health Lebanon; 2015.

25. Republic of Lebanon Ministry of Health. *Mental health and substance use: prevention, promotion and treatment, situation analysis and strategy for Lebanon 2015–2020.* Beirut: Republic of Lebanon, Ministry of Public Health; 2015.

26. World Health Organization. *Mental health action plan.* Geneva: World Health Organization; 2013.

27. Kim JY, Farmer P, Porter M. Redefining global health-care delivery. *The Lancet.* 2013;382(9897):1060–9.

28. Anderson AA. *The community builder's approach to theory of change.* New York: The Aspen Institute Roundtable on Community Change; 2006. 37 p.

29. Breuer E, De Silva MJ, Shidaye R, Petersen I, Nakku J, Jordans MJ, Fekadu A, Lund C. Planning and evaluating mental health services in low-and middle-income countries using theory of change. *The British Journal of Psychiatry.* 2016;208:55–62.

30. Agency for Healthcare Research and Quality. Section 4: ways to approach the quality improvement process [Internet]. [cited 2019 February 2]. Available from: https://www.ahrq.gov/cahps/quality-improvement/improvement-guide/4-approach-qi-process/index.html

31. Instructionaldesign.org. Instructional systems design. [Internet]. [cited 2019 February 2]. Available from: https://www.instructionaldesign.org/

32. Raviola G, Eustache E, Oswald C, Belkin GS. Mental health response in Haiti in the aftermath of the 2010 earthquake: a case study for building long-term solutions. *Harvard Review of Psychiatry.* 2012;20(1):68–77.

33. Raviola G Rose A, Fils-Aimé JR, Therosme T, Affricot E, Valentin C, Daimyo S, Coleman S, Dubuisson W, Wilson J, Verdeli H. Development of a comprehensive, sustained community mental health system in post-earthquake Haiti, 2010–2019. *Global Mental Health.* 2020;7. pp. 1–12.

34. Echeverri C. Assessment of the mental health system in Haiti: needs and perspectives. *Pan-American Health Organization and Zanmi Lasante/Partners in Health,* 2016. pp. 1–30.

35. Raviola G, Smith S, Rose A, Coleman S, Eustache E. Mental health planning matrix to achieve universal health coverage. In: PIH Cross-Site Mental Health Strategic Planning Conference; Boston; 2016.

36. McGriff SJ. Instructional system design: using the ADDIE model. [Internet]. [cited 2019 February 2]. Available from: https://www.lib.purdue.edu/sites/default/files/directory/butler38/ADDIE.pdf

37. Raviola G, Smith S, Manzi A, Forbush L. Training process map. In: PIH Cross-Site Mental Health Strategic Planning Conference; Boston; 2016.

38. Raviola G, Manzi A, Rose A, Smith S, Jerome G, Fenelon D. Mental health monitoring and evaluation process map. In: PIH Cross-Site Mental Health Strategic Planning Conference; Boston; 2016.

39. Schneiderman N, Ironson G, Siegel SD. Stress and health: psychological, behavioral, and biological determinants. *Annual Review of Clinical Psychology.* 2005;1:607–28.

40. Hierholzer E, Bellamy N, Mannix B. *SAMHSA disaster technical assistance center supplemental research bulletein: disaster behavioral health interventions inventory.* Washington, DC: US Department of Health and Human Services, SAMHSA; 2015.

41. Mitchell GSE, Jeffrey T. *Critical incident stress debriefing (CISD): an operations manual for the prevention of traumatic stress among emergency service and disaster workers,* 2nd ed. Ellicot City: Chevron Publishing Corporation; 1997. 223 p.

42. United Nations High Commissioner for Refugees (UNHCR). Guiding Principles on Internal Displacement. Geneva, Switzerland: UN High Commissioner for Refugees; 1998. 14 p.

Chapter 11

Neurology in Global Mental Health Delivery and Training

J. Reginald Fils-Aimé and Aaron L. Berkowitz

Summary points

- Neurologic disorders are a major contributor to global disability-adjusted life years (DALYs) and global mortality.
- Neurologic disorders may present to mental health providers with psychiatric symptoms or comorbidities, especially in resource-limited settings with few or no neurologists.
- Mental health professionals can help to reduce the treatment gap associated with neurological disorders in resource-limited settings.
- Implementation of global mental health and neurology programs can benefit from being integrated into existing community-based primary care structures.
- Programs that have successfully integrated neurology and mental health in primary health-care structures have used task-sharing models by training non-neurologist providers in basic care of neurologic diseases.
- Neurology training should be integrated at all levels of global mental health training so that mental health professionals (whether visiting or local) are able to provide basic neurologic care, training, and supervision in the context of global mental health delivery.
- Global mental health practitioners and trainees should understand that effective neurologic care requires genuine attention to the local historical, sociocultural, and geopolitical context; moreover, local partnership and bidirectional learning have an essential place in improving the quality of care.

Introduction

Just as there can be "no health without mental health,"[1] there can be no mental health without neurologic health. Despite the large burden of neurologic disease, there are often few or no neurologists in resource-limited settings. Patients with neurologic disorders therefore often present to primary care providers such as general physicians, internists, pediatricians, nurses, or mental health practitioners. Because many patients with neurologic disorders present with or develop psychiatric symptoms or comorbidities, primary healthcare practitioners are often the first point of contact between patients with neurologic diseases and the health system in settings where there are few or no neurologists.

In this chapter, we describe the global burden of neurologic disease, contrast it with the global scarcity of neurologists, and argue that the challenge of distinguishing between neurologic and psychiatric conditions—both for laypersons and practitioners—creates an unacceptable treatment gap in low-resource contexts. Against this backdrop, we discuss models for the integration of basic neurology training for mental health providers in resource-limited settings as an essential tool for closing this treatment gap and improving healthcare delivery.

DOI: 10.4324/9781315160597-15

We will focus on epilepsy in particular here because of its high burden of disease,[2] high treatment gap in low-income countries (LICs),[2,3] high incidence of psychiatric comorbidities,[4,5] associated stigma,[6,7] the frequent presentation of patients with epilepsy to mental health practitioners, and the large number of programs designed to address epilepsy in LICs described in the literature. Although there are psychiatric comorbidities of other neurologic diseases such as stroke, dementia, and head trauma, we do not address these neurologic conditions because their psychiatric features (e.g., post-stroke depression, dementia-related psychosis) are generally diagnosed and managed symptomatically by mental health practitioners separately from the treatment of the underlying disease per se. Epilepsy not only has psychiatric comorbidities, but also may itself be mistaken as primary psychiatric disease.

We will also draw on our experience providing mental health and neurologic care in Haiti. Once one of the most lucrative European colonies, Haiti is now one of the world's poorest countries (see Table 11.1). Haiti was founded following history's only successful slave revolt, becoming the second European colony to declare independence after the United States. As the first free Black republic, Haiti was shunned by the international community: US slavery still existed at the time of Haiti's independence and France, Haiti's former colonizer, would not recognize Haiti's independence until Haiti paid an indemnity that ruined the already fragile nascent economy. Political and economic instability has been perpetuated by corrupt misrule and continuous foreign intervention, and compounded by the highest number of natural disasters (e.g., hurricanes and earthquakes) among the nations of Central America and the Caribbean, from 1971 to 2014.[8] These natural disasters have caused unparalleled loss of life and infrastructure due to the fragility of the country as a result of limited environmental policy and urban planning. For example, a major earthquake centered near Port-au-Prince in 2010 resulted in an estimated several hundred thousand deaths, millions of displaced individuals,[9] and approximately 300,000 persons injured,[10] increasing the local burden of patients with neurologic and mental health conditions.

In the setting of increased health needs in this post-earthquake context, the non-governmental organization (NGO) Zanmi Lasante (ZL), the Haiti-based sister organization of the US-based NGO Partners In Health, expanded its mental health program. This expansion quickly required increasing neurology capacity, as presentations of psychiatric and neurologic conditions can be similar or overlapping. Moreover, since many local community members placed both psychiatric

Table 11.1 Selected demographic, socioeconomic, and health indicators in Haiti

Indicator	Value
Total population[11]	10,911,819
Economic indicators	
Poverty headcount ratio at $1.90 a day, % of the population (2011 Purchasing Power Parity)[12]	25%
Gini Index[8]	0.61
Human development index (rank)[13]	168
Health and health system indicators	
Life expectancy at birth (years) (UNDP)[13]	63.6
Physicians per 1000 population[14]	0.2
Absolute number of neurologists (for the whole country)[15]	3
Absolute number of psychiatrists (for the whole country)[16]	20
Proportion of the health budget in the national budget in 2021[17]	3.8%
Percentage of births attended by skilled health staff[18]	42%

and neurological diseases under the same label of "head diseases" (*maladi tèt*), individuals presented to the mental health clinic in search of care for neurological disorders such as epilepsy, Parkinson's disease, and migraine. Both authors have participated in the analysis of and response to the increased need for neurologic care in this setting.

The global burden of neurologic disease

Recent Global Burden of Disease (GBD) study data underscore the considerable health burdens associated with neurological disorders, which in 2019 comprised the eleventh leading contributor to disability-adjusted life years (DALYs), the seventh leading cause of death, and the fifth leading cause of years of life lived with disability (YLDs) globally.[19] In another analysis, which aggregated an expanded category of neurologic disease—including meningitis, stroke, and other conditions that affect the brain that had been classified elsewhere—the estimated health burdens attributable to neurological disorders and conditions were even greater; this study estimated that neurological disorders were the leading cause of DALYs (11.6% of global DALYs) and second leading cause of death (16.5% of global deaths) worldwide in 2016.[20] These figures almost certainly represent underestimates given the lack of access to diagnostic tests, such as neuroimaging, in LICs.[21] Since neurologic disease prevalence increases with age, the relative burden of neurological disease will likely continue to increase as the population ages.

The global burden of neurologic disease is inequitably distributed, with low- and middle-income countries (LMICs) bearing the greatest burden of incidence, mortality, and DALYs for many neurologic disorders. For example, stroke incidence is not only higher in LMICs, but mortality-to-incidence ratio is also greater; in other words, individuals are not only more likely to have a stroke in such settings, but also more likely to die of one as well.[22] In addition, 90% of the world's estimated 63 million people suffering from epilepsy live in LMICs,[23] where epilepsy incidence is nearly twice that of high-income countries.[24,25]

Beyond the conventional population health metrics of disability and mortality, the psychosocial and socioeconomic burden of neurological disorders in resource-limited settings is also immense. For example, patients with epilepsy have increased risk of psychiatric disorders such as depression, anxiety, psychosis, and attention deficit disorder.[7] They face stigma that may result in physical, sexual, or civil rights abuses and in social exclusion; for example, rape is more common in women with epilepsy than in other women.[26] People with epilepsy are more likely to have poorer employment status, fewer years of schooling, poorer housing, and higher food insecurity.[26–28] The burden of disabling neurologic disorders is further amplified—but unmeasured—by their broad impacts on families and caregivers: it is estimated that approximately 500 million people worldwide are family members or colleagues of people with epilepsy.[29]

The global workforce shortfall of neurologists

Despite this enormous burden of neurologic disease in LMICs, there is very limited access to neurologic care in low-resource regions. According to the 2017 Neurological Atlas, there is a median of 4.75 neurologists per 100,000 population in HICs in contrast to a median of only 0.03 and 0.13 neurologists per 100,000 population in LICs and LMICs, respectively.[30] This lack of human resources for neurologic care results in enormous gaps in care for neurologic diseases in resource-poor regions,[31] compounding other structural, economic, and social barriers to accessing care for neurologic illness. For example, it is estimated that although fewer than 10% of epilepsy patients remain untreated in HICs, more than 75% of individuals with epilepsy remain untreated in LICs, with an even higher treatment gap in rural areas—some with treatment gaps of 100%.[3]

The paucity of health providers with specialty training in neurologic disease not only affects access to direct patient care, but also leaves a vacuum in the training of primary healthcare providers in the diagnosis and treatment of neurologic disorders. As a result, patients have limited or no access to specialists in settings in which generalists' clinical skills to care for neurologic disorders are often inadequate. Closing this treatment gap in low-resource settings thus requires training models that equip health providers with the knowledge and skills needed to diagnose and treat patients with neurologic conditions through shared delivery infrastructure using existing healthcare systems.[32] Moreover, a successful approach will include diverse providers from across clinical domains, including psychiatrists, psychologists, internists, pediatricians, family physicians, nurses, and other primary care providers as well as traditional healers.[33,34]

Relationship between neurologic and mental disorders

Many neurologic disorders have psychiatric symptomatology or psychiatric comorbidities at presentation or during the course of the illness. For example, epileptic seizures may present in some instances with hallucinations or behavioral disturbances and may be complicated by post-ictal psychosis. Dementia may present with changes in personality and can be complicated by depression and/or hallucinations. Infectious diseases that affect the nervous system such as HIV and syphilis can develop neuropsychiatric manifestations (such as HIV-associated dementia, depression, psychosis, and delirium).[35] Thus, mental health and neurologic care often require integration and mental healthcare providers should be equipped to recognize both neurologic and psychiatric causes of behavioral, cognitive, mood, and psychotic symptoms and respond with appropriate management, triage, or referral. The detection and assessment of underlying and comorbid neurological disorders is, therefore, a critical component of mental health clinical training. Such training will bolster clinician capacity to deliver effective treatments for the psychiatric aspects of these disorders and appropriately integrate mental health treatment with neurological interventions.

The clinical specialties now comprising psychiatry and neurology were not initially viewed as distinctive domains. For example, the iconic Sigmund Freud, a pioneer in the history of psychiatry and neurology, practiced both disciplines.[36] In Haiti, the country's first psychiatrist, Louis Mars, was a neuropsychiatrist who cared for patients with neurologic disease, including epilepsy and neurodevelopmental disorders.[37,38] The Mars and Kline center that Dr. Louis Mars built in Haiti's capital, Port-au-Prince, has retained its old name, "Centre de Psychiatrie et de Neurologie Mars and Kline," without having a neurologist working there.[39,40] The certifying board for both psychiatry and neurology in the United States continues to be combined as the American Board of Psychiatry and Neurology, even as training in these domains has diverged as these two fields have developed as distinctive disciplines. The majority of clinicians who practice in HIC settings can avail themselves of neurologic specialty consultation. In contrast, primary care and mental health providers in LMIC settings rarely have access to neurologists for patient care, consultation, or continuing medical education. Training of these providers in diagnosis and management of neurologic disorders is therefore essential to respond to the full spectrum of patient needs presenting in both primary care and mental health settings.

Neurology training and neurological care delivery across diverse social contexts

Based on our experience, we argue that meeting some of the challenges of diagnosis and management of neurologic disease inherent to low-resource settings requires an understanding of the local historical, sociocultural, and geopolitical contexts. Here, we explore some of those issues with respect to epilepsy in Haiti.

History is often important in helping us understand the current perceptions of a disease. For example, when Haiti was under French colonial rule prior to independence in 1804, the presence of a slave with epilepsy on a slaves' ship would make the price of all the slaves on the boat drop significantly.[41] If a slave manifested signs of epilepsy within one year after purchase, he or she could be returned to the seller.[41] Many in Haiti still believe that epilepsy is contagious, illustrating how stigma and some misconceptions regarding epilepsy are historically rooted.

Arthur Kleinman and colleagues described how our cultural beliefs affect the way "we communicate about our health problems, the manner in which we present our symptoms, when and to whom we go for care, how long we remain in care and how we evaluate that care."[42(p.141)] Providers must understand not only how culture may affect care-seeking behavior, but also how it shapes patients' explanatory models that manifest, among other ways, in their descriptions of symptoms, the meaning they give to the disease, and the expectations they have from the treatment (see also Chapter 2, this volume). In Haiti, many patients use metaphors in the local language (*Kreyòl Ayisyen*, or Haitian Creole) to describe symptoms that they may not have experienced or heard of before. For example, one patient in a rural Haitian clinic presented her chief concern as "it is raining in my head and there is a music in my ears." As an illustration of how her expressed concerns were initially misunderstood in this clinical encounter, the general physician referred her for a mental health evaluation, assuming she was describing hallucinations; however, further exploration revealed that she was referring to tinnitus.

A common chief concern for absence seizure in children in Haiti is "*li pa kenbe leson*" ("he cannot memorize school lessons") or "*li pa la*" ("he is not there"), each illustrating expressions that may be mistaken for learning disability and attention disorders, respectively. The medical word for seizure in Haitian Creole is *kriz* (literally, "crisis"), which is used colloquially by patients to refer to any medical "crisis" including hypertension, stroke, or a psychotic episode, in addition to epileptic seizures. One can also hear absence seizure or other alterations of consciousness described as "*bon anj li pati*" or "*bonnanj li pa sou li*" ("his good angel went/is away"). These expressions are linked to the conceptualization of personhood in Haitian Vodou (or Voodoo), which is thought to be a composite of the "*Kò kadav*" ("the body"), the "*Gwo bonnanj*" ("the big good angel," which represents the source of physical strength that is the soul), and the "*Ti bonnanj*" ("the little good angel," which represents the guardian and the source of consciousness, affect, and dreams). The *Gwo bonnanj* is the component thought to be superseded by the spirit during a Vodou spirit possession; it is also believed that a sorcerer can replace it, for example, by a bad spirit causing diseases or by the soul of a dead person who had mental illness, epilepsy, or any other disease, creating that disease in the cursed person.[43,44]

Therefore, clinicians must be keenly aware of local ways of describing neurologic diseases and their corresponding explanatory models. As local generalist health providers develop expertise in detection and assessment of neurologic disorders and their manifestations, they may improve their identification of them in their patients and register any unique local descriptions of them. In turn, local providers can help non-local neurologic specialists to enhance local application of their diagnostic skills by providing training on how patients conceive of their illnesses. Global experts will take the opportunity to learn from local expressions, approaches, and practices, and eventually draw lessons for global applications, such as described in the World Health Organization (WHO)/ International League Against Epilepsy (ILAE)/ International Bureau for Epilepsy (IBE) "Out of the Shadows" Global Campaign against Epilepsy.[45,46] Such bidirectionality not only enhances collaboration toward the goal of adapting diagnosis and treatment to local contexts, but also can promote training approaches that are culturally attuned for both local and global experts.

Notwithstanding the potential relevance of cultural beliefs, practices, and preferences to help-seeking for neurological illness in some settings, invoking cultural factors as the sole explanation for poor uptake of health services may obscure social structural barriers that undermine access to care in low-income communities. Indeed, this "culturalist" approach has been critiqued for displacing attention onto patient behavior from social structural factors[47,48]—such as poor access to transportation, unaffordability of medicines and services, and unacceptable opportunity costs of taking time to seek health services—that need to be taken into consideration. For example, in Haiti, epilepsy is sometimes believed by patients and patients' families to be caused by a magic spell or by a Vodou spirit as a punishment. A case series described five patients whose seizures were ascribed to a Vodou spirit by them, their family members, and/or a *mambo* (traditional healer) who was treating them.[49] The authors attributed the patients' delay in accessing care to their religious views and initiatives:

> These cases demonstrate that beliefs and folklore are not always harmless in that, at times, they can adversely affect clinical management. In addition to being a source of great anxiety, they may delay appropriate diagnosis and treatment.[49(p.239)]

Although the authors focused on the "beliefs and folklore" as having the potential to "adversely affect clinical management" and "delay appropriate diagnosis and treatment,"[49(p.239)] the accessibility (in terms of distance and expense) and quality of medical care in the area where the patients were living were not discussed. However, a careful read of the paper reveals that each of these patients subsequently eventually accessed medical care and, in some cases, this was after traveling or emigrating to the United States. Although the authors do not provide narrative data that explain this pivot in care-seeking, it raises an important question about the role of access to health care as a primary driver in decision-making. In this illustration, we argue that there has been a premature attribution of lack of care-seeking in the professional health sector to "beliefs" without sufficient consideration of structural conditions—transportation and affordability to name just two—that may have undermined clinic access.

Indeed, a study conducted in Central Haiti showed that Vodou explanatory models were not primary barriers to seeking psychiatric treatment.[50] Rather, structural factors such as lack of treatment resources and lack of quality care were the greatest obstacles. According to recent surveys, the most common reasons people cite for not going to the hospital when they are sick are lack of money (58%)[18] and traveling distance to care facility.[18] Therefore, it is essential for global mental health trainees and practitioners to learn about not only the local culture, but also the local history and both the socioeconomic and the geopolitical context, which can all have major impacts on how neuropsychiatric care is provided in the country in which they work.

Integrating neurologic care into existing mental healthcare infrastructure

One model for global health delivery emphasizes the importance of developing a shared delivery infrastructure across medical conditions, leveraging existing health system infrastructure and resources to incorporate care for additional conditions.[51] Since many of the patients with mental disorders in resource-limited settings come to the primary and community healthcare setting and since local facilities are often relatively more accessible to patients (i.e., in contrast to urban specialized ones, when they exist), one effective strategy to expand coverage of neurologic needs is through augmentation of the training of local primary care providers. Although the traditional model of separate, isolated psychiatric institutions still exists in many LMICs, a model for shared delivery infrastructure is aligned with the World Health Organization's (WHO) promotion of deinstitutionalization and integration into primary health care.[52,53]

The integration of neurology programs into a shared delivery platform requires the training of a wide range of care providers including not only physicians, but also psychologists, nurses, community health workers, and even traditional healers. Traditional healers are often the first recourse of patients with neurologic diseases such as epilepsy. In Haiti, for example, 70% of the population first seeks medical care from traditional healers.[54] Studies in settings where patients commonly seek care from traditional healers have demonstrated that healers can provide great assistance in referring patients into the medical system for conditions such as epilepsy[55,56] and mental illness,[57-60] providing a bridge with the biomedical healthcare system that allows patients to benefit from both medical and spiritual care.

Examples of epilepsy training and care programs integrated into shared delivery infrastructures

There is substantial experience incorporating epilepsy care into community-based health systems in LMICs, as it is a chronic disease requiring diagnosis, long-term care, and medication titration similar to other non-communicable diseases (NCDs) cared for in the community primary care setting. In this section, we discuss how this approach has been implemented and suggest how it might be extrapolated to the integration of treatment of other neurologic disorders into primary and mental health care in LMICs.

In 1997, the WHO, the International League Against Epilepsy (ILAE), and the International Bureau for Epilepsy (IBE) launched the "Global Campaign against Epilepsy" with the goal of bringing epilepsy "out of the shadows" to improve accessibility of diagnosis and treatment of epilepsy worldwide.[28] A WHO/ILAE demonstration project was carried out in rural China; aspects of this program can serve as a good model for informing the implementation of epilepsy care in other resource-limited areas. In that project—carried out in primary care settings with community participation in six non-contiguous Chinese rural provinces—primary care physicians and local medical staff received basic training in diagnosis and management of epilepsy, as well as on the use of a screening questionnaire. Following the pre-existing hierarchical team structure, village health workers were supervised by town hospital primary care physicians, themselves supervised by neurologists. The village health workers identified the suspected cases of epilepsy; the primary healthcare physicians were responsible for making the diagnosis and providing medical management under the supervision of neurologists. The intervention was preceded by a free educational program for the public consisting of lectures and discussions with patients and community leaders, distribution of printed materials, and educational interventions in televisions and newspapers.[28]

That intervention confirmed that convulsive seizures could easily be identified by village health workers in this setting and that most patients responded to a one-drug treatment regimen: phenobarbital. They used phenobarbital as first-line therapy and demonstrated clinical improvement with this low-cost medication, presenting it as a cost-effective option for other limited-resource settings. After two years of treatment, 25% of patients were seizure free and another 45% of them had symptomatic improvement. At the end of the intervention, an evaluation survey showed that there was a significant reduction of the epilepsy treatment gap from 63% to 50%.[61] The authors defined treatment gap in the paper as "the difference between the number of people with active epilepsy and the number whose seizures were being appropriately treated in a given population at a given point in time, expressed as a percentage."[61] The success of the project prompted the proposed epilepsy care to be integrated in the primary care system all over rural China.[28,61,62]

Comparable programs have been similarly successful in rural India. In a program named "Epilepsy Control Programme in India through a District Model," which was carried out from

1999 to 2000 in several states, neurologists took part in the design of the program and trained district medical officers including psychiatrists, pediatricians, and other physicians. These district medical officers, in turn, trained and supervised primary healthcare (PHC) medical officers holding a basic medical degree (MBBS), who diagnosed and treated epilepsy cases referred by peripheral health workers working at the community level. From 1999 to 2001, six training workshops took place for the district medical officers, each lasting two to three days. These trainings covered the public health aspects of epilepsy, the diagnosis and management of epilepsy, and its legal, social, and psychological aspects. Pre- and post-test evaluation showed a clear increase of knowledge and skills. The participants showed satisfaction at the end of the training and were eager to start both epilepsy clinics and training for additional PHC medical officers. However, to take that district model to a larger scale, the implementers underlined the need for refresher courses, developing training manuals in local languages and taking into account the local sociocultural practices, customs and beliefs, and increasing government support.[63] The program described in this study is an elegant example of how psychiatrists can be trained not only as providers of neurologic care but also as trainers of PHC doctors with respect to neurologic care.

Another project in India trained paramedical practitioners in "epidemiological methods, practical management of epilepsy, case ascertainment, and health education"[64] to raise awareness, screen, and refer cases to primary care physicians and neurologists who successfully managed the cases clinically—without further neurological investigations—and with phenobarbital or/ and phenytoin as treatment.[64]

Nurses constitute a large professional workforce from which global neurology interventions should tap more and more. Interventions in which nurses are tasked with caring for a range of neurological and mental health conditions in the primary care or community setting have been effective in countries such as Zimbabwe[65] and Cameroon.[66] In Zimbabwe, Adamolekun and colleagues[65] described an epilepsy care program run by nurses in Chitungwiza, a town of 100,000 inhabitants situated 20 kilometers from Harare. At the time of the study, Chitungwize had a 200-bed hospital with specialists and general practitioners, and four health centers run by nurses. Epilepsy patients were diagnosed and initiated on treatment by physicians and subsequently followed closer to their homes at the health centers by community health nurses for routine care and monitoring of drug therapy. The Epilepsy Support Program, supported by several partners, organized a monthly epilepsy support group for users, parents, and relatives. The support group discussed the importance of parental understanding and participation in the care of patients with epilepsy, as well as the importance of drug adherence. The program also organized vocational and rehabilitative trainings, and members of the group shared personal experiences and took part in outreach activities. An epilepsy clinic was integrated into the epilepsy support group to allow a neurologist to evaluate the clinical management of the patients by the health centers' nurses. Among the 114 patients seen at the epilepsy support group, 46 (40.3%) were seizure-free for more than the six months preceding the evaluation; 59.6% of the patients were on monotherapy; and 71.9% were on phenobarbital either as monotherapy or in combination with another drug. No corrective intervention was needed from the neurologist in 43.8% of the consultations. The most important intervention that the neurologist had to do for patients with inadequate seizure control was to order an increase in dose in 29% of the consultations. The authors conclude that, while the program revealed the potential benefit of written protocols specifying anti-seizure medication maintenance doses and titration, it also provided a basis for the planning of training on epilepsy comprehensive care for community health nurses.[65] However, the study did not include an assessment before the intervention that could allow for post-intervention comparison, nor did it evaluate the impact of the vocational aspect of the program.

At Zanmi Lasante, a successful epilepsy program has been built by the mental health department involving the existing community healthcare infrastructure for chronic diseases, which includes community health workers, generalist physicians, nurses, and mental health professionals, such as psychologists and social workers.[33,34,67] The mental health program leaders have developed the curriculum for all of the aforementioned cadres of providers in collaboration with a US-based neurologist (the co-author ALB). The curriculum covers epilepsy diagnosis and management and includes an interview form for first and follow-up visits written in the local languages, Haitian Kreyòl and French. It also includes a medication titration algorithm for prescribing physicians with typical starting, maintenance, and maximum doses; titration protocols; and side effects of each medicine listed. Importantly, the neurologist accompanied local experienced medical providers in conducting a "train the trainers" program to equip them not only to practice patient care, but also to teach other local providers how to manage epilepsy. In addition to on-the-ground training, complex cases are discussed virtually (while protecting patients' confidentiality by removing all personal identifiable information) with the collaborating US-based neurologist or with a local physician undergoing neurology training by visiting faculty to allow for both specialist opinions on clinical care and continuing education.

Standardized protocols for care of neurologic and psychiatric disorders: The WHO mhGAP Intervention Guide (mhGAP-IG)

To facilitate implementation efforts aimed at reducing the gap in care for mental, neurological, and substance use disorders, the WHO has developed an evidenced-based intervention guide for non-specialists, which was published in 2010 and updated in 2015. The WHO's *mhGAP* [Mental Health Gap Action Programme] *Intervention Guide for mental, neurological and substance use disorders in non-specialized health settings* (mhGAP-IG),[52] responds to a critical need for standardized protocols for some of the most prevalent mental, neurological, and substance use conditions for guidance in regions where specialty training may not be available. The mhGAP-IG includes protocols addressing three neurological conditions that have either overlap or are often comorbid with psychiatric conditions: epilepsy, developmental disorders, and dementia.

One study conducted in Nigeria described how the mhGAP-IG was integrated into a "cascade-training model" in which a few psychiatrists, called "Master trainers," trained some non-specialists such as generalists, practitioners, and nurses.[68] These latter clinicians, in turn, were facilitators of the end-users' training that included medical doctors, nurses, and community health officers (i.e., professionals with a two-year diploma in community health). The psychiatrists took part in developing the teaching materials and adapting the mhGAP-IG to the local context. After the completion of all the levels of training, a strong monitoring and supervision structure was set in place. The psychiatrists supervised the facilitators who, in turn, supervised the frontline providers, and refresher trainings were conducted. The paper concludes that this "well-supervised cascade training model" for integrating mental health into primary health care using the mhGAP-IG in Nigeria was feasible.[68] Although the paper does not specifically address how neurologic disorder protocols from mhGAP were incorporated into training, the project demonstrates how protocols from the mhGAP might be usefully incorporated into a training program. However, the mhGAP-IG may still be challenging to implement without access to the necessary specialist expertise to teach how it should be used and mentor local providers in practice, particularly with respect to neurologic disorders. Additionally, providers must follow local protocols and medication formularies, which may make general guidelines challenging to apply across different contexts.

Conclusion

When psychiatrists and other mental health professionals and trainees from relatively well-resourced settings collaborate in global mental health program development or care delivery, they may encounter clinical service needs relevant to neurologic disease, for which they have little prior postgraduate training and minimal access to local specialty neurologic expertise and resources. Even when health professionals have received some neurological training within other postgraduate programs, limitations in the formulary and laboratory capacities, as well as in imaging modalities, may present diagnostic and management challenges; thus, without additional training, supervision, and opportunities for consultation, they may feel ill-equipped to address neurological issues clinically or programmatically. We therefore recommend integrating neurology training into all levels of global mental health training when possible. Psychiatrists in global mental health fellowships should ideally receive some training in the basics of neurologic diagnosis and treatment and seek access to a neurologist consultant or colleague who can help address challenging cases and broader issues that may arise with respect to care of neurologic disease in resource-limited settings.

The above examples demonstrate some successful models in which local or external neurologic specialists developed training materials and programs to integrate neurologic care into existing local health infrastructure in LMICs. At a programmatic level, global mental health services should ideally integrate or coordinate with a local neurologist (or collaborating consulting neurologist if a local provider is not available) both for clinical consultation and to assist in the development of protocols, training materials, and—most importantly—training programs on how to utilize such materials. Moreover, these trainings should not be limited to physicians, but rather should include training of all frontline providers including nurses, community health workers, and traditional healers to develop and strengthen collaborative community health infrastructure to diagnose and care for patients with neurologic disorders.

We recommend that such training ideally happen on-site using an existing platform, such as a governmental or non-governmental healthcare facility, and that it be supported by Internet-based trainings and tele-consultation. Crucial for any such collaboration is the development of a shared vision toward collaborative preparation of the curricula, care pathways, protocols, and decision support tools that incorporate local context and resources. Programs should be rigorously monitored and evaluated for further improvement of the program and supported with specialist mentorship, coaching, and regular refresher training. Finally, the collaborative structure should facilitate bidirectional learning, which will ultimately improve the training process and the care provided.

References

1. Prince M, Patel V, Saxena S, Maj M, Maselko J, Phillips MR, et al. No health without mental health. *The Lancet.* 2007;370(9590):859–77.
2. Birbeck LG. Epilepsy care in developing countries: part I of II. *Current Review in Clinical Science.* 2010;10(4):75–9.
3. Meyer A-C, Dua T, Ma J, Saxena S, Birbeck G. Global disparities in the epilepsy treatment gap: a systematic review. *Bulletin of World Health Organization.* 2010;88(4):260–6.
4. Tsigebrhan R, Hanlon C, Medhin G, Fekadu A. Help seeking and suicidality among people with epilepsy in a rural low income country setting: cross-sectional survey. *International Journal of Mental Health Systems.* 2017;11(1):44.
5. Mula M, Sander JW. Psychosocial aspects of epilepsy: a wider approach. *B J Psych Open.* 2016 Aug 17;2(4):270–4. doi: 10.1192/bjpo.bp.115.002345. PMID: 27703786; PMCID: PMC4995176.
6. Jacoby A, Snape D, Baker GA. Epilepsy and social identity: the stigma of a chronic neurological disorder. *The Lancet Neurology.* 2005;4(3):171–8.
7. de Boer HM, Mula M, Sander JW. The global burden and stigma of epilepsy. *Epilepsy and Behavior.* 2008;12(4):540–6.
8. Singh RJ, Barton-Dock M. *Haiti - Toward a new narrative.* World Bank; 2015.
9. Farmer PE. Haiti after the earthquake. *Public Affairs.* New York; 2011. p. 119.

10. Lou L, Shi P. Haiti 2010 earthquake: how to explain such huge losses? *International Journal of Disaster Risk Science*. 2011;2(1): 25–33.

11. Institut Haïtien de Statistique et d'Informatique (IHSI). Estimation de la Population Haitienne en 2015 [Internet]. IHSI. 2015 [cited 2020 February 22]. Available from: http://www.ihsi.ht/

12. World Bank. Poverty headcount ration at $1.90 a day - Haiti (2012, most recent data) [Internet]. 2019 [cited 2020 February 22]. Available from: https://data.worldbank.org/indicator/SI.POV.DDAY?locations=HT

13. United Nations Development Programme. Human development report 2019 [Internet]. 2019 [cited 2020 Feb 22]. Available from: http://hdr.undp.org/en/countries/profiles/HTI

14. World Bank. Physicians per 1000 population in Haiti. 2018. https://data.worldbank.org/indicator/SH.MED.PHYS.ZS?locations=HT. Accessed August 8, 2022.

15. Fils-Aimé JR. Unpublished data estimating the number of neurologists in Haiti. 2022.

16. Department of Mental Health and Substance Abuse WHO. Mental health atlas 2011 [Internet]. Vol. 113. 2014. Available from: who.int/publications/i/item/9799241564359

17. Ministère de l'Economie et des Finances d'Haiti. *Budget rectificatif 2022–2021* [Internet]. MEF. 2022 [cited 2022 August 22]. Available from: https://mef.gouv.ht/index.php?page=Budget2021

18. Institut Haïtien de l'Enfance (IHE) et ICF. *Enquête Moralité, Morbidité et Utilisation des Services (EMMUS-VI) 2016–2017*. Pétion-Ville, Haïti, et Rockville, Maryland, USA: IHE et ICF. 2018.

19. Institute for Health Metrics and Evaluation GBD 2019. University of Washington, 2022. https://vizhub.healthdata.org/gbd-compare/ Accessed July 20, 2022.

20. GBD 2016 Neurology Collaborators. Global, regional, and national burden of neurological disorders, 1990–2016: a systematic analysis for the global burden of disease study 2016. *The Lancet Neurology*. 2019;18:459–80.

21. Mclane HC, Berkowitz A, Patenaude BN, Mckenzie ED, Wolper E, Wahlster S, et al. Availability, accessibility and affordability of neurodiagnostic tests in 37 countries. *Neurology*. 2015;85 (18): 1614–22.

22. Feigin VL, Forouzanfar MH, Krishnamurthi R, Mensah GA, Connor M, Bennett DA, et al. Global and regional burden of stroke during 1990–2010: findings from the global burden of disease study 2010. *The Lancet*. 2014;383(9913):245–54.

23. Ngugi AK, Bottomley C, Kleinschmidt I, Sander JW, Newton CR. Estimation of the burden of active and life-time epilepsy: a meta-analytic approach. *Epilepsia*. 2010;51(5):883–90.

24. Ngugi AK, Kariuki SM, Bottomley C, Kleinschmidt I, Newton CR. Incidence of epilepsy a systematic review and meta-analysis. *Neurology*. 2011; 77(10):1005–12.

25. Scott R a, Lhatoo SD, Sander JW. The treatment of epilepsy in developing countries: where do we go from here? *Bulletin of the World Health Organization*. 2001;79(4):344–51.

26. Birbeck G, Chomba E, Atadzhanov M, Mbewe E, Haworth A. The social and economic impact of epilepsy in Zambia: a cross-sectional study. *The Lancet*. 2010;6(1):39–44.

27. Birbeck GL, Chomba E, Atadzhanov M, Mbewe E, Haworth A. Women's experiences living with epilepsy in Zambia. *American Journal of Tropical Medicine and Hygiene*. 2008;79(2):168–72.

28. World Health Organization. Epilepsy management at primary health level in rural China: WHO/ILAE/IBE a Global Campaign Against Epilepsy Demonstration Project. Geneva: WHO. 2009:1–32.

29. Kale R. The treatment gap. *Epilepsia*. 2002;43(Suppl.6):31–3.

30. World Health Organization. *ATLAS: countries resources for neurological disorders*. 2nd ed. Geneva: World Health Organization; 2017.

31. Programme for Neurological Diseases and Neuroscience, Department of Mental Health and Substance Abuse, World Health Organization. *Atlas country resources for neurological disorders*. Geneva: World Health Organization; 2004.

32. Cochran MF, Berkowitz AL. A global health delivery framework approach to epilepsy care in resource-limited settings. *Journal of the Neurological Sciences*. 2015;358(1–2):263–5. Available from: http://dx.doi.org/10.1016/j.jns.2015.09.007

33. Raviola G, Rose A, Fils-Aime J, Thérosmé T, Affricot E, Valentin C, et al. Development of a comprehensive, sustained community mental health system in post-earthquake Haiti, 2010–2019. *Global Mental Health*. 2020;7:e6.

34. Grelotti DJ, Lee AC, Fils-aimé JR, Jean JS, Therosmé T, Petit-homme H, et al. A pilot initiative to deliver community-based psychiatric services in rural haiti after the earthquake. *Annals of Global Health*. 2015;2(74):718–24.

35. Dube B, Benton T, Cruess DG, Evans DL. Neuropsychiatric manifestations of HIV infection and AIDS. *Journal of Psychiatry and Neuroscience*. 2005;30(4):237–46.

36. Boller F, Barba GD. The evolution of psychiatry and neurology. In: Jeste DV, Friedman JH, editors. *Current clinical neurology: psychiatry for neurologists*. NJ; Humana Press. 2006. pp. 11–15.

37. Mars L. *L'hygiène mentale et la communauté haitienne*. Bulletin du Bureau d'ethnologie de la République d'Haïti. 1947; Serie II(3): 22–40.

38. Kline N, Mars L. *The Haiti Psychiatric Institute; Centre de Psychiatrie*. Psychiatry in the underdeveloped countries: a report of a roundtable discussion at the 116th annual meeting at the American Psychiatric Association. 1960. pp. 48–51.

39. Bijoux L. Évolution des conceptions et de l'intervention en santé mentale en Haïti. *Revue Haïtienne de Santé Mentale*. 1:83–90; 2010.

40. Farmer P. The birth of the klinik: A cultural history of Haitian professional psychiatry. In: *Ethnopsychiatry*. Gaines A., ed. Albany: SUN; 1992. pp. 251–72.

41. Debien G. L'etat sanitaire des esclaves. In: *Les eclaves aux Antilles (XVIIe-XVIIIe Siecles)*. Fort-de-France: Societe d'Histoire de la Martinique; 1975. pp. 298–337.

42. Kleinman A, Eisenberg L, Good B. Culture, illness, and care clinical lessons from anthropologic and cross-cultural research. *Annals of Internal Medicine*. 1978;88(2):251–8. Available from: http://dx.doi.org/10.7326/0003-4819-88-2-251

43. Kiev A. Folk psychiatry in Haiti. *Journal of Nervous and Mental Disease*. 1961;132(3):260–5.

44. WHO/PAHO. *Culture et Sante Mentale en Haiti: Une Revue de litterature*. Geneva: WHO; 2010.

45. Boer HM De. "Out of the shadows": A global campaign against epilepsy. *Epilepsia*. 2002;43(Suppl. 6):7–8.

46. World Health Organization, International League Against Epilepsy, International Bureau for Epilepsy. *"Out of the shadows" Global campaign against epilepsy: An introduction to the campaign and its demonstration projects*. ILAE/IBE/WHO. 2001. Paswerk Bedrijven Cruquius, the Netherlands

47. Farmer P. An anthropology of structural violence. *Current Anthropology*. 2004;45:305–25.

48. Farmer P. On suffering and structural violence: a view from below. *Daedalus*. 1996;125:261–83.

49. Carrazana EJ, DeToledo J, Tatum W, Rivas-Vasquez R, Rey G, Wheeler S. Epilepsy and religious experiences: Voodoo possession. *Epilepsia*. 1999;40(2):239–41.

50. Khoury N, Kaiser B, Brewster A-R, Keys H, Kohrt B. Explanatory models and mental health treatment: is Vodou an obstacle to psychiatric treatment in rural Haiti? *Culture Medicine and Psychiatry*. 2012;36(3):514–34.

51. Kim JY, Farmer P, Porter ME. Redefining global health-care delivery. *The Lancet*. 2013;382(9897):1060–9.

52. World Health Organization. *mhGAP intervention guide for mental, neurological and substance use disorders in non-specialized health settings - version 2.0*. 2015.

53. World Health Organization. *World family doctors caring for people: integrating mental health into primary care: a global perspective*. World Health Organization. Singapore; 2008. https://apps.who.int/iris/handle/10665/43935

54. Ministère de la Santé Publique et de la Population. *Politique nationale de Santé*. Official document. MSPP. 2012. Retrieved at https://www.mspp.gouv.ht/documentation/?txt_date_debut=&start=0&txt_date_fin=&txt_categorie=0&txt_mot_cle=politique+nationale&btn_search=. Accessed on 03/05/2023

55. Baskind R, Birbeck GL. Epilepsy care in Zambia: a study of traditional healers. *Epilepsia.* 2008;23(1):1–7.
56. Kendall-taylor N, Kathomi C, Rimba K, Newton CR. Traditional healers and epilepsy treatment on the Kenyan Coast. *Epilepsia.* 2013;49(9):1638–9.
57. Gureje O, Nortje G, Makanjuola V, Oladeji B, Seedat S, Jenkins R. The role of global traditional and complementary systems of medicine in treating mental health problems. *The Lancet Psychiatry.* 2015;2(2):168–77.
58. Abbo C, Okello ES, Musisi S, Waako P, Ekblad S. Naturalistic outcome of treatment of psychosis by traditional healers in Jinja and Iganga districts, Eastern Uganda – A 3- and 6 months follow up. *International Journal of Mental Health Systems.* 2012;6(1):13.
59. Abbo C, Ekblad S, Waako P, Okello E, Musisi S. The prevalence and severity of mental illnesses handled by traditional healers in two districts in Uganda. *African Health Sciences.* 2009;9(Suppl 1):S16–22.
60. Abbo C. Profiles and outcome of traditional healing practices for severe mental illnesses in two districts of Eastern Uganda. *Global Health Action.* 2011;4:1–15.
61. Wang W, Wu J, Dai X, Ma G, Yang B, Wang T, et al. Global campaign against epilepsy: assessment of a demonstration project in rural China. *Bulletin of the World Health Organization.* 2008;86(12):964–9.
62. Ding D, Hong Z, Chen GS, Dai XY, Wu JZ, Wang WZ, et al. Primary care treatment of epilepsy with phenobarbital in rural China: cost-outcome analysis from the WHO/ILAE/IBE global campaign against epilepsy demonstration project. *Epilepsia.* 2008;49(3):535–9.
63. Gourie-Devi M, Satishchandra P, Gururaj G. Epilepsy control program in India: a district model. *Epilepsia.* 2003;44(Suppl. 1):58–62.
64. Mani KS, Rangan G, Srinivas H V., Srindharan VS, Subbakrishna DK. Epilepsy control with phenobarbital or phenytoin in rural south India: the Yelandur study. *The Lancet.* 2001;357(9265):1316–20.
65. Adamolekun B, Mielke J, Ball D, Mundanda T. An evaluation of the management of epilepsy by primary health care nurses in Chitungwiza, Zimbabwe. *Epilepsy Research.* 2000;39:177–81.
66. Kengne AP, Fezeu LL, Awah PK, Sobngwi E, Dongmo S, Mbanya JC. Nurse-led care for epilepsy at primary level in a rural health district in Cameroon. *Epilepsia.* 2008;49(9):1639–42.
67. Fils-aimé RJ, Grelotti DJ, Therosme T, Kaiser BN, Raviola G, et al. A mobile clinic approach to the delivery of community-based mental health services in rural Haiti. *PLoS One.* 2018;13(6):1–15.
68. Gureje O, Abdulmalik J, Kola L, Musa E, Yasamy MT, Adebayo K. Integrating mental health into primary care in Nigeria: report of a demonstration project using the mental health gap action programme intervention guide. *BMC Health Services Research.* 2015;15(1):242.

Chapter 12

Substance Use Disorders in Global Mental Health Delivery and Training

Hilary S. Connery, R. Kathryn McHugh, Meghan E. Reilly, Sonya Shin, and Shelly F. Greenfield

Acknowledgments: The authors would like to acknowledge Laurel Meyer, BA for her assistance on preparation of this manuscript for publication. In addition, a previous version of this chapter was published as Connery HS, McHugh RK, Reilly M, Shin S, Greenfield SF. Substance use disorders in global mental health delivery: epidemiology, treatment gap, and implementation of evidence-based treatments. *Harvard Review of Psychiatry.* 2020 Sep-Oct; 28(5): 316–327. https://journals.lww.com/hrpjournal/pages/default.aspx

Summary points

- Substance use disorders (SUDs) account for a significant proportion of global morbidity and mortality, and financial and social burden, yet the majority of those living with SUDs in both low- and middle-income countries (LMICs) and high-income countries (HICs) never receive treatment specific to SUDs.
- Stigma and legal discrimination associated with SUDs continue to hinder public understanding of SUDs as a treatable mental health condition, and to impede global health efforts to reduce SUD prevalence and costs.
- Evidence-based, behavioral therapies and pharmacotherapies to treat SUDs are effective but most individuals with SUDs have no access to these treatments, especially in LMICs.
- Capacity-building for SUD treatment delivery in LMICs and HICs is optimized when clinical expertise is partnered with regional community stakeholders and government in a unified strategy to expand services for those with SUDs.
- SUD-relevant training must be included in mental health, primary care, and community health settings in order to build capacity for treatment.
- Several strategies have been successfully employed to build capacity such as collaborative care models for mental health including SUDs; clinician/researcher collaborations for adaptation of evidence-based treatments to specific settings; train-the-trainer models; expansion of virtual technologies and telemedicine; and booster sessions to clinicians for ongoing implementation.
- Workforce expansion for SUD treatment delivery is optimal when it engages community stakeholders to participate actively, as family and peer supports, and as trained lay health workers. Longitudinal supervision of this workforce and appropriate incentives for service are required components of a sustainable community-based model for SUD treatment.

Background

Substance use disorders (SUDs) are highly prevalent worldwide and are among the leading causes of morbidity and mortality globally.[1,2] In 2016, 1.3% of all disability adjusted life years

DOI: 10.4324/9781315160597-16

(DALYs) globally were attributable to drug use and 4.2% of all DALYs were attributable to alcohol use.[3] Alcohol use is a major cause of disease and injury,[4] with an estimated 283 million people aged 15+ years having an alcohol use disorder (AUD; representing 5.1% of adults) in 2016.[5] Globally, alcohol use is both a causal factor for hundreds of disease and injury conditions and is responsible for millions of deaths annually.[6] Moreover, harmful alcohol use is responsible for 5.7% of the global burden of disease including 7.1% in males and 2.2% in females.[1] For males between the ages of 15 and 24 years, alcohol misuse is the leading cause of death and disability in most regions of the world (except for in the eastern Mediterranean region) and, similarly, it is the leading cause of death and disability for females in high-income countries and in the Americas.[6] Furthermore, the health burdens related to alcohol use extend well beyond measured alcohol-attributable disability and deaths insofar as AUD elevates risk for other mental health disorders[4] and harmful consequences of alcohol use—including alcohol-related injuries, violence, and fetal alcohol spectrum disorders—can have serious collateral effects on other individuals in the family and community, especially women and children.

In addition to the global burden of disease caused by harmful alcohol use and AUD, more than 270 million people (5.5%) worldwide between the ages of 15 to 64 years used drugs in 2017, of whom 35 million had a drug use disorder.[7] Of these, approximately 11 million injected drugs and roughly 12.5% of these individuals were living with HIV.[7] It is now estimated that the drug-attributable disease burden accounts for approximately 1.3% of the global burden of disease overall.[3]

In addition to this estimated disease burden, SUDs contribute to additional morbidity and mortality because they are associated with a myriad of medical conditions such as infectious diseases including Hepatitis B and C, HIV, and tuberculosis (TB), as well as many cancers and chronic pulmonary, cardiovascular, and gastrointestinal disorders.[8] According to the WHO, alcohol use causes a staggering number of deaths associated with infectious diseases; for example, it is estimated that 19.6% of deaths from tuberculosis (representing 254,000 deaths globally in 2016) and 3.3% of deaths from HIV/AIDS as well as 3.3% of deaths from lower respiratory infections are caused by alcohol use.[5] The age-standardized alcohol-attributable burden of infectious diseases varies considerably across regions, with the highest burden being in Africa (where the rate was 24.8 deaths per 100,000 people) and the lowest in the Eastern Mediterranean Region (where the rate was fewer than 0.3 deaths per 100,000 people).[5] If we include tobacco-related disorders, all of these burdens amplify considerably.[9] In 2016, tobacco use caused more than 7.1 million deaths worldwide with 5.1 million and 2.0 million deaths in men and women, respectively.[10]

Substance use disorders have a profoundly negative effect on overall mental health. SUDs are also highly comorbid with other mental health disorders.[11–13] This comorbidity can complicate treatment course and recovery from both the SUD and virtually all other mental health disorders, especially anxiety, depression, personality disorders, and post-traumatic stress disorder (PTSD). In addition, SUDs contribute significantly to intimate partner violence, family violence, overdose and suicide, and other injury deaths (e.g., related to firearms, motor vehicles, and drowning).

Given the significant morbidity and mortality associated with SUDs, there are fortunately a broad range of evidence-based treatments for alcohol, tobacco, opioid, and other substance use disorders. These include brief behavioral therapies that can be delivered in individual and group formats, peer-led supportive treatments, family treatments, mutual help programs, and medication treatment (e.g., also termed pharmacotherapy).[11,14] Yet despite these evidence-based treatments for SUDs, and the overwhelming data demonstrating morbidity and mortality associated with SUDs, the vast majority of the world's population affected by SUDs receives no treatment. Moreover, although many scientific advances in behavioral and pharmacologic interventions have been achieved in the last two decades, the treatment gap for SUDs globally remains among the widest of all medical and mental health disorders.

This treatment gap is highly consequential. The Organization for Economic Co-operation and Development (OECD) estimated that if there was an increase in access within primary care settings to provide screening and advice to 30% of eligible heavy drinking patients, the overall prevalence of harmful use of alcohol could decrease by 10–15% across OECD member countries with a concomitant reduction in the incidence of AUD by 5–14%.[15] Significant rates of death, disease, and disability could be avoided if consumption were modestly reduced. For example, in 2000, the attributable overall DALYs from alcohol were 713 million.[16] The estimated avoidable disease burden in 2010 if consumption had been cut by 25% in the intervening decade was 195 million DALYs and by 2020, 220 million DALYs.[16] Another study demonstrated that in the European Union, if 40% of people with AUD were treated with effective alcohol pharmacotherapy, approximately 13% and 9% of alcohol-attributable deaths in males and females, respectively, would be averted in a 12-month period.[17]

What, then, are the reasons that we do not respond as a global community to narrow the treatment gap in HIC and LMIC health systems? Recent economic studies demonstrate the cost-effectiveness of investing in up-front resources, especially in brief intervention and treatment programs for heavy drinking and AUDs as well as for pharmacologic treatment for opioid use disorders.[18] Why the treatment gap remains in both HICs and LMICs may be explained by some combination of lack of: 1) universal access to health and mental health care; 2) availability of evidence-based treatments in a specific region; 3) clinical skills among healthcare providers to deliver the interventions; and 4) political will and/or financial resources. Additionally, each of these factors is magnified by historical stigma and discrimination of individuals with SUDs cutting across diverse cultural settings.

Stigma and legal and economic discrimination toward people with alcohol and drug use disorders have contributed to marginalization of individuals with these disorders across many societies and communities. This marginalization is compounded by self-stigma that results in avoidance of help-seeking, social isolation of individuals with SUDs and their families, ongoing ignorance of healthcare and governmental leaders about the availability of effective treatments, and lack of systematic education of health and mental healthcare providers about evidence-based treatments for patients with SUDs. To mitigate the social and health impacts of this pervasive stigma, therefore, it is of particular importance that all health clinicians, inclusive of mental healthcare providers, in HICs/LMICs learn to integrate prevention, early intervention, treatment and recovery approaches, strategies, and evidence-based treatments into their work with patients with mental health disorders who have, or are at risk for, SUDs.

Historical roots of global stigma and discrimination of persons with substance use disorders

Substance use disorders are mental health disorders that manifest in individuals based on the complex interaction of genetic risk with a range of social determinants of health including those characterized by individual disempowerment and discrimination, as well as childhood and adult trauma, and lack of access to education, secure housing, food, and water. Although prospective patients encounter many social barriers to accessing quality care for SUDs, stigma and discrimination are particularly important factors operating at both the provider and the health systems level.[19] This stigma is fueled by ignorance and false beliefs regarding SUDs, including their etiology and the efficacy of treatments.[20,21] This stigma is powerfully reified in the language routinely used to describe individuals with an SUD. For example, in a study of non-SUD trained mental healthcare practitioners attending professional conferences in the United States, when a person with an SUD was described as a "substance abuser," clinicians were less likely to believe they deserved treatment for their disorder(s) compared with when the person was more accurately described as "a person with a substance use disorder."[22]

Individuals with SUDs may also not recognize that they have an illness, or that it is treatable. This lack of knowledge may, in part, reflect the lack of awareness or knowledge in their local community or society. There is also a long-standing, well-documented disapproval of those with SUDs.[23] Self-stigma may reflect the individual's perceived disapproval by others in one's society or community, contributing to a sense of shame and fear of rejection, abandonment, or punishment.[24] Self-stigma has been defined as the process in which persons with mental illness internalize negative public attitudes about mental illness and apply these attitudes to themselves.[25] Self-stigma leads individuals to self-discrimination including self-isolation. This has many detrimental effects on the individual including decreased health services use, poor health outcomes, and lower quality of life. In addition, self-stigma can lead to lower self-esteem and reduced self-efficacy, which can, in turn, lead to individuals not accessing opportunities that might promote employment, independent living, or other social advantages.[26] Even insofar as individuals might seek health care, lower self-efficacy among those individuals with self-stigma can lead to reductions in adherence to treatment recommendations and reduced positive treatment outcomes. In response to considerable public misinformation about SUDs, the World Health Organization published a fact sheet in multiple languages for policymakers entitled "What do people think they know about substance dependence?" as an effort aimed at dispelling eight myths about SUDs.[27]

Thus, stigma creates a significant barrier to treatment access and treatment delivery for SUDs in both LMICs and HICs. Effective education of healthcare providers and health systems leaders who are dedicated to reducing suffering, morbidity, and mortality from SUDs in the population they serve is one necessary (even if not sufficient) approach to implementing screening, early interventions, and treatment for individuals with SUDs.

Epidemiology, disease burden, and costs of substance use disorders globally

The WHO held their first Forum on Alcohol, Drugs, and Addictive Behaviors (FADAB) in June 2017.[2] The FADAB reported that in 2008, 155–250 million people or 3.5–5.7% of the world's population between ages 15 and 64 years used substances such as cannabis, amphetamines, cocaine, opioids, and non-prescribed prescription medicines.[12] Globally, cannabis is used by 129–190 million people, and this is followed in prevalence of use by amphetamines, stimulants, cocaine, and opioids.[28] The WHO estimates that 0.7% of the global burden of disease in 2004 was due to cocaine and opioid use[29] and the social costs such as arrests, injuries, violence, and other family consequences of illicit substance use was approximately 2% of the GDP.[30] The 2008 data estimated that, globally, 69,000 people die from opioid overdose annually[31] while over 15 million consumed illicit opium, morphine and/or heroin.[28] According to the Global Burden of Disease study, the most common drug use disorders in 2016 were cannabis use disorders (22.1 million or age-standardized prevalence of 289.7 cases per 100,000 people) and opioid use disorders (26.8 million or age-standardized prevalence of 353.0 cases per 100,000).[3] In spite of this, in 2008 only 30% of countries had effective medication available (e.g., in this study, narrowly defined as opioid agonist pharmacotherapy for maintenance treatment of opioid dependence) to treat opioid dependence.[32]

As of March 2018, global alcohol consumption was equal to 6.4 liters of pure alcohol consumed per person per year for those 15 years and older,[33] which can be understood as an estimate of approximately one bottle or one liter of wine per week per person.[34] Almost 25% of alcohol consumed was illegally produced or sold.[5] In 2016, globally, 16% of drinkers 15 years and older engaged in heavy episodic drinking with HICs having the highest alcohol per capita consumption.[5]

Globally, 26.5% of all 15–19-year-olds, or 155 million adolescents, are current drinkers.[5] The prevalence rates of current drinking are highest among 15–19 year-olds in the WHO European Region (43.8%) and lowest in the Western Pacific Region (37.9%), which is similar to the 38.2% prevalence in the Region of the Americas.[5] Globally an estimated 46 million women and 237 million men have alcohol use disorders.[5]

In 2016, daily tobacco smoking (nicotine use disorder) resulted in a staggering US$2 trillion global economic burden, associated with healthcare costs of tobacco-related illnesses and lost productivity due to premature morbidity and mortality. The majority of smoking-related deaths occur in LMICs, and men have significantly higher death rates compared with women in most countries. Regional variation in cigarette consumption continues to associate lower socioeconomic status with greater consumption, even in LMICs, and China has suffered sustained growth in consumption, consuming more cigarettes now than all other LMICs combined.[9] Mental health disorders including other SUDs are associated with vulnerability to nicotine use disorder.[35]

According to one study, as far back as 2000, 4% of the global burden of disease measured in disability-adjusted life years (DALYs) was attributed to alcohol, 4% to tobacco, and 0.8% to illicit drugs.[16] In countries with emerging economies, alcohol use was the most important of all factors identified in this comparative risk analysis study in affected youth with respect to disability and mortality, exceeding even the importance of tobacco in this population.[16] In 2016, 4.2% of all global DALYs were attributable to alcohol use and 1.3% were attributable to drug use.[3] Whereas alcohol accounted for 76% of the global substance use attributable health burden measured in DALYs, a majority of this burden was, by contrast, attributable to drugs in high-income North America and in the North Africa and the Middle East region. The overall disease burden attributable to alcohol and drugs varies greatly among countries and regions. For example, Lesotho, Burundi, Russia, Ukraine, Belarus, and Central African Republic were the leading countries with respect to the highest rates of alcohol-attributable age-standardized DALYs whereas the United States, Russia, Mongolia, Ukraine, and Greenland led with respect to drug-attributable burden using that indicator. Importantly, disease burden attributable to substance use was associated with socioeconomic development. Much regional variation is associated with the effects of alcohol and drug use on other health outcomes with countries with higher Socio-Demographic Indices (SDI) having a higher burden of disease due to drugs and those with a low and middle SDI having the highest alcohol-attributable burdens of disease.[3]

There is also approximately a 4-to-1 gender ratio of disease burden associated with most specific substance use disorders worldwide, with men more affected than women. Considerable variation of drinking and abstention rates in both women and men occurs based on cultural norms and prohibitions from region to region. For example, according to the WHO statistics in 2016, the global prevalence of AUDs demonstrated a large variation by sex, with 8.6 percent of adult men having an AUD as compared with only 1.7 percent of adult women.[5] For both men and women, AUD prevalence is highest in the European and the Americas regions (14.6% for men and 3.5% for women, respectively for the former and 11.5% of men and 5.1% of women, respectively, for the latter).[5] This gender difference is most likely attributable to regional variation in social acceptability and its impact on lifetime exposure. For example, in the United States and many European countries, there is a growth in any drinking as well as heavy drinking among women resulting in a narrowing of the gender gap in both prevalence of use and health consequences.[36]

Given the epidemiology and the vast associated population health burdens, it is critical for practitioners—and trainees—of global mental health to appreciate that SUDs are rarely present on their own. Multiple epidemiologic studies confirm the high rates of co-occurring SUDs among individuals with other mental health disorders including depression, anxiety, psychosis, and post-traumatic stress disorders.[37,38] Just as primary care medicine practitioners globally are advised to screen and provide appropriate interventions for SUDs for patients with other medical conditions, so can mental health practitioners mitigate the burden of SUDs and enhance clinical outcomes for their patients with depression, anxiety, psychotic, post-traumatic stress, and other related disorders by screening and providing appropriate interventions for SUDs. Such efficacious interventions, including behavioral and pharmacologic treatments, are discussed in depth in the next sections. This is followed with a discussion of the scalability and implementation of such evidence-based treatments, and how SUD care can be tailored to fit the needs and resources in LMICs.

Availability of effective treatments

Behavioral treatments

Behavioral treatments for SUDs leverage techniques for modifying behavior, cognition, and motivation to target key processes that maintain substance use, such as ambivalence about change, maladaptive strategies for managing stress, and environmental risk factors. Although not all behavioral treatments are equally effective, several types of treatments have demonstrated efficacy for SUDs.[39] For example, cognitive-behavioral therapies have demonstrated efficacy across a number of clinical trials.[40] The vast majority of research on behavioral therapies has been conducted in high-income countries. Nonetheless, some studies have provided support for behavioral interventions—with modifications to tailor to the local culture—in LMICs, such as interventions for stimulant use in Cambodia.[41] However, the effectiveness of these interventions can be hampered when access to medication or other health care is limited. For example, in a study of behavioral therapy for smoking cessation in Syria, quit rates were very low (<17%), which may have been attributable to the lack of ability to provide concurrent nicotine replacement therapy to manage nicotine withdrawal.[42] Motivational Interviewing (MI)[43] is a technique for enhancing motivation to change behavior. This approach focuses on a non-judgmental, empathic, and patient-centered tone to engage intrinsic motivation rather than prescribing change. MI is often combined with other behavioral treatments, such as cognitive-behavioral therapy, or can be used to encourage treatment initiation when implemented within a general medical setting. MI is a key component of Screening, Brief Intervention and Referral to Treatment (SBIRT) approaches, which aim to identify and prevent problematic substance use and to facilitate treatment initiation among those with SUDs. SBIRT has been implemented across a wide array of settings (e.g., primary care, emergency departments), although the success of this strategy appears to vary somewhat based on the setting and the illness severity of specific populations.[a]

The strongest effects for behavioral treatments have been observed with Contingency Management (CM) approaches.[44] Such approaches use the basic behavioral principle of reinforcement to modify behavior. Specifically, CM approaches provide reward (i.e., positive reinforcement) for desired behaviors to encourage and sustain those behaviors. This often will take the form of providing rewards for substance abstinence (e.g., as documented by negative urine toxicology screens), but has also been applied to other behaviors such as treatment attendance. Although the evidence for these approaches is based on data from high-income countries, data suggest that the lower-cost incentives are efficacious.[45] Nonetheless, the costs of these programs are a likely barrier to implementation in low-resource settings.

---

a For a review of SBIRT in clinical settings, please read Agerwala SM, McCance-Katz EF. Integrating screening, brief intervention, and referral to treatment (SBIRT) into clinical practice settings: a brief review. J Psychoactive Drugs. 2012 Sep-Oct;44(4):307–17. doi: 10.1080/02791072.2012.720169.

Delivering behavioral treatments

Behavioral therapies can be delivered in either individual or group formats, and the few trials that have compared these delivery methods have generally not supported the superiority of either format.[46] Group is the predominant format of therapy delivery in many treatment settings because it allows for more efficient allocation of therapist time. This delivery method may be particularly well suited to LMICs. For example, a study examined the efficacy of group behavioral therapy for PTSD for female sexual violence survivors in the Democratic Republic of Congo delivered by paraprofessionals in the community (people with some post-primary education and experience with case management or supportive counseling). The treatment was associated with large symptom improvements and was superior to a comparison support condition.[47] These treatments appear to be particularly effective when family supports are leveraged, and can be administered in the format of family- or couples-based interventions.

Among the greatest challenges in improving access to behavioral therapies for SUDs is that providers of behavioral therapy (e.g., psychologists, social workers, community health workers) require significant training, a challenge that has hampered the successful dissemination of behavioral therapies across psychiatric and behavioral health conditions.[48] Studies of clinician training in behavioral treatments have consistently found that a one-time workshop is insufficient to achieve successful training outcomes, even among highly trained mental health professionals.[49] The gold standard for training in behavioral therapies is resource intensive, and entails didactic training as well as practice-based learning followed by ongoing supervision and feedback. However, this approach can be costly and requires a significant allocation of clinician time, which is a particularly salient consideration in settings with health workforce shortfalls or high rates of staff turn-over.[50] Such challenges are particularly stark for LMIC settings.

Accordingly, efforts to make this process more efficient have been undertaken, including the consideration of "stepped" training approaches, in which more intensive training is only provided to those who do not quickly achieve competence.[51] Successful components of large-scale efforts to implement behavioral treatments include the availability of funding, program "champions," and the ability to manage the unique challenges of each service setting through setting-specific adaptations.[52] Such setting-specific adaptations may include changes to both adapt the treatment to the available infrastructure (e.g., availability of mental health professionals) and also to adapt the treatment content to be culturally responsive while also maintaining the core "active ingredients" of the treatment. For example, studies of behavioral therapies for psychiatric disorders leveraging community mental health workers have shown beneficial outcomes in settings with limited availability of specialized mental health professionals, such as communities in Iraq[53] and Pakistan.[54] Adaptations of behavioral treatments for psychiatric disorders to include culturally relevant content, such as the use of salient metaphors and consideration of local customs and values, have also demonstrated efficacy.[55] Guidance on the process of adapting the format and content of a treatment to fit local needs and cultures has been published, using the example of post-traumatic stress disorder.[56] An adaptation of alcohol use disorder treatment in Tomsk, Russia is described in detail below.

Technology-based treatment is another promising approach for delivering behavioral treatments for psychiatric disorders, including SUDs. The use of computer-based administration of behavioral therapies has shown promise and may be a way to expand access to high-quality behavioral interventions while requiring only minimal training for clinical support staff.[57] This may be particularly critical given the training burden when considering the number of specific behavioral treatments that may be relevant in any given setting (e.g., CM, MI, gender-specific treatments). Development efforts are underway for other technologies, such as mobile phone applications[58] and various forms of telehealth (communication with a professional at a distance via video, voice, or text[59]). During the COVID-19 global pandemic, the use of telehealth to extend services for alcohol and drug treatment expanded rapidly;[60] however, significant concerns remain regarding the equitable distribution of these services based on access to devices and adequate broadband coverage.[61] These approaches offer substantial promise to expand evidence-based treatments to low-resource settings. However, the delivery of such advancements also is subject to barriers such as inconsistent or limited access to Internet, cellular, and electric power services. Moreover, evaluation of the efficacy of these approaches will be critical, as this research agenda in mental health broadly, and SUDs in particular, has at times been met with disappointing results.[62]

Mutual support formats

Alcoholics Anonymous (AA), along with other mutual help groups such as Narcotics Anonymous (NA) and Self-Management and Recovery Training (i.e., SMART Recovery), are available globally and represent the most accessible form of SUD treatment in many areas. As of 2019, AA reported that it was active in an estimated 180 countries with an estimated 1,967,613 members and 120,455 groups[63] with members from AA service structures in North and South America extending services assistance to others in remote communities.[64] Although these organizations do not conduct research into the efficacy of their programming, researchers have attempted to characterize the effectiveness of these programs, with data generally showing favorable results.[65] Greater engagement in these groups (e.g., participating actively in meetings) and attending a group well targeted to the individual (e.g., meetings with participants of similar ages) are associated with superior outcomes.[66,67]

Importantly, AA is free; there are no membership fees or costs to attend. Although AA continues to be the most widely available mutual support group, there may be significant barriers in some countries such as legal consequences (e.g., termination of a driver's license, mandated treatment) for those who identify themselves with an AUD, for example, but for whom there is no protection of confidentiality. For others, the spiritual aspect of AA may be undesirable and other options may be preferable. SMART Recovery is a mutual support group that focuses on the development of behavioral skills, such as coping with urges to use substances, within a group format. Mutual support groups are also available for family members. These include groups such as Al-Anon (groups for family members concerned about someone's alcohol use). Information on how to start a new mutual support group is available from organizations' websites (e.g., www.aa.org; smartrecovery.org).[68,69]

Recovery coaching is a rapidly expanding mutual support format that uses an individual mentorship model and can extend the reach of treatment supports beyond traditional treatment settings. A recovery coach is typically a peer who can play a wide range of roles, such as supporting motivation to change, helping to manage stressful or high-risk situations, facilitating treatment attendance, and supporting other behavioral and functional goals (e.g., applying for jobs). Although systematic studies are not yet available for these individual peer services, recovery coaching and other peer-support models (e.g., peer navigators) are generally low-cost interventions relative to professional services and are associated with less training burden on a system. Accordingly, this approach—with central supervision to ensure evidence-based approaches—may be particularly well suited to LMIC settings, with the benefits of both expanding treatment capacity and leveraging local expertise (e.g., understanding of social support systems).

Pharmacotherapies

Medication interventions for SUDs provide significant support for safety (e.g., detoxification and prevention of life-threatening withdrawal syndromes such as may occur with AUD; stabilization of alcohol and drug poisoning), comfort, and cessation of conditioned substance use behavior.[70] All medication interventions for SUDs require patient and community health education on the biopsychosocial hazards of substance misuse and SUDs in order to achieve optimal public health prevention. For prescribers, it is important to be mindful that local formularies may constrain available medication treatment approaches as can legal frameworks in some instances, especially regarding medications for opioid use disorders. Medication treatments directed at maintaining abstinence from SUDs are optimally paired with individualized behavioral treatment and objective monitoring of progress (observed mental status stabilization, role performance improvement, toxicological evidence of abstinence or substance use reduction, and self-reported improvements in quality of life).

In considering medication availability in lower-resourced regions, priority must be given to life-saving interventions and protocols, including benzodiazepine stabilization of alcohol and sedative withdrawal syndromes, drug poisoning reversal treatments (e.g., antagonist therapies such as naloxone for opioid overdose and flumazenil for benzodiazepine overdose), and non-specific supportive medical interventions for substance-related delirium (e.g., thiamine and folate replacement, haloperidol for psychosis/delirium, hydration and oxygenation). These treatments will save lives but do not prevent future substance misuse and must be considered emergency interventions rather than effective SUD treatment.

Evidence-based medications to treat SUDs are available with demonstrated effectiveness for opioid use disorder, nicotine (tobacco) use disorder, and alcohol use disorder. Only nicotine use disorder treatments have been assessed to be equally effective in those with or without co-occurring mental health disorders.[71] General principles of SUD maintenance therapies include partial or full substitution therapies, in which the medication effectively replaces and stabilizes neural pathways destabilized by chronic substance use, and antagonist therapies, in which the medication blocks future substance access to receptors within affected, SUD-reinforcing neural pathways. Examples of the former include buprenorphine and methadone for opioid use disorder, nicotine replacement and varenicline for nicotine use disorder, and acamprosate, topiramate, and gabapentin for AUD. Examples of antagonist therapy include naltrexone for opioid use disorder as well as AUD, and bupropion for nicotine use disorder. Some medications, such as the partial agonists buprenorphine and varenicline, provide unique pharmacological aspects of both agonist and antagonist prevention against future substance use. Disulfiram is an aversive medication used to treat AUD. Alcohol is metabolized to acetaldehyde which is in turn metabolized by the enzyme acetaldehyde dehydrogenase. If alcohol is consumed, the inhibition by disulfiram of acetaldehyde dehydrogenase will cause a build-up of acetaldehyde producing unpleasant side effects including flushing and nausea, and potential increased heart rate, hypotension, and chest pain. Prioritization may be considered for utilizing medications with low incidence of adverse effects and good tolerability (e.g., buprenorphine, varenicline, acamprosate) over medications with more serious adverse effects requiring laboratory monitoring (e.g., methadone, disulfiram) or lower tolerability. It is also useful to caution against somatic treatments that may be in use and for which there is no empirical support.

Gender-specific treatment

With increased recognition of the array of sex/gender differences in SUDs, including a range of treatment needs that are unique to (or disproportionately affect) women, gender-specific treatment approaches have been of significant interest in recent years. Such treatments take into account considerations such as trauma exposure, co-occurring mental health disorders prevalent among women, family concerns, pregnancy, parenting, child care, etc., and have demonstrated efficacy in the treatment of women with SUDs in high-income countries.[72] For example, the

Women's Recovery Group—a manualized group therapy for women with SUDs—utilizes both gender-specific content and an all-women format that facilitates affiliation among group members.[73] Investigation of these approaches in low- and middle-income countries, including the need for cultural adaptations, is an important future research direction.

Although gender differences in response to pharmacotherapies are largely unknown due to poor representation of women in many clinical trials, evidence is beginning to emerge suggesting that men and women may respond differently to a range of medications for SUDs. For example, a meta-analytic review identified superior treatment outcomes for nicotine-dependent women treated with varenicline relative to nicotine replacement therapy, a finding not observed for men.[74] However, another review cited several pharmacotherapy studies demonstrating that when gender differences were observed in SUD treatment outcome, outcomes were worse for women receiving medication compared to women in the placebo groups.[75] Most studies have shown comparable clinical outcomes for women and men for buprenorphine/naloxone treatment for opioid use disorder.[75]

One domain of gender-specific treatments of particular importance is treatment for pregnant and post-partum women with SUDs. Most addictive substances cross the placenta and some are known or suspected teratogens. Accordingly, efforts to engage pregnant women with SUDs in prenatal and substance use care are critically important for both the health of the mother and the developing fetus. Both behavioral therapies[76] and several pharmacotherapies have demonstrated efficacy for the treatment of pregnant women in recent years. For example, a large randomized clinical trial (i.e., the MOTHER trial) compared buprenorphine and methadone for the treatment of pregnant opioid-dependent women, and demonstrated benefits to both the mother and the fetus (e.g., continued engagement in prenatal care and planned delivery services required to mitigate neonatal abstinence syndrome in infants and promote developmental bonding between mother and child in the post-partum period) with buprenorphine treatment resulting in shorter duration of neonatal abstinence syndrome in the neonates.[77]

Implementation of evidence-based treatments for substance-related disorders

Bridging the treatment gap requires strategic choice, adaptation, and delivery of evidence-based treatments in LMICs, taking into account local disease burden and epidemiology, existing health infrastructure, and local social, cultural, and religious contexts. Planning and implementation are iterative, bidirectional processes, involving mental health specialists and other healthcare providers. Multi-disciplinary teams must include all relevant providers, including psychiatrists and psychologists, along with primary care providers, teams focused on co-occurring medical and other mental health conditions, as well as community-based health workers, and peer and lay counselors to arrive at the most effective model of training to implement evidence-based care for patients with SUDs in the local health system and social context. In many global health settings, robust delivery platforms—such as national programs in HIV, TB, and maternal-child health—also require strong buy-in from decision makers in the Ministries of Health, as well as private-sector organizations and other public-sector entities (e.g., Ministries of Finance, elected leaders at the district or municipality level, etc.). Getting such support is key, since layering SUD treatment onto these existing healthcare platforms can optimize assets such as national treatment protocols, supply chain, and community health worker networks.[78]

The selection of appropriate evidence-based interventions is based upon consideration of the cultural context of providing care, availability of existing resources, and best opportunities to expand capacity to meet local needs in the specific context where the care will be delivered. For instance, pharmacologic treatment may not be ideal in settings where medication supply chains are weak; on the other hand, the choice and deployment of behavioral treatments may depend on the number, availability, and skills of the healthcare providers who would deliver the intervention, as well as local capacities for their oversight. In this respect, non-mental health practitioners can provide key information on acceptable and unacceptable interventions, as well as implications for delivery. Surveys or interviews with providers and patients can not only "paint the landscape" of mental health and SUD treatment needs, but also potentially reduce stigma and build buy-in through open dialogue about concerns and treatment options.

Once interventions are identified, implementation processes should be created to address screening and referral, clarify provider roles and systems for inter-provider communication, and optimize patient engagement and retention. In the global context, treatment programs may require building out additional teams and/or community-based delivery platforms as needed to reach those individuals who are not accessing healthcare systems. Iterative discussions are often needed to sensitize program directors and frontline providers to the relevance of treating SUDs as well as other co-occurring mental health conditions and embracing "program accountability" for individuals typically excluded from health care.

Long-term, sustained training is essential to support providers across the continuum of healthcare delivery, especially for those providers administering active therapeutic interventions such as medications for recovery, behavioral therapies, and in-home coaching interventions. Ongoing supervision and feedback-related problem-solving is the most effective means of building self-efficacy among providers who initially may be unfamiliar and uncomfortable with providing SUD care.[79–81] Although resource intensive, the up-front investment of a collaborative supervision model for adapting evidence-based SUD treatments to global health settings can provide significant gains in providing effective cultural innovations of evidence-based treatments that may be sustained locally. Several strategies have been successfully employed in such collaborative care models for mental health including SUDs and are becoming increasingly affordable and accessible with expansion of virtual technologies and platforms to support global collaborations (Table 12.1). These strategies harness the evidence-based treatment expertise of clinical/research teams paired with the cultural expertise of local healthcare leadership teams to adapt evidence-based treatment to local resources, training needs, delivery platforms, quality assessment, evidence-based treatment performance, and patient acceptance, leading to optimal local integration and outcomes (institutional pairing). Initial planning includes an intensive process of mutual engagement around targeted goals, training in all aspects of an evidence-based treatment protocol, and implementing innovation needs of the region that may reflect regional resource gaps or cultural stigma ("train-the-trainer" models for

Table 12.1 Collaborative strategies supporting evidence-based SUD treatment dissemination[79–81]

Training strategy	Rationale
Institutional pairing	Experienced clinical/research team pairs with local leadership to adapt EBT to local culture, train delivery personnel, and provide longitudinal quality monitoring, adaptations, and updates.
Train the trainer	Experienced clinical/research team trains local leadership to sustain local EBT fidelity/adherence and critically assess performance gaps. Local leadership advises on regional SUD stigma barriers that may obstruct EBT implementation.
Telemedicine	Virtual consultation technology allows interim quality assurance and collaborative problem-solving and innovation as needed.
Booster sessions and ongoing assessment of treatment delivery	Routinely scheduled supervision and objective performance feedback sustains local EBT skills and maintains timely updates to new evidence and innovative best practices.

EBT: *evidence-based treatment*

disseminating evidence-based treatment). Next phases provide structured staff training, set-up, and piloting of adapted evidence-based treatment for initial cultural acceptance and fit. Once achieved, a structured schedule of collaborative quality assessment of implementation and iterative feedback to optimize evidence-based treatment delivery and outcome can yield both local sustainability and interim adaptability to changing trends or medical updates to evidence-based treatment. The use of technology to bridge geographical training barriers and planned collaborative booster supervision are essential strategies to achieving this end.

Incorporating tools for monitoring and evaluation is essential for tracking program goals. Because SUDs may be under-diagnosed, universal simple screening for tobacco, alcohol, and drug use is recommended in all adolescent and adult healthcare settings, and more extensive and targeted screening is appropriate within high-risk populations (e.g., infectious disease, mental health) and among those receiving longer-term SUD care. Application of evidence-based screening standards would help to quantify service needs, the association of SUDs with other health conditions, and treatment response to SUD care, including behavioral health care. Especially when providers are new to delivering behavioral interventions, monitoring treatment fidelity and providing ongoing, real-time feedback to providers are critical to achieving competence in treatment delivery and sustaining the adoption of these interventions. Programs should also incorporate algorithms to make iterative programmatic changes based on data.

Although the co-occurrence of SUDs with other medical conditions magnifies the impact of SUDs on global disease burden, this phenomenon also presents unique opportunities for treatment delivery: programs focused on specific health problems may offer a platform to reach those at greatest risk of SUDs, even where infrastructure for mental health and primary care is weak. Furthermore, because SUDs have such a profound impact on disease outcomes, programs targeting local disease burden (for example, HIV, TB, maternal-child health, depression, post-traumatic stress disorder) are most likely to achieve their desired outcomes if SUD treatment is integrated into their package of care. For example, TB treatment involves daily directly observed therapy (DOT) for at least six months, and therefore offers an ideal "delivery platform" for intensive AUD and potentially other SUD care. Several examples of successful implementation strategies are illustrated in Box 12.1 and Box 12.2.

BOX 12.1. INTEGRATED MANAGEMENT OF AUDs WITH CO-OCCURRING MEDICAL CONDITION

The TB program in Tomsk Oblast located in western Siberia, Russia, incorporated alcohol treatment into routine TB care. AUDs were known to be highly prevalent among TB patients in this setting.[82,83] However, patients rarely received specialized care by "narcologists" due to stigma and cost.[84] In response, a team of US-based addictions and TB specialists collaborated with local leadership and physicians to incorporate three components of alcohol care into their TB program: screening and referral; evidence-based treatments (EBTs) adapted to the local context; and delivery across a spectrum of care settings. The team integrated pharmacologic and behavioral interventions for AUDs into TB management as follows:

- System for screening and referral: The Alcohol Use Disorders Identification Test (AUDIT) was locally validated and implemented by TB physicians, with treatment algorithms based on AUDIT scores.[85] In addition to introducing universal screening and referral, the incorporation of this tool into the routine intake process began to normalize discussions of alcohol use with their patients.

- Adaptation of EBTs to the local context: Using the bidirectional approach described above, the cross-cultural team adapted a brief counseling intervention (BCI) for this population and setting; a key modification included scripted discussions designed to motivate patients to reduce their alcohol intake to improve their chance of TB cure. TB providers were trained on AUD interventions, including BCI delivery and naltrexone management, including issues specific to TB therapy (e.g., side-effect management, peri-operative management of naltrexone).

- Delivery across the care spectrum: Naltrexone was administered along with TB medications under DOT. As patients recovered, they routinely transitioned from inpatient care to day hospitals and clinic posts. To ensure continuity of care, all DOT workers were trained to administer naltrexone and track naltrexone adherence on the patient's "TB treatment card." BCI was incorporated into routine monthly TB follow-up evaluations; however, for patients who moved back to remote villages, sporadic follow-up resulted in fewer BCI encounters.

- Program evaluation and improvement: The clinical trial to evaluate this model found that naltrexone adherence was high, with 75% of planned doses achieved through DOT; among individuals who had previously attempted to quit, naltrexone improved TB treatment outcomes (92% versus 76% had favorable outcomes, p=0.04).[86] On the other hand, BCI proved more challenging to deliver and did not improve outcomes, with patients receiving only 50% of planned BCI encounters. Providers identified the main barrier to BCI delivery as the transition to outpatient care, since many patients transitioned to remote villages where providers were not trained to deliver BCI. To improve continuity of care, a community outreach program, Sputnik, was subsequently implemented.[87] Through home visits, trained nurses now work with patients to address alcohol use and other psychosocial issues, resulting in greater retention and improved TB outcomes.

The experience described above suggests that treatment programs can overcome barriers of stigma and limited access to specialty services by folding SUD care into existing healthcare platforms in global health settings.[78]

BOX 12.2. COMMUNITY INVOLVEMENT IN ADAPTATION AND IMPLEMENTATION EFFORTS

CHOICES (Changing High-risk Alcohol Use and Increasing Contraception Effectiveness Study) was developed as a preconception intervention to reduce alcohol-exposed pregnancies among women engaged in risky drinking.[88] Originally developed for high-risk populations in urban and suburban communities, the intervention applied motivational interviewing to target behavior change in two areas: contraception uptake and reduction in alcohol use.[88] Delivered as four clinic-based counseling sessions and one contraception consultation visit, CHOICES was shown to reduce risky drinking and increase contraception use in a multi-site clinical trial.[89] The team then partnered with the Oglala Sioux Tribe (OST) to adapt the CHOICES curriculum with extensive community input from clinic staff and leadership, throughout the implementation process as follows:

- Adaptation and implementation: Tribal clinic providers tailored the intervention to their own preferences and needs. For example, they determined that women would feel most comfortable working with established clinic providers and tribal members. The CHOICES materials were also modified to include local images, statistics, and treatment options. Flexibility was allowed to accommodate the specific context of each clinic in terms of recruitment strategy (e.g. recruitment fliers versus provider referral), interventionist background (e.g., nurse practitioner, behavioral health specialist), and number of sessions (two versus four).[90]
- Program evaluation and improvement: The OST clinical trial resulted in significantly reduced alcohol-exposed pregnancy risk.[91] Alongside the trial, a community-based needs assessment was conducted and identified the importance of social support from relatives, elders, and community members through shared cultural practices and teachings.[92] A subsequent iteration was therefore developed to test group delivery of the CHOICES intervention.[93]

This program highlights how an evidence-based treatment can be successfully transitioned from research to programmatic implementation through strong community engagement and program flexibility to build upon the varying strengths of local implementation sites.

For vulnerable populations who are marginalized from health care, these approaches can have synergistic positive effects on SUDs and other co-occurring health outcomes.[94,95] Because of underlying risk factors for both SUDs and co-occurring conditions, integrated care may be ideal for delivering gender-specific interventions.[96,97] Systematic reviews and implementation research reinforce the importance of five core components for successfully integrated SUD programs: 1) political will; 2) longitudinal training for frontline providers; 3) standardized protocols for screening, treatment, and referral; 4) patient-centered, holistic approaches to managing comorbid conditions; and 5) service delivery that maximizes efficiency and retention.[79,80,98–101]

Training of lay, community, and peer support persons

Given the paucity of specialized SUD/mental health services broadly available in both HICs and LMICs, and the strain on primary care in LMICs especially, dissemination of evidence-based treatment will of necessity include building a workforce that includes non-medical/non-clinical lay staff as well as supportive involvement of family, friends, and other community stakeholders to serve roles of extended care management. Mental health studies utilizing these approaches have demonstrated modest efficacy in LMIC regions[47,102] but with only limited data showing positive trends for reducing problematic alcohol consumption. Global SUD peer recovery support programs, typified by 12-step programs such as Alcoholics Anonymous (www.aa.org),[68] also provide extended stabilization resources through the social networking of recovering peers actively assisting and engaging peers in early recovery phases of treatment. It has been noted, however, that these programs are effective only in culturally accepting regions and do not effectively engage SUD populations in regions having strong barriers of stigma and legal discrimination against SUDs, such as in Russia,[81] or in regions lacking familiarity with 12-step programs, such as in Brazil.[103]

Case management intervention studies generally offer mixed results with strongest efficacy in patient engagement and retention in care, compared with other measured outcomes.[104] Therefore, in strategic planning for development of lay health worker and peer support services, a needs assessment should consider regional barriers to care in order of need priority/severity, and use this to guide selection of their participatory services best suited to plug gaps in SUD care, while also incentivizing lay health workers to actively participate. For example, recruiting and reimbursing transportation services to health clinicians may in some cases be more urgently needed than training lay health workers to deliver mobile care remotely. These decision points are best collaboratively determined by a community-wide needs assessment process. Indeed, lessons learned from large-scale GMH studies in LMICs aimed at integrating mental health and AUD care within primary care services confirm this approach, and further outline eight core considerations during implementation: 1) use participatory workshops during the design and planning phases, bringing together as many community stakeholders as possible to achieve unity in purpose and vision; 2) engage healthcare providers in allowing non-stigmatized health services to be a point of contact in which to identify and engage individuals with more stigmatized mental health/SUD service needs; 3) use screening instruments that employ culturally appropriate concepts and case vignettes; 4) train lay health workers in the use of manualized treatment interventions; 5) provide longitudinal fidelity/adherence supervision support, and assessment of intervention goals achievement; 6) adequately compensate lay health workers for their services; 7) implement more robust mental health/SUD care when systems need to be re-built after natural disasters; and 8) rapidly respond to opportunities in which political will and/or funding is aligned with strengthening regional mental health/SUD care.[105]

Summary

Substance use disorders are highly prevalent globally resulting in great morbidity and mortality. In addition to their associated high burden of disease, SUDs cause significant additional harm to others, especially women and children, through substance-related injuries, violence, adverse effects on fetal development, disruption in parenting, and other mental health effects through the complex interplay between SUDs and other conditions including depression, anxiety, post-traumatic stress, and psychotic disorders. There are additional costs to communities and societies including family and social disruption, financial costs, and economic burden. Despite the existence of evidence-based treatments, implementation of behavioral, pharmacologic, and community-based services in both LMICs and HICs remains severely limited and, globally, the treatment gap is vast. Culturally appropriate adaptation of evidence-based treatments is a necessary step in implementation of innovative systems of care and can be informed through, and complement, community-wide needs assessments. Models of integration of SUD treatment into existing platforms of medical and mental health care can be culturally adapted and expanded through training lay workers. Innovations in the use of technology show promise in providing training, consultation, and extended recovery treatment support. Compelling evidence demonstrates that increasing access to SUD treatment in LMICs and HICs can significantly reduce morbidity and mortality from SUDs and related conditions, decrease economic burdens in multiple domains, and improve individual, family, and community health.

References

1.   World Health Organization. Health topics: alcohol 2021 [cited 2022 August 30]. Available from: https://www.who.int/health-topics/alcohol#tab=tab_1

2.   World Health Organization. *1st WHO forum on alcohol, drugs and addictive behaviours.* Geneva, Switzerland: World Health Organization; 2017. [cited 2022 August 30]. Available from: https://www.who.int/news-room/events/detail/2017/06/26/default-calendar/who-forum-on-alcohol-drugs-and-addictive-behaviours#:~:text=The%20primary%20goal%20of%20this,alcohol%2C%20drugs%20and%20addictive%20behaviours

3. GBD 2016 Alcohol and Drug Use Collaborators. The global burden of disease attributable to alcohol and drug use in 195 countries and territories, 1990–2016: a systematic analysis for the Global Burden of Disease Study 2016. *The Lancet Psychiatry.* 2018;5(12):987–1012.

4. Rehm J, Gmel GE Sr., Gmel G, Hasan OSM, Imtiaz S, Popova S, et al. The relationship between different dimensions of alcohol use and the burden of disease-an update. *Addiction.* 2017;112(6):968–1001.

5. World Health Organization. *Global status report on alcohol and health 2018.* Geneva: World Health Organization; 2018.

6. Jernigan D. Global developments in alcohol policies: progress in implementation of the WHO global strategy to reduce the harmful use of alcohol since 2010: background paper developed for the WHO Forum on Alcohol, Drugs and Addictive Behaviours 2017. [cited 2022 August 30]. Available from: https://wwwapp.bumc.bu.edu/BEDAC_Camy/_docs/resources/ publications/Global%20Developments%20in%20Alcohol%20Policies.pdf

7. United Nations Office on Drugs and Crime. World drug report 2019: 35 million people worldwide suffer from drug use disorders while only 1 in 7 people receive treatment [Internet] 2019. [cited 2022 September 11]. Available from: https://www.unodc.org/unodc/en/ frontpage/2019/June/world-drug-report-2019_-35-million-people-worldwide-suffer-from -drug-use-disorders-while-only-1-in-7-people-receive-treatment.html

8. World Health Organization. *Global status report on alcohol and health 2014.* Geneva, Switzerland: World Health Organization; 2014. 392 p.

9. The American Cancer Society, The World Lung Foundation. *The Tobacco Atlas.* [Internet] Atlanta, Georgia; 2015. [cited 2022 August 26]. Available from: http://www.tobaccoatlas.org/

10. The Tobacco Atlas. Issue: deaths: American Cancer Society, Inc. and vital strategies [Internet] 2020. [cited 2022 August 26]. Available from: https://tobaccoatlas.org/topic/deaths/

11. Galanter M, Kleber HD, Brady KT. *The American psychiatric publishing textbook of substance abuse treatment,* 5th ed. Washington, DC: American Psychiatric Publishing Inc; 2015. 980 p.

12. Odlaug BL, Gual A, DeCourcy J, Perry R, Pike J, Heron L, et al. Alcohol dependence, co-occurring conditions and attributable burden. *Alcohol.* 2016;51(2):201–9.

13. Lai HM, Cleary M, Sitharthan T, Hunt GE. Prevalence of comorbid substance use, anxiety and mood disorders in epidemiological surveys, 1990–2014: a systematic review and meta-analysis. *Drug and Alcohol Dependence.* 2015;154:1–13.

14. National Institute on Drug Abuse. NIDA. *Principles of drug addiction treatment: a research-based guide,* 3rd ed. [Internet] December 1, 2012. [cited 2022 August 26]. Available from: https://www.drugabuse.gov/publications/principles-drug-addiction-treatment-research -based-guide-third-edition

15. OECD. Tackling harmful alcohol use: economics and public health policy [Internet]. OECD Publishing; 2015. [cited 2022 September 12]. Available from: https://www.oecd.org/health /tackling-harmful-alcohol-use-9789264181069-en.htm

16. Rehm J, Taylor B, Room R. Global burden of disease from alcohol, illicit drugs and tobacco. *Drug and Alcohol Review.* 2006;25(6):503–13.

17. Rehm J, Shield KD, Gmel G, Rehm MX, Frick U. Modeling the impact of alcohol dependence on mortality burden and the effect of available treatment interventions in the European Union. *Eur Neuropsychopharmacology.* 2013;23(2):89–97.

18. Wilson DP, Donald B, Shattock AJ, Wilson D, Fraser-Hurt N. The cost-effectiveness of harm reduction. *International Journal of Drug Policy.* 2015;26(1):1.

19. CASA. Addiction medicine: closing the gap between science and practice [Internet]. *The National Center on Addiction and Substance Abuse (CASA) at Columbia University, New York.* 2012. 586 p.

20. Botticelli MP, Koh HK. Changing the language of addiction. *JAMA.* 2016;316(13):1361–2.

21. Barry CL, McGinty EE, Pescosolido BA, Goldman HH. Stigma, discrimination, treatment effectiveness, and policy: public views about drug addiction and mental illness. *Psychiatric Services.* 2014;65(10):1269–72.

22. Kelly JF, Westerhoff CM. Does it matter how we refer to individuals with substance-related conditions? A randomized study of two commonly used terms. *International Journal of Drug Policy.* 2010;21(3):202–7.

23. Cunningham JA, Sobell LC, Chow VM. What's in a label? The effects of substance types and labels on treatment considerations and stigma. *Journal of Studies on Alcohol.* 1993;54(6):693–9.

24. Luoma JB, Twohig MP, Waltz T, Hayes SC, Roget N, Padilla M, et al. An investigation of stigma in individuals receiving treatment for substance abuse. *Addictive Behaviors.* 2007;32(7):1331–46.

25. Corrigan PW, Larson JE, Kuwabara SA. Social psychology of the stigma of mental illness: public and self-stigma models. In: Maddux JE and Tangney JP, eds. *Social psychological foundations of clinical psychology.* New York: The Guilford Press; 2010. pp. 51–68.

26. Corrigan PW, Rao D. On the self-stigma of mental illness: stages, disclosure, and strategies for change. *The Canadian Journal of Psychiatry.* 2012;57(8):464–9.

27. World Health Organization. What do people think they know about substance dependence? [Internet]: WHO 2001. [cited 2022 August 30]. Available from: https://apps.who.int/iris/handle/10665/66978

28. United Nations Office on Drugs and Crime. *World drug report 2010 (united nations publication, sales no. E.10.XI.13) [Internet].* [cited 2022 September 12]. Available from: https://www.unodc.org/documents/wdr/WDR_2010/World_Drug_Report_2010_lo-res.pdf

29. World Health Organization. *The global burden of disease: 2004 update.* Geneva: World Health Organization; 2008. [updated 2008]. Available from: https://apps.who.int/iris/handle/10665/43942

30. United Nations Office on Drugs and Crime. *World drug report 2016* (United Nations publication, Sales No. E.16.XI.7) [Internet]. [cited 2022 September 12]. Available from: https://www.unodc.org/doc/wdr2016/WORLD_DRUG_REPORT_2016_web.pdf

31. World Health Organization. *Community management of opioid overdose [Internet].* Geneva: World Health Organization; 2014. [cited 2022 August 26]. Available from: https://www.ncbi.nlm.nih.gov/books/NBK264311/

32. World Health Organization. Global Health Observatory (GHO) data: opioid agonist pharmacotherapy for the maintenance treatment of opioid dependence [Internet]. [cited 2022 September 12]. Available from: https://www.who.int/data/gho/indicator-metadata-registry/imr-details/2718

33. World Health Organization. World health statistics data visualization dashboard 2016 [Internet]. [updated March 20, 2018; cited 2022 August 26]. Available from: https://apps.who.int/gho/data/node.sdg.3-5-viz?lang=en

34. Ritchie H, Roser M. Alcohol consumption [Internet]. Published online at ourworldindata.org 2018 [updated January 2022; cited 2022 August 26]. Available from: https://ourworldindata.org/alcohol-consumption

35. Kalman D, Morissette SB, George TP. Co-morbidity of smoking in patients with psychiatric and substance use disorders. *American Journal on Addictions.* 2005;14(2):106–23.

36. Grant BF, Chou SP, Saha TD, Pickering RP, Kerridge BT, Ruan WJ, et al. Prevalence of 12-month alcohol use, high-risk drinking, and DSM-IV alcohol use disorder in the United States, 2001–2002 to 2012–2013: results From the national epidemiologic survey on alcohol and related conditions. *JAMA Psychiatry.* 2017;74(9):911–23.

37. European Monitoring Centre for Drugs and Drug Addiction (EMCDDA). Comorbidity of substance use and mental disorders in Europe [Internet] 2015. [cited 2022 September 21]. Available from: https://www.emcdda.europa.eu/publications/insights/comorbidity-substance-use-mental-disorders-europe_en

38. Kessler RC, Aguilar-Gaxiola S, Alonso J, Chatterji S, Lee S, Ormel J, et al. The global burden of mental disorders: an update from the WHO World Mental Health (WMH) surveys. *Epidemiologia e Psichiatria Sociale.* 2009;18(1):23–33.

39. Carroll KM, Rounsaville BJ. Perhaps it is the Dodo Bird Verdict that should be extinct. *Addiction.* 2010;105(1):18–20.

40. Carroll KM, Onken LS. Behavioral therapies for drug abuse. *American Journal of Psychiatry*. 2005;162(8):1452–60.

41. Page K, Carrico AW, Stein E, Evans J, Sokunny M, Maly P, et al. Cluster randomized stepped-wedge trial of a multi-level HIV prevention intervention to decrease amphetamine-type stimulants and sexual risk in Cambodian female entertainment and sex workers. *Drug and Alcohol Dependence*. 2019;196:21–30.

42. Asfar T, Weg MV, Maziak W, Hammal F, Eissenberg T, Ward KD. Outcomes and adherence in Syria's first smoking cessation trial. *American Journal of Health Behavior*. 2008;32(2):146–56.

43. Miller WR, Rollnick S. *Motivational interviewing: helping people change*, 3rd ed. New York: Guilford Press; 2012. 482 p.

44. Petry NM, Alessi SM, Olmstead TA, Rash CJ, Zajac K. Contingency management treatment for substance use disorders: how far has it come, and where does it need to go? *Psychology of Addictive Behaviors*. 2017;31(8):897–906.

45. Sigmon SC, Stitzer ML. Use of a low-cost incentive intervention to improve counseling attendance among methadone-maintained patients. *Journal of Substance Abuse Treatment*. 2005;29(4):253–8.

46. Sobell LC, Sobell MB, Agrawal S. Randomized controlled trial of a cognitive-behavioral motivational intervention in a group versus individual format for substance use disorders. *Psychology of Addictive Behaviors*. 2009;23(4):672–83.

47. Bass JK, Annan J, McIvor Murray S, Kaysen D, Griffiths S, Cetinoglu T, et al. Controlled trial of psychotherapy for Congolese survivors of sexual violence. *New England Journal of Medicine*. 2013;368(23):2182–91.

48. McHugh RK, Barlow DH. The dissemination and implementation of evidence-based psychological treatments: a review of current efforts. *The American Psychologist*. 2010;65(2):73–84.

49. Sholomskas DE, Syracuse-Siewert G, Rounsaville BJ, Ball SA, Nuro KF, Carroll KM. We don't train in vain: a dissemination trial of three strategies of training clinicians in cognitive-behavioral therapy. *Journal of Consulting and Clinical Psychology*. 2005;73(1):106–15.

50. Squires DD, Gumbley SJ, Storti SA. Training substance abuse treatment organizations to adopt evidence-based practices: the addiction technology transfer center of New England science to service laboratory. *Journal of Substance Abuse Treatment*. 2008;34(3):293–301.

51. Martino S, Canning-Ball M, Carroll KM, Rounsaville BJ. A criterion-based stepwise approach for training counselors in motivational interviewing. *Journal of Substance Abuse Treatment*. 2011;40(4):357–65.

52. Babor TF, Del Boca F, Bray JW. Screening, brief intervention and referral to treatment: implications of SAMHSA's SBIRT initiative for substance abuse policy and practice. *Addiction*. 2017;112(Suppl 2):110–17.

53. Weiss WM, Murray LK, Zangana GA, Mahmooth Z, Kaysen D, Dorsey S, et al. Community-based mental health treatments for survivors of torture and militant attacks in Southern Iraq: a randomized control trial. *BMC Psychiatry*. 2015;15(249):015–0622.

54. Rahman A, Hamdani SU, Awan NR, Bryant RA, Dawson KS, Khan MF, et al. Effect of a multicomponent behavioral intervention in adults impaired by psychological distress in a conflict-affected area of Pakistan: a randomized clinical trial. *JAMA*. 2016;316(24):2609–17.

55. Hinton DE, Otto MW. Symptom presentation and symptom meaning among traumatized cambodian refugees: relevance to a somatically focused cognitive-behavior therapy. *Cognitive and Behavioral Practice*. 2006;13(4):249–60.

56. Applied Mental Health Research Group. *Design, implementation, monitoring, and evaluation of mental health and psychosocial assistance programs for trauma survivors in low resource countries: a user's manual for researchers and program implementers (adult version)*. Baltimore, MD: Johns Hopkins University School of Public Health; 2013. 66 p.

57. Carroll KM, Kiluk BD, Nich C, Gordon MA, Portnoy GA, Marino DR, et al. Computer-assisted delivery of cognitive-behavioral therapy: efficacy and durability of CBT4CBT among

cocaine-dependent individuals maintained on methadone. *American Journal of Psychiatry.* 2014;171(4):436–44.

58. Rizvi SL, Dimeff LA, Skutch J, Carroll D, Linehan MM. A pilot study of the DBT coach: an interactive mobile phone application for individuals with borderline personality disorder and substance use disorder. *Behavior Therapy.* 2011;42(4):589–600.

59. Ben-Zeev D, Kaiser SM, Krzos I. Remote "hovering" with individuals with psychotic disorders and substance use: feasibility, engagement, and therapeutic alliance with a text-messaging mobile interventionist. *Journal of Dual Diagnosis.* 2014;10(4):197–203.

60. Busch AB, Sugarman DE, Horvitz LE, Greenfield SF. Telemedicine for treating mental health and substance use disorders: reflections since the pandemic. *Neuropsychopharmacology.* 2021;46(6):1068–70.

61. Harker N, Johnson K, Erasmus J, Myers B. COVID 19—Impact on substance use treatment utilization and provision in South Africa. *Substance Abuse Treatment, Prevention, and Policy.* 2022;17(1):15.

62. Witkiewitz K, Desai SA, Bowen S, Leigh BC, Kirouac M, Larimer ME. Development and evaluation of a mobile intervention for heavy drinking and smoking among college students. *Psychology of Addictive Behaviors.* 2014;28(3):639–50.

63. Alcoholics Anonymous. Estimated Worldwide A. A. Individual and Group Membership 2021 [updated December 21, 2021; cited 2022 August 26]. Available from: https://www.aa.org/sites/default/files/literature/smf-132_Estimated_Membership_EN_1221.pdf

64. Alcoholics Anonymous. North/South connections virtual special forum — A.A. in remote communities [Internet]. [cited 2022 August 26]. Available from: https://www.aa.org/North-South-Connections-Forum-AA-in-Remote-Communities

65. Timko C, Moos RH, Finney JW, Lesar MD. Long-term outcomes of alcohol use disorders: comparing untreated individuals with those in alcoholics anonymous and formal treatment. *Journal of Studies of Alcohol.* 2000;61(4):529–40.

66. Kelly JF, Myers MG, Brown SA. The effects of age composition of 12-step groups on adolescent 12-step participation and substance use outcome. *Journal of Child and Adolescent Substance Abuse.* 2005;15(1):63–72.

67. Weiss RD, Griffin ML, Gallop RJ, Najavits LM, Frank A, Crits-Christoph P, et al. The effect of 12-step self-help group attendance and participation on drug use outcomes among cocaine-dependent patients. *Drug and Alcohol Dependence.* 2005;77(2):177–84.

68. Alcoholics Anonymous. Alcoholics anonymous [Internet]. [cited 2022 August 26]. Available from: https://www.aa.org/

69. Smart Recovery. Smart recovery. [cited 2022 September 7]. Available from: smartrecovery.org

70. World Health Organization. mhGAP Intervention Guide for mental, neurological and substance use disorders in non-specialized health settings, Version 2.0 [Internet] 2016. [cited 2022 August 26]. Available from: http://www.who.int/substance_abuse/publications/treatment/en/

71. Anthenelli RM, Benowitz NL, West R, St Aubin L, McRae T, Lawrence D, et al. Neuropsychiatric safety and efficacy of varenicline, bupropion, and nicotine patch in smokers with and without psychiatric disorders (EAGLES): a double-blind, randomised, placebo-controlled clinical trial. *The Lancet.* 2016;387(10037):2507–20.

72. Greenfield SF, Grella CE. What is "women-focused" treatment for substance use disorders? *Psychiatric Services.* 2009;60(7):880–2.

73. Greenfield SF, Sugarman DE, Freid CM, Bailey GL, Crisafulli MA, Kaufman JS, et al. Group therapy for women with substance use disorders: results from the women's recovery group study. *Drug and Alcohol Dependence.* 2014;142:245–53.

74. Smith PH, Weinberger AH, Zhang J, Emme E, Mazure CM, McKee SA. Sex differences in smoking cessation pharmacotherapy comparative efficacy: a network meta-analysis. *Nicotine Tobacco Research.* 2017;19(3):273–81.

75. Sugarman DE, Reilly ME, Greenfield SF. Treatment outcomes for women with substance use disorders: a critical review of the literature (2010–2016). *Current Addiction Reports.* 2017;4(4):482–502.

76. Tappin D, Bauld L, Purves D, Boyd K, Sinclair L, MacAskill S, et al. Financial incentives for smoking cessation in pregnancy: randomised controlled trial. *BMJ (Clinical research ed)*. 2015;350:h134.

77. Jones HE, Kaltenbach K, Heil SH, Stine SM, Coyle MG, Arria AM, et al. Neonatal abstinence syndrome after methadone or buprenorphine exposure. *The New England Journal of Medicine*. 2010;363(24):2320–31.

78. Shidhaye R, Lund C, Chisholm D. Closing the treatment gap for mental, neurological and substance use disorders by strengthening existing health care platforms: strategies for delivery and integration of evidence-based interventions. *International Journal of Mental Health Systems*. 2015;9(40):015–0031.

79. Edelman EJ, Hansen NB, Cutter CJ, Danton C, Fiellin LE, O'Connor PG, et al. Implementation of integrated stepped care for unhealthy alcohol use in HIV clinics. *Addiction Science and Clinical Practice*. 2016;11(1):015–0048.

80. Savic M, Best D, Manning V, Lubman DI. Strategies to facilitate integrated care for people with alcohol and other drug problems: a systematic review. *Substance Abuse Treatment and Prevention Policy*. 2017;12(1):017–0104.

81. Connery H, Greenfield S, Livchits V, McGrady L, Patrick N, Lastimoso CS, et al. Training and fidelity monitoring of alcohol treatment interventions integrated into routine tuberculosis care in Tomsk, Russia: the IMPACT effectiveness trial. *Substance Use and Misuse*. 2013;48(9):784–92.

82. Mathew T, Shields A, Yanov S, Golubchikova V, Strelis A, Yanova G, et al. Performance of the alcohol use disorders identification test among tuberculosis patients in Russia. *Substance Use and Misuse*. 2010;45(4):598–612.

83. Mathew TA, Ovsyanikova TN, Shin SS, Gelmanova I, Balbuena DA, Atwood S, et al. Causes of death during tuberculosis treatment in Tomsk Oblast, Russia. *International Journal of Tuberculosis and Lung Disease*. 2006;10(8):857–63.

84. Mathew TA, Shields AL, Imasheva A, Shin SS, Mishustin SP, Peremitin GG, et al. Knowledge, attitudes, and practices of physicians in Tomsk Oblast tuberculosis services regarding alcohol use among tuberculosis patients in Tomsk, Russia. *Culture, Medicine and Psychiatry*. 2009;33(4):523–37.

85. Mathew TA, Yanov SA, Mazitov R, Mishustin SP, Strelis AK, Yanova GV, et al. Integration of alcohol use disorders identification and management in the tuberculosis programme in Tomsk Oblast, Russia. *European Journal of Public Health*. 2009;19(1):16–8.

86. Greenfield SF, Shields A, Connery HS, Livchits V, Yanov SA, Lastimoso CS, et al. Integrated management of physician-delivered alcohol care for tuberculosis patients: design and implementation. *Alcohol: Clinical and Experimental Research*. 2010;34(2):317–30.

87. Gelmanova IY, Taran DV, Mishustin SP, Golubkov AA, Solovyova AV, Keshavjee S. 'Sputnik': a programmatic approach to improve tuberculosis treatment adherence and outcome among defaulters. *International Journal of Tuberculosis and Lung Disease*. 2011;15(10):1373–9.

88. Velasquez MM, Ingersoll KS, Sobell MB, Floyd RL, Sobell LC, von Sternberg K. A dual-focus motivational intervention to reduce the risk of alcohol-exposed pregnancy. *Cognitive and Behavioral Practice*. 2010;17(2):203–12.

89. Floyd RL, Sobell M, Velasquez MM, Ingersoll K, Nettleman M, Sobell L, et al. Preventing alcohol-exposed pregnancies: a randomized controlled trial. *American Journal of Preventive Medicine*. 2007;32(1):1–10.

90. Hanson JD, Pourier S. The Oglala Sioux tribe CHOICES program: modifying an existing alcohol-exposed pregnancy intervention for use in an American Indian community. *International Journal of Environmental Research and Public Health*. 2015;13(1):ijerph13010001.

91. Hanson JD, Nelson ME, Jensen JL, Willman A, Jacobs-Knight J, Ingersoll K. Impact of the CHOICES intervention in preventing alcohol-exposed pregnancies in American Indian women. *Alcohol: Clinical and Experimental Research*. 2017;41(4):828–35.

92. Hanson JD, Jensen J. Importance of social support in preventing alcohol-exposed pregnancies with American Indian communities. *Journal of Community Health*. 2015;40(1):138–46.

93.   Hanson JD, Ingersoll K, Pourier S. Development and implementation of CHOICES group to reduce drinking, improve contraception, and prevent alcohol-exposed pregnancies in American Indian Women. *Journal of Substance Abuse Treatment*. 2015;59:45–51.

94.   Braithwaite RS, Nucifora KA, Kessler J, Toohey C, Mentor SM, Uhler LM, et al. Impact of interventions targeting unhealthy alcohol use in Kenya on HIV transmission and AIDS-related deaths. *Alcohol: Clinical and Experimental Research*. 2014;38(4):1059–67.

95.   Fuller BE, Loftis JM, Rodriguez VL, McQuesten MJ, Hauser P. Psychiatric and substance use disorders comorbidities in veterans with hepatitis C virus and HIV coinfection. *Current Opinions in Psychiatry*. 2009;22(4):401–8.

96.   Carter AJ, Bourgeois S, O'Brien N, Abelsohn K, Tharao W, Greene S, et al. Women-specific HIV/AIDS services: identifying and defining the components of holistic service delivery for women living with HIV/AIDS. *Journal of the International AIDS Society*. 2013;16(1):17433.

97.   Grella CE. From generic to gender-responsive treatment: changes in social policies, treatment services, and outcomes of women in substance abuse treatment. *Journal of Psychoactive Drugs*. 2008;5:327–43.

98.   Go VF, Morales GJ, Mai NT, Brownson RC, Ha TV, Miller WC. Finding what works: identification of implementation strategies for the integration of methadone maintenance therapy and HIV services in Vietnam. *Implementation Science*. 2016;11(54):016–0420.

99.   Nguyen Bich D, Korthuis PT, Nguyen Thu T, Van Dinh H, Le Minh G. HIV patients' preference for integrated models of addiction and HIV treatment in Vietnam. *Journal of Substance Abuse Treatment*. 2016;69:57–63.

100.   Haldane V, Cervero-Liceras F, Chuah FL, Ong SE, Murphy G, Sigfrid L, et al. Integrating HIV and substance use services: a systematic review. *Journal of the International AIDS Society*. 2017;20(1):1–14.

101.   Meyer JP, Althoff AL, Altice FL. Optimizing care for HIV-infected people who use drugs: evidence-based approaches to overcoming healthcare disparities. *Clinical Infectious Diseases*. 2013;57(9):1309–17.

102.   van Ginneken N, Tharyan P, Lewin S, Rao GN, Meera SM, Pian J, et al. Non-specialist health worker interventions for the care of mental, neurological and substance-abuse disorders in low- and middle-income countries. *Cochrane Database Systems Review*. 2013;19(11):1–366.

103.   Terra MB, Barros HM, Stein AT, Figueira I, Palermo LH, Athayde LD, et al. Do alcoholics anonymous groups really work? Factors of adherence in a Brazilian sample of hospitalized alcohol dependents. *American Journal on Addictions*. 2008;17(1):48–53.

104.   Penzenstadler L, Machado A, Thorens G, Zullino D, Khazaal Y. Effect of case management interventions for patients with substance use disorders: a systematic review. *Frontiers in Psychiatry*. 2017;8:51.

105.   Davies T, Lund C. Integrating mental health care into primary care systems in low- and middle-income countries: lessons from PRIME and AFFIRM. *Global Mental Health*. 2017;4:e7.

Index